KENT'S FORGOTTEN AIRFIELD
THROWLEY
1917 – 1919

KENT'S FORGOTTEN AIRFIELD

THROWLEY

1917 – 1919

ANTHONY J. MOOR

TEMPUS

First published 2007

Tempus Publishing Limited
The Mill, Brimscombe Port,
Stroud, Gloucestershire, GL5 2QG
www.tempus-publishing.com

British Library Cataloguing in Publication Data.
A catalogue record for this book is available from the British Library.

ISBN 978 0 7524 4269 3

Typesetting and origination by Tempus Publishing Limited.
Printed in Great Britain.

Contents

Acknowledgements

I would like to thank Robin A. Brown who, having served with 112 Squadron RAF, researched their history and kindly helped with documents and photographs of the squadron during its service in the First World War at Throwley. Robin has written and had published a book on the complete history of 112 (Shark) Squadron RAF.

I was also given much help from E.F. Cheesman, who over the years has established himself as one of a select few of First World War aviation historians and has himself, with the late Christopher Cole, written a history of the Home Defence of Great Britain from 1914–18.

To locate all the pilots and ground crew who were based at Throwley is, for obvious reasons, an impossible task. However, I once wrote to perhaps the last of these pilots, A.C.S. Irwin, who replied to my letter, recalling his memories of that time. He ended by saying that his flying career spanned forty years, during which time he flew with the RFC, the RAF and the Fleet Air Arm. Later he became the editor of the *Illustrated London News*. He concluded by saying he was in his eighties and could no longer ride a bike! What characters these pilots were. I dedicate this short history to their memory and those that followed in their footsteps.

A recent photograph of Stede Court, Harrietsham, Kent, which was the HQ of No. 53 (Home Defence) Wing. This grand old estate was the ideal location for the HQ as it was close to Detling Airfield near Maidstone. Throwley was only a few miles over the North Downs and at Frinsted there was an Emergency Landing Ground. (A.J. Moor)

No. 53 Wing (Home Defence) at Harrietsham. Several well-known wartime pilots can be recognised in this group, including Wing Commanders A.A.B. Thomson, G.S.M. Insall, VC (fifth from right, front row), W. Sowrey, F. Sowrey, Collis, Cook, Usborne, Potter and Irwin (fourth from left, front row). (R.A. Brown)

THROWLEY AERODROME
1917 - 1919

PLUMFORD
To Throwley

To Faversham

Bells Forstal

North

AIRFIELD

Cadmans Farm

To Charing & Harrietsham

Details of airfield buildings by courtesy of ex-squadron members and from aerial photographs by No.80 Squadron RAF.

THROWLEY AERODROME 1917–19

A. 112 Squadron 'A' Flight Bessoneau Hangar
B. 112 Squadron 'B' Flight Bessoneau Hangar
C. 112 Squadron 'C' Flight Bessoneau Hangar
D. 'Old Thatch' (House since demolished.)
E. 112 Squadron Guard Room (now a bungalow)
F. Camp Recreation Building
G. Large Buildings (use not known)
H. Workshops
I. Semi-Underground Ammunition & Pyrotechnic Store
J. 188 Squadron Wooden Hangar
K. Water Tower & Pump
L. New Brick Hangar (not completed)

M. Compass Swinging Base
N. Two Bessoneau Hangars
P. Officers' & Airmen's Huts
Q. Gun Firing Butts
R. 188 Squadron Tents (until August 1918)
S. Medical Officers' Hut
T. Officers' Mess
U. Cookhouse
(A.J. Moor)

Introduction

For the people of Great Britain who endured the horrors of the Blitz in the Second World War, the Zeppelin and, later, the bomber raids of the First World War would have likely appeared to be insignificant. However, at the time, this was far from being the case for it must not be forgotten that it was only the lack of technical knowledge that prevented the Germans from destroying our towns and cities from the air. Aerial bombardment was a threat as early as 1910, when the Admiralty met to discuss the defence of dockyards and munitions factories. Two years later the Committee of Imperial Defence also considered the seriousness of this threat; needless to say, neither party could agree.

It was the opinion of the Army that they should be responsible for Home Defence, including Naval establishments. The Royal Navy could, they said, protect themselves by using their own aircraft if they wished. When war came, all the RFC fighters were sent to France, and, had the Germans attacked from the air, they would have met with little opposition. The only airborne defence would have been from the few RNAS aircraft based at certain points. It was Winston Churchill who realised that this defence was inadequate and set about forming units of aircraft for improving the situation in 1912. As the Army could not offer a solution to the problem of defence, responsibility was passed to the Admiralty on 1 July 1914. The RFC Naval Wing became the Royal Naval Air Service. It was not until 1 August 1915 that the RFC and RNAS were made separate organisations.

At this time the Germans had only six Zeppelins in service, and of these three were shot down, another crashed at sea and one was destroyed by fire. It was some time before enthusiasm for the Zeppelin returned, but when it did new bases were established. Following attacks on Fredrichshaven and Düsseldorf airship sheds by the RNAS, permission was given by the German General Staff to attack London. Guns and searchlights had been positioned within the London area and some aircraft were assigned to coastal areas.

The first Zeppelin raid occurred on 19 January 1915 over Norfolk, causing some minor damage. Meanwhile across England blackouts were enforced and large cities such as Sheffield were protected by guns. The Chatham and Sheerness areas became the most heavily defended.

By the end of 1916, after a reign of terror on the British population, it was felt that the Zeppelin menace was over and guns were sent to arm the merchant fleet against the U-boats. This was a fatal decision, for on 16 March 1917 the Zeppelins returned. On 25 May 1917 a new threat appeared in the skies, in the shape of the Gotha twin-engined bomber. They attacked the south-east and returned to their base in Belgium without being hindered. Ninety-five civilians were killed and 200 injured. It was obvious following this raid that Home Defence, such as it was, had been totally inadequate. More raids followed on 5 and 13 June, which resulted in a public outcry and the decision was made to double the number of RFC Fighter Squadrons.

A committee was formed by the Government, headed by General Smuts, to improve the country's Home Defence. Shortly afterwards three new squadrons were formed to defend London; from one of these units, 'B' Flight of 50 Squadron, 112 Squadron was formed. Their base was to be an airfield already used by 50 Squadron, based at Bekesbourne, as an emergency or relief landing strip close to the village of Throwley, between Faversham and Charing.

On 10 September 1917 the newly formed squadron received orders to patrol a line from Throwley to Judds Hill and Wardens Point. The plan was to intercept Gotha bombers intent on raiding London and towns in the south-east. From May 1917 until the Armistice in 1918, German bomber squadrons raided England on no less than twenty-seven occasions. The strength of these raids varied between one and forty-three aircraft, and it was reported that one enemy aircraft was destroyed for each raid.

A Little Bit of Heaven

The following are the words to the popular tune 'A Little Bit Of Heaven', which was the song adapted by airmen at 112 Squadron Concert Party at Throwley.

The poem was compiled by Mrs N. Ricketts, a civilian subordinate at Throwley Airfield.

Have you ever heard the story how our aerodrome got its name.
If you'll listen you will understand from whence this place first came.
No wonder the boys all want their tickets, to get away you see.
 For here's the way-a chap who knew once told the tale to me.

Chorus:
Just a little bit of rain and sleet fell from out the sky one day.
And settled in a mud heap in a spot so far away.
And when the Brass Hats came to view this scene of desolation.
They said, 'Lets build an aerodrome five miles from town or station'.
Then they sprinkled it with wooden huts and a Bessoneau hangar or two,
And a row of Squadron Offices that entirely spoiled the view.
Then dotted it with the RDC's who should have been at home.
Put a few fed-up mechanics there and called it Throwley 'drome'.

Note: RDC = Royal Defence Corps. These were old-time-serving soldiers, usually fifty years of age or over, recalled and enlisted to carry out general duties at the airfield or other related sites.

one

The establishment of the home
defence airfield at Throwley, and
formation of new squadrons
by the Royal Flying Corps

Villagers were no doubt curious when RFC work parties arrived in their trucks in late October 1916. These advanced guards were to erect three Bessoneau hangars, canvas-covered structures, to accommodate the squadron's Sopwith Pup fighter aircraft. Needless to say, accommodation was basic, consisting of simple tents for the airmen; later, however, as the airfield became more established, permanent buildings were erected under the shelter of Dodds Willows, becoming home to both officers and airmen.

A wooden hangar was also constructed for the No.6 Motor Transport Squadron. Hedges were cut down on either side of the road from Bells Forstal to Throwley to assist aircraft on landing and take off. The tented area was located close to the farm which included the all-important cookhouse and the medical officers' quarters.

The main officers' mess was located at Bells Forstal Farm, a house with a delightful location and beautiful gardens within sight of the airfield. Earl Sondes of Lees Court, between Clares Forstal and Bells Forstal, owned the land on which the airfield was constructed, not more than a mile from Throwley church.

One of the problems with the airfield's location was the shortage of water, which may have been due to the area being on high ground. For this reason a water tower was built and a bore hole sunk; despite this innovation NCOs and other ranks were permitted to travel into Faversham for a weekly bath. This was a good opportunity to meet the local female population and some enjoyable hours would be spent at Faversham Roller Skating Rink!

Under the command of Major Gerald Allen, 112 Squadron was officially formed at Throwley on 30 July 1917, having been established as a Home Defence unit from 'B' Flight 50 Squadron. Two Wings had been created to defend Britain, Northern and Southern, controlled by Home Defence Headquarters based at Adastral House in London. However, in September 1917 it was to become The Home Defence Brigade and was later known as the 6th Brigade. The brigade was split into three wings: Northern and Eastern, operating by day, and Southern, which operated by night; the latter two formed the Defence of London.

That October 6th Brigade was divided into five wings: Northern 49 Wing, South Midland 47 Wing, North Midland 48 Wing, Eastern 46 Wing, and Southern 50 Wing. Major B.F. Moore was given command in November 1917 but requested a transfer to the Western Front and Major C.A. Ridley became the new CO. Although 112 Squadron was officially a Home Defence unit, it was to become better known as a Night Fighter Squadron and most probably for this reason command was handed over to Major C.J.Q. Brand DSO, MC, DFC, on 13 February 1918. Brand, who served with 70 Squadron in France, a Night Fighter Squadron, was a South African who in 1920 made an epic flight in a Vickers Vimy, which will be described later. Here he describes his posting to the newly formed Home Defence squadron, which he would command:

On the 14th February 1918, I was transferred to Throwley, Kent to command 112 Squadron, equipped with 100hp Nome Sopwith Pups. I set about training pilots for night flying. At the same time appealing to GO.C 6 Brigade Gen. T.C.R Higgins, to be re-equipped with the 110

Location map of south-east Kent, dated 1917/18, showing the proximity of Throwley to other airfields.

hp Le Rhone Sopwith Camels as I did not consider the Nome a suitable engine for night operations. A Le Rhone Camel duly arrived with the promise that if results were satisfactory, there would be more to follow.

All pilots passed out satisfactorily on this machine and after very little delay the entire squadron was equipped with this wonderful type the Le Rhone Camel and serious training began. The programme of daily work being the same as that carried out at Hainault Farm, Essex and at other stations but with the addition of Aerial Gunnery at towed targets by day. Practice fighting by day using dark coloured goggles followed by actual practice when proficient.

Night-flying training began with dusk landings without flares, and went on to include testing night-flying landings in all weather conditions, using searchlights on occasions. This provided valuable practice for searchlight personnel in locating and holding machines fully illuminated in the concentration of beams.

Meanwhile, some of the more experienced pilots had taken part in the two or three raids, but without success. Eventually, on 19 May 1918, on the occasion of the German bombers' last night attack on London, when they suffered the loss of seven machines, the squadron scored its first success – a twin-engined Gotha being destroyed in flames over Faversham.

A short time prior to this last raid on England, the enemy had turned his attentions to intensive bombing of areas in France, Abbeville suffering particularly. As a result of an urgent appeal from France for a Night Fighting Scout squadron, No.151 Squadron was hastily equipped, having been formed from part of No.44, No.78 and No.112 Squadrons. No.151 Squadron, commanded by Major G.W. Murlis Green DSO, MC, proceeded overseas on 20 June 1918 and officially took up station at Fontaine-sur-Maye, near the Forêt de Crécy, and began operations.

The squadron, once alerted to an impending raid, was ordered to patrol a line from Throwley to Judds Hill and Warden Point. Orders had been given to pilots in the air by a series of forty ground signals. However, from June 1918 this was done by wireless transmission and later in August an attempt was made using Radio Transmission. This was not a great success, as A.W. James, who was based at Throwley, recalled some years later:

> I remember seeing one of 112 Squadron pilots speaking into a microphone to a pilot, telling him to turn left, right, climb and turn, plus a few choice words, for it seemed the pilot could not hear!

There is no account of how often the squadron was ordered into the air to seek out enemy aircraft but they had no success until the night of 19/20 May 1918.

By June the squadron comprised some twenty pilots, sixty airmen and NCOs, and was formed into A, B and C flights as well as a Headquarters Flight. On charge were twenty-four aircraft, of which only four were not flying, and although they had a permanent base, this squadron could have moved to another location given very short notice. During June 1918, No.112 Squadron was called upon to form the nucleus of No.151 Squadron at Throwley, which became the first Night Fighter unit.

The London Air Defence Area (LADA) was formed at the end of July 1917 and was intended to cover the south-east. Brigadier General Edward B. Ashmore returned from France to take command of the LADA. He was well qualified for the position, being a regular artillery officer, and he had become a pilot as early as 1912. He took flying lessons at four in the morning so that he could be at work by nine.

Two wings had been formed to defend northern and southern Britain; they were both based at Adastral House, London. In September 1917 it became known as The Home Defence Brigade and then, later in December 1918, the 6th Brigade RAF; its motto was 'By Day and By Night'. (R.A. Brown)

Ashmore's answer to bombing raids was the Balloon Barrage; these were already in use by the Germans against Austrian bombers. An 'apron' of 1,000ft streamers was suspended by between three and five balloons joined together by steel cables. The apron was anchored at three points and could be raised to any height between 7,500 and 10,000ft. The main purpose of the balloons was to force the German bombers to fly at predictable heights to enable guns and Home Defence pilots to locate the intruders. The other danger to the enemy was the possibility that they could fly into the apron. Twenty such aprons were planned to defend the eastern and northern approaches to London but due to problems in finding the right type of balloon only half this number were in position when the German raids ended in May 1918.

Ashmore realised that the fighters of the Home Defence squadrons would be more successful than guns if the bombers could be found. Patrol lines were organised to give pilots a broad search zone. Free of anti aircraft guns, which were replaced by searchlights, pilots were instructed to remain in the patrol zone at night. Therefore, any aircraft heard outside the zone would be considered hostile. The guns removed were re-sited to extend the outer aircraft defences. A system of barrage fire was devised to combat the incoming raiders and the London Metropolitan area was divided into numbered squares. Enemy aircraft were plotted by their sound and 'curtains' of shells were aimed in their flight path as they passed from square to square.

Each curtain was given a code name: 'Woodpecker' extended across the Thames between Dartford and Gravesend; the 'Ace of Spades' curved to the south-east of Woolwich; 'Pot Luck', 'Pip Squeak' and 'Cosy Corner' protected London from the north; 'Dandy Dick', 'No Trumps' and 'Cold Feet' ran between Croydon and the Thames to the south. Another innovation was the 'sound detector'; one of these was installed on the south-east coast, a concave surface carved in a cliff face, the idea being that it would pick up sound waves.

Another device consisted of two pairs of gramophone trumpets mounted on poles. It had the effect of a hearing aid and the direction of sound was relayed to the searchlight and gun crews. Over the next few years many types of detectors were constructed. Some still remain today, scattered along the Kent coast. And, of course, in the Second World War Britain would have radar.

Escorting Marshal Foch, discipline
at Throwley, problems with
the local business community,
and members of the public

The French destroyer *Francis Carnier* steamed into Dover harbour during December 1918. On board was the Commander in Chief of the Allied Forces in France, Marshal Foch. He was accompanied by the French Prime Minister, M. Clemençeau, and Lord Derby. At the same time another destroyer, the *Temeraire*, arrived with its VIPs, the Italian Prime Minister Signor Orlando and the Italian Foreign Minister Baron Sonnio. The *Captain Meld* sailed with the two destroyers to protect them from any possible attack. This ship had previously been in action with the *Broke* and the *Morris* in a successful engagement with German destroyers off Dunkirk. The crossing was in rough seas and had originally been arranged to take place on the Saturday, destination Folkestone.

Despite the change of plans for the visit, a Guard of Honour comprising three Battalions of the Buffs was drawn up to receive the guests; the Battalion's colours had been brought from Canterbury Cathedral the previous day. The distinguished party was met by Rear Admiral Dampier, General Sir Charles Wolland, Brigadier General C.J. Hopkirk, CO of the Dover Garrison, and the Mayor of Dover. During the inspection 'The Marseillaise' was played and the Battalion's colours lowered, an honour usually given only to the ruler of a nation. Due to the weather it was not possible for airships or seaplanes to escort the destroyers; however, some twenty-three aircraft managed to escort the convoy into Dover.

As the train left Dover several of the aircraft formed up and followed the train to London, despite high winds. One of these pilots was Lt A.C.S. Irwin; he had been assigned to this duty from Throwley. A photograph of Irwin in his Sopwith Camel was taken from inside a carriage as he drew up alongside the train. The train arrived in London without any incident being reported. They returned to France in *Le Nord*, one of the cross-Channel ships owned by Nord Railway.

By the end of October 1918 Major Osborne, who was then CO of 112 Squadron, was concerned about the level of discipline within the squadron. In a letter to the officer commanding No. 53 Wing, he expressed his concern over one of his senior officers, Capt. T.M.B. Newton:

The above mentioned Officer has been with this squadron for 15 months and was, I believe, highly thought of by his late Squadron Commander. He has however not nearly enough 'ginger' to please me, largely due I believe, to having been here for so long. The squadron is in a very bad way both in discipline and moral and being senior Flight Commander, I consider it to be this Officers fault and lack of keenness. This officer being a clever pilot and well trained in all branches of night operations, I ask for his removal so that I may put Lt W.D.H Baird in charge of his flight.

In a similar letter Major Osborne expressed his concern over another of his men, Captain Collier:

My complaints about him are very minor, chiefly, that he has not enough go, he does not exercise his abilities, but leaves matters to take care of themselves. A case in point occurred

An unusual photograph taken from inside the speeding train of Lt A.C.S. Irwin as he flew alongside acting as escort to Marshal Foch on his journey from Dover to London. This photograph appeared in an edition of the *Illustrated London News*. (A.C.S. Irwin)

on Thursday night when Lt. Baird's holt flares failed. He was instructed to have the cause investigated but at 12.30 next day he had not taken the trouble to find out the cause of the failure, although the Flight Sergeant had looked into the case first thing. This Officer is an extremely capable and well trained night pilot and if removed, I strongly recommend that he be retained in his present kind of work.

Discipline appeared to be a problem at Throwley; in particular the behaviour of some of the officers was troublesome. On one occasion, a Lt W. Casson was accused of 'diving' at

Two unknown pilots are seen here attired in the famous 'Sidcot' flying overalls. These overalls were an important innovation as they were both lighter and warmer than previous flying suits. In the background stands a Sopwith Camel; its squadron is not identified but it could be a member of 112 Squadron or perhaps it was just visiting the airfield.

Note the twin Vickers machine guns mounted on top of the fuselage in front of the pilot's cockpit and the opening in the upper wing enabling the pilot to see above. (I. McKay)

Lt Jenkinson, who was walking across the airfield at the time. This incident turned out to have been falsified. Jenkinson did, however, have a narrow escape when an aircraft of 188 (Training) Squadron, landing with engine failure, nearly hit the unfortunate officer as he strolled around the airfield.

Lt Jenkinson had reported the alleged breach of flying discipline to junior officers visiting squadrons from Headquarters. He was warned to use more discretion and tact when discussing matters of such importance. Of a more serious nature was a communication received by the CO from a Lt Col RAMC Officer in Charge of the Military Hospital at Canterbury:

> I beg to invite your attention to the fact that airmen are in the habit of flying low over the hospital and grounds. No doubt the airmen do not realise that there are cases of Neurasthenia and shell shock in bed and that they are terrified by the noise of the machines so close overhead. Could the matter be brought to their notice with a view to abating the noise, the same state of affairs applies the V.A.D hospitals in the locality.

Perhaps the incident which caused most concern, particularly to the residents of Faversham who remembered the horrific explosion in 1916 in which many workers were killed, involved the premises of Curtis & Harvey Ltd who owned the gunpowder mills in the town. According to the works manager, a Mr Mirtel, at 11 a.m. on 20 August 1918 a spent cartridge case fell onto the skylight of a Danger House, smashing the glass and falling into the building below; fortunately no explosion occurred. The manager pointed out that firing guns over the vicinity should cease as it would end in loss of life or another explosion.

Despite the fact that there were no pilots killed as a result of enemy action, there were several pilots who lost their lives in flying accidents. A local resident of Throwley, Mr Manuel, remembers that an airman was killed − he believes decapitated − when struck by a Camel coming into land. This was, in fact, an observer pupil pilot of 188 Squadron who was just walking across the airfield. Another story was that one of the pilots committed suicide by crashing his aircraft into woods close to the airfield. Upon reaching the wreckage it was discovered that the pilot's tongue had been severed on impact. Local legend says that the unfortunate pilot haunts the woods looking for his tongue!

On another occasion a Camel was having difficulty taking off and flew straight into one of the Bessoneau hangars in which many airmen were working. If the reader visits Throwley churchyard, to the rear of the church they will find the graves of two pilots: Lt E.W.F. Hopgood, who was killed on 14 October 1918 when he lost control at 4,000ft and got into a spin from which he didn't recover; and 2nd Lt J.T. Mitchell, who was killed on 24 January 1919 when he to got into a spin and crashed in Hockley Wood. The wreckage was not located until an aerial search took place.

During the summer of 1918 a Wing Review took place at Throwley which was taken by an Air-Vice Marshall who, upon landing, caused quite a stir amongst the onlookers. The aircraft, a Bristol M1C, was indeed an unusual sight in the skies over Kent as it was one of the earliest monoplanes (of single-wing construction). To the local population the event was very exciting as many different aircraft arrived in the area, including Bristol Fighters, FE2bs, SE5s and Sopwith Camels.

At a similar event, taking place at Ashford and reviewed by General French, a young pilot, 2nd Lt Turton (who allegedly held the record for the number of crash landings) excelled himself by landing his aircraft on top of a tree overlooking the parade. There he stayed until the end of the spectacle. The local press, who were characteristically unsympathetic, had a field day with this unexpected development and a report on the review was suitably headed, 'Airman gets a Grandstand View'.

An officer standing by an AW.FK8 in full flying kit waits for his pilot or observer. Note the markings on the side of the aircraft, in this case an arrow. The 'torpedo'-like device fixed to the upper wing is a fuel tank. (I. McKay)

Although the training of pilots at Throwley was going well, there still occurred certain incidents which sometimes led to strained relationships. On one occasion a letter was received from a resident of Whitstable, Harry Funnington, who wrote to the Commanding Officer on 14 August 1918:

> Will you kindly give instructions to the members of your Flying Corps to avoid flying so near to the houses situated in Joy Lane.
> I have an invalid at home and it is no uncommon occurrence for members to just miss the roof of my house! This naturally causes great distress to anyone lying in bed ill.

At the time this complaint was received pilots were using buoys off the south-east coast for unofficial target practice. As a result Trinity House notified the HQ at Stede Court, Harrietsham, that they were aware of this practice. A notice was served to the effect that a reward of £5 would be paid to anyone:

> ... giving such information to the corporation of Trinity House, as will lead to the identification of the persons or persons by whom such damage is or has been done and enable proceedings to be instituted and a conviction secured against the offending parties.

Notice was also given that under Section 666 of the Merchant Shipping Act 1894:

> It is an offence to wilfully or negligently damage Seamarks, and that such offence is punishable by a fine not exceeding £50, in respect of such an offence, in addition to the cost of making good the damage!

This was brought to the notice of the young pilots at Throwley, who no doubt ignored or at least did not agree with severity of the problem.

The RAF crest of 112 Squadron, a cat sejant, based at Throwley; the squadron's motto is 'Swift In Destruction'. (Red Lion Press)

three

Pilots training, flying aircraft
at Throwley, encounters with
Zeppelins and the new menace,
the Gotha bombers

Many pilots during the First World War did not receive much training before being posted to an operational unit. This was mainly due to the big German offensive in France known as the 'Big Push' when the Germans broke right through, threatening the Channel Ports. Because the RFC suffered heavy loses all the available pilots had to be found to replace them in England; one of these pilots was A.B. Yuille DFC.

Yuille was not a fully trained pilot and had only flown a Sopwith Pup for twenty minutes. Instead of being sent to a flying training school, graduating to the Sopwith Camel when gaining his wings, a process which could take three months, he found himself posted to 112 Squadron destined to fly Night Fighters at Throwley. Fortunately for Yuille, having such an experienced pilot as his new CO, Major Quintin Brand, would give him the opportunity to gain skills he needed for the task. Brand had lost an arm fighting in France, which impressed the young pilot as it did not prevent him from flying.

Yuille remembers his CO's words, 'Well the first thing you chaps have to get to do is to teach yourselves to fly.' Later when pilots were allocated Sopwith Pups, he told them:

Fly it whenever you get the chance all over the country, where you like. Nobody will worry, just get into it and fly and when you can fly it properly, then we will see what we can do.

This advice was taken literally and sometimes Yuille flew his machine four or five times a day. Eventually the CO said, 'I think you look as if you can fly the Pup now.' Taking this as a green light, Yuille used to fly down to Eastbourne to have lunch with his sister who was at school there. At other times he would fly south to Hastings, more or less at sea level all the way round the coast past Dover, Margate and up the river to Faversham, then turning into Throwley. On occasion he would loop the Pup, spinning it in a similar fashion to when he used to fly the Avro 504. Sometimes he would take off with Brand to practice manoeuvring alongside, thus gaining confidence in flying close to other aircraft.

The CO was very keen on Formation Flying and would take the whole squadron up. The inexperienced pilots would fly the Pups and they had to fly with the Camels in as tight formation as nerves would allow. They would form into three flights in 'V' formation, one in front and one each side to the rear. With five aircraft in each flight they would get so close they could have had a 'chat', if it wasn't for the roar of the engines. Good training, for unless the fighter flew close to its prey the pilot would open fire and miss his target.

The Sopwith Camel had similar controls to the Pup but the engine was much more powerful. Yuille recalled in an interview:

The Camel was very tricky to fly primarily because of the right-hand torque and the small wing span and the powerful engine. If you put your right wing down in a right hand turn and were not careful you spun down on the torque. Conversely turning to the left was fairly heavy, you had to push the joystick over to get the left hand turn, your left hand bank , but on going to the right it was so light that you were over and spinning before you knew where you were. But you were told all about that before you ever went up in a Camel and its advice you never forgot.

I flew several times at night in a Pup before I flew a Camel and it's funny, night flying. It's not really so different or so difficult except to know where you are because you can't see the ground so well. You get a very good horizon to fly against. The horizon is there and you can see water very clearly at night underneath you, but of course you can't pick out roads or railways or anything like that particularly if blacked out because of the war. The main thing is to keep your eye on the horizon and not find yourself getting into a dive when you don't mean to.

It's more difficult to judge your height in coming into land particularly as Throwley wasn't very well lit. You had to get your height check the wind direction. That was done for you with these three red lights. You landed over the one into the two which were set correctly into the wind, so that you would land in the right direction. There were no runways, you were just landing on grass. But it wasn't all that easy to get your exact height off the ground and you could land a little bit high and break the undercarriage.

Being a Night Fighter pilot was a lonely existence as then there was no contact with Throwley by radio-telephone or any other means. Pilots could be on patrol for two hours and it was quite common for pilots to arrive back at base, hoarse, through singing at the top of their voice to keep themselves company.

Every morning there was a Rota posted informing pilots of their flying duties. Usually patrols started at 10.00 p.m., each lasting two hours before other pilots in readiness would take-off to relieve them. However there was no patrolling unless German activity was reported, this was because they had to fly from bases in Belgium and needed to gain elevation, useful knowledge for pilots on patrol.

Despite constant training, very little was seen of the Germans during April/May 1918. Navigating at night was not easy, although pilots could always see water at Throwley – the Thames. To assist

Crowds always gathered when an aircraft made a forced landing in rural areas. This Sopwith Camel B5215 appears damaged and the pilot is checking the full extent of the problem with the airmen who have been called out to assist. The circumstances of this incident are not known. (I. McKay)

The fuselage is ripped open folding back the fabric, thus exposing the airframe, but the pilot does not seem unduly worried. The location of this incident and the pilot's name are not known. The damage to the fabric-covered fuselage is clearly visible. (I. McKay)

returning pilots there was a lighthouse, which blinked a Morse letter, and there were lights on the ground; many pilots relied on instinct to find their way home.

Subsequent to his tour of duty at Throwley, Yuille was posted to France, north of Abbeville, where he served under Brand, night flying. He was credited with shooting down a German bomber near Ypres and the crews were taken prisoner. This was the first Gotha bomber shot down by the RFC in France. Later he achieved fame when he shot down another German bomber; this incident just happened to be seen by King George, who was visiting France.

On the night of 16/17 February 1917 an airship was sighted off Walmer. Its engines had been heard by people living in coastal areas, although it didn't drop any bombs. Lt Butler of 50 Squadron 'B' Flight, Throwley, flying a BE12-6493, returned to base due to poor weather. Other pilots who had been dispatched from Manston, Dover and Bekesbourne to search for the intruder also returned home unsuccessful. At that time Zeppelin raids continued to occupy the Home Defence squadrons.

It was no surprise when a force of four Naval Zeppelins were reported heading for London on the night of 16/17 March 1917. That evening 37 Squadron, 39 Squadron, 78 Squadron and 50 Squadron were on patrol. The airborne planes were a BE2c flown by 2nd Lt A.J. Arkell, 'B' Flight, Throwley, and Capt. R.C.H. Murray, BE12a of HQ, Flight Frinsted. The four 'R'-class airships, including the new 'S'-class L42, were developed to reach higher altitudes. Poor weather had spoilt their plans for attack, so they scattered their bomb load, but no casualties were reported. Separating from the other Zeppelins, L39 and L35 came in over Thanet at 10.00 a.m. and headed towards Ashford, where L35 turned south towards Dover.

L39 continued south-west, leaving the coast for its base over Pevensey; later this airship was shot down by gunfire over France, crashing at Compiegne. L40 made landfall over New Romney. Experiencing engine problems, L42 passed over Winchelsea and Dungeness, returning to base. The remaining Zeppelins at an altitude of 17–19,000ft were caught by 45mph high winds. Wireless frequencies were jammed by the British which prevented the Germans from obtaining accurate fixes. Drifting south of their intended routes, they had to run the gauntlet of French Defences. Home defence units were soon alerted and aircraft dispatched from Throwley. 2nd Lt A.J. Arkell, 50 Squadron, took off to be joined in the hunt by pilots from Manston and Bekesbourne.

They were all airborne before the first Zeppelin crossed the coast, but due to poor weather they were unable to intercept. Even the searchlights scanning the sky could not penetrate the

In 1959 Robin A. Brown, who had served with 112 Squadron flying Hawker Hunters, managed to persuade a Photograph Reconnaissance Canberra to fly over the site of Throwley Airfield. The outline of the hangars was still visible while the Compass Swinging Base, camp hut and guardhouse had survived. There was still some evidence of buildings but they were almost hidden from view in Dodds Willows, Bells Forstal Farm is to the top of the photograph. (R.A. Brown)

Fortunately LAC A.W. James saved this wall chart, which was displayed in the 112 Squadron crew room during 1918/19 when the squadron was disbanded. It reappeared in 1957 when Mr James presented it to the squadron. It was framed and hung in the crew room. When 112 Squadron was disbanded in 1957 the picture was loaned to the Imperial War Museum where it was exhibited. (RAF Bruggen Photograph Section No.259)

The three hangars of 'A', 'B' and 'C' Flights (112 Squadron) were constructed close to the lane which led from the road onto the airfield. In the distance is the Guardroom which is still clearly visible today. (Mrs N. Ricketts)

An interesting view looking across the airfield. On the left are the two wooden hangars and to the right two of the three Bessoneau hangars. A few years ago the outline of the wooden hangars was still visible when the ground dried in summer. (A.B. Yuille)

A Sopwith Camel named 'Twinkle'; note that this aircraft has a foot plate to assist the pilot into the cockpit at night. Just visible are the first two digits of its serial number, D64. (A.B. Yuille)

Above: A remarkable photograph, in which the Camel in the foreground carries a swastika on its fin, then a good-luck symbol. The aircraft behind appears to be named 'Madge II'. Many aircraft in the First and Second World Wars were named after wives and girlfriends. (A.B. Yuille)

Left: A layer of snow covers Throwley Airfield during the winter of 1918. This aerial photograph reveals the new brick hangar still under construction (but which was never completed), along with the wooden hangar. Bessoneau hangars and wooden huts were erected in Dodds Willows. The aircraft visible are believed to be Avro 504s of 188 Night Training Squadron. (C.J. Chabot)

Lt A.C.S. Irwin with his two dogs 'Tinker' and 'Tip', standing by a Sopwith F1 Camel of 112 Squadron, probably during the summer of 1918. This aircraft is in Night Fighter colours; the nacelle and metal parts were darkened and the white of the fuselage and upper wing roundels were painted over. Beneath the port wing, protected by a canvas cover (only when parked), is a 'Holt' flare. The white rectangle should contain the aircraft's serial number D6415; on the rudder is Flight Commander's pennant. (A.C.S. Irwin)

Lt W.G. Scotcher at the controls of 'Pixie II'. Both pilot and plane were part of 112 Squadron. The aircraft displays a Swastika on the fin. The hangars in the background, one which is under construction, indicate that the location may not be Throwley Airfield. (C.F. Wooley)

thick cloud formation. The enemy had the advantage, being able to fly at higher altitudes than the fighters. Arkell, who was flying at 9,000ft above the cloud for thirty minutes, saw nothing and set off for Throwley in heavy rain. He was forced to land eventually with engine trouble at the second-class airstrip at Marden. Captain R.G.H. Murray of 50 Squadron, HQ Flight based at Frinsted, returned having observed nothing despite experiencing better weather.

On 25 May 1917 twenty-three Gothas of Kagol 3 headed for England, their target being London. Approaching the English coast they split into two defensive formations. One of these was seen by the Tongue lightship crew; they estimated its height as being 15,000ft. Crossing the coast between Blackwater and Crouch they set course for London. Due to poor visibility they turned south to find an alternative target. Flying in a curve over Kent they managed to drop bombs on Lympne Airfield, the main attack concentrated on Folkestone. Lt H.T.Q. Windsor and Captain T.R. Irons, 50 Squadron, 'B' Flight, were airborne on patrol. One Gotha was destroyed by other aircraft; both pilots returned having observed nothing.

During the course of this raid seventy-seven sorties were flown by Home Defence units and ninety-five people were killed. Two weeks later, on 5 June, Gothas took off to attack Sheerness. One Gotha was destroyed, crashing in the sea off Bartons Point after being hit by gunfire. But for the two luckless pilots of 'B' Flight, 50 Squadron, on patrol from Throwley, there was to be no interception. Captain C.R. Rowden, flying an Armstrong Whitworth F.K8, and 2nd Lt A.J. Arkell in an RE8 were disappointed with the day's events, Arkell's aircraft having suffered engine trouble.

The first patrol involving pilots of the newly formed 112 Squadron took place during daylight on 12 August 1917, when thirteen Gothas were despatched to attack Southend. Eight Sopwith Pups were airborne that day; Captain S.H. Pratt returned to Throwley with gun trouble, as did 2nd Lt J.W.R. Thompson. During a night-time raid which took place on 5/6 December 1917, 2nd Lt W.R. Oulton, a pilot of 50 Squadron, had a narrow escape when the 160hp Beardmore engine of his FK.8 shed a cylinder. Its connecting rod cut through the crankcase sump and an engine bearer. It was only due to his flying skill that he was able to glide down, landing at Throwley somewhat relieved to be on the ground again.

four

The last Gotha raid of 1918,
the successful interception of one
of the intruders and its dramatic
destruction, and captured German
bomber crews interrogated

Following the formation of the 6th Brigade, it was soon apparent that the trusty BE2c was not the right aircraft to combat the menace of the Gotha bombers, which now posed a major threat. Despite the fact that Home Defence squadrons were gradually being re-equipped with single and two-seat fighters, as yet no one had attempted to fly the Sopwith Camel at night. On 3 September 1917 Major Murlis-Green, then CO of 44 Squadron, who later became CO of 112 Squadron, was granted permission to carry out a night patrol to test the Camel's suitability as a Night Fighter. He was accompanied by Capt. C.J.Q. Brand and Lt C.C. Banks. The three pilots duly took off and on return they were delighted with the Camel's performance. By the spring of 1918 the Gotha raids had increased, although there were losses. On 18 December 1917 Murlis-Green had intercepted a Gotha which he attacked and damaged, eventually crashing in the sea off Folkestone. As well as the Gotha destroyed on 19 May by Brand, a second was attacked by Major F. Sowrey, CO of 143 Squadron.

On 19 May Captain Ernst Brandenburg, Commander, Bombengeschwader 3, who was planning yet another raid on London, assembled 38 Gotha V bombers, 3 Giant bombers and two Rumpler CVII reconnaissance aircraft. These smaller aircraft were to fly ahead of the main force to observe weather conditions. They had orders to drop the few bombs they were able to carry on Dover as an alternative target if London could not be reached. The main force comprised the 15 Flight Bombengeschwader 3, who were stationed in Belgium. As Captain Richard von Bentivegni, CO of 501 Staffel, prepared his remaining three Giants (the surviving aircraft from a raid on 9 May), weather conditions were favourable. This was the first evening of many which seemed suitable for air raids, with the coastline free of fog and an anticyclone extending over England.

The barometer was rising slowly and stood at 30.27in. Surface winds were 8 to 10mph from east-north-east and at 10,000ft the wind was 10mph from the south-west. Despite patches of mist inland, which interfered with searchlights, the visibility was good. Brandenburg and his officers could not have hoped for better conditions. That evening an aircraft was heard circling off the North Foreland on the coast of Kent. British observers were puzzled as it hovered in the moonlit sky without heading inland. The intruder left a flare burning brightly over the sea and its drone faded away; German bombers were already heading towards England.

The flare had been a signal to tell them that the weather was clear. At 10.42 p.m. London was alerted to the impending raid. From then until midnight German aircraft flew in at five-minute intervals. The telephone lines were jammed with reports to the Defence Sub Commands and the Home Guard. The night air was filled with the drone of the bombers which crossed and re-crossed; some aircraft passed out to sea and others came in. English pilots who flew out to meet the threat were amazed, as the sky seemed full of German machines. Major Quentin Brand, CO of 112 Squadron, took off from Throwley in his Sopwith Camel to patrol the area. Attracted by the searchlights, which scanned the night skies between Canterbury and Faversham, he soon intercepted a Gotha. Major Brand's own combat report reads as follows:

I arrived over the vicinity still climbing, my height being something in the region of 7,000ft. The concentration of lights above (about four in number)was searching just North East of me and while looking in their direction, something passing above and to my left caught my attention. It proved to be a twin-engined machine about 500ft or so above me turned to engage the enemy aircraft (whose identity was perfectly definite) by approaching from his rear and below his own height. His rear gunner opened fire, I immediately returned his fire and a subsequent burst apparently put his starboard engine out of order. The aircraft did a rapid turn with its nose well down and passed beneath me. I turned keeping it in sight and got to very close quarters. He was going down rapidly, soon after opening fire the German machine burst into flames, which enveloped my own aircraft for an instant.

The Gotha bomber of Bombengeschwader 3, Staffel 15, No.979, flew in over Sandwich at 11 p.m.; it was west of Canterbury ten minutes later. Following the Stour Valley south-westward to Chilham, the aircraft came under fire near Canterbury. To avoid the guns of Godmersham and Wye it turned north-west and when over Faversham, flying west-north-west, was shot down by Brand. Crashing at 11.29 p.m., it fell about one and a half miles east of Harty Ferry, close to the sea wall.

This was seen from as far away as the keep at Dover Castle and Foreness. Prior to this action it had dropped a 50kg bomb at Faversham and one on the village of Davington, causing damage to doors, roofs and windows.

An incendiary was dropped at Graveney Marshes, which failed to ignite, and other bombs were believed to have fallen in the Swale. The Gotha was totally destroyed. Despite this, a barograph found in the wreckage indicated that the ill-fated bomber had set out at 9.30 p.m. and flew over England at an altitude of 3,100m.

The instrument recorded the crash as occuring at 11.36 p.m. The Imperial War Graves Commission has identified the crew as Lt Rudolf Bartikowski, Vizefeldwebel Fritz Bloch and Vizefeldwebel Heinrich Heiligers. All three were buried at Leysdown (St Clements') churchyard but later moved to Cannock Chase War Graves Cemetery.

The flaming Gotha had been seen from Throwley and on Major Brand's return he was enthusiastically 'chaired' into his office but with such vigour that his bearers banged his head on the door! Major Brand later had one of the propellers from the Gotha mounted with a clock set in its centre. When asked why he kept firing after the Gotha was in flames, he replied, 'To make sure that the fire stayed alight'. He had taken off alone in complete darkness, without the aid of flares, climbing to meet the incoming stream of bombers. Because of his conspicuous gallantry he was awarded the DSO. Brand's Camel did not escape undamaged, as one of the airmen at Throwley, A. W. James, noticed. The propeller and the fabric of the wings were severely blistered. Major Brand's engine fitter, J. Tucker, also recalled that the underside of the aircraft was ripped open from nose to tail.

Major Sowrey engaged a Gotha in the neighbourhood of Detling, flying at 8,000ft. He was able to get quite close and fired off his drum before trouble with his guns enabled the enemy to escape. Lt W.G. Scotcher witnessed the combat and flew in their direction but by the time he arrived the combat was over and there was no sign of the enemy. The speed of the Gotha was estimated as being 80mph. At about 12.25 a.m. when in the vicinity of Maidstone, Major Sowrey encountered an enemy machine flying almost due north. He fired off two double drums but, in attempting to use his Vickers gun, his machine stalled and by the time he had righted her, his opponent had got away. This was thought to be the aircraft brought down at Frinsted by Lt E.E. Turner and Lt H.B. Barwise in a Bristol Fighter C851 of 141 Squadron Biggin Hill.

One of the crew who survived the attack was later questioned and confirmed that the Gotha had been attacked previously by a single-seater fighter. This aircraft was in fact flown by Major Sowrey of 143 Squadron, Detling, in his SE5a, who intercepted the Gotha but did not damage it.

Lt Turner was proceeding in the direction of South Ash when he spotted the aircraft to the south of his position, flying east. His Observer, Lt H.B. Barwise, opened fire and hit one of the engines with his first burst. Owing to engine problems Lt Turner was unable to keep the Gotha in his sight. There was no doubt that that this was indeed the aircraft which crashed at Frinsted. It had been a successful night for pilots of Home Defence units in Kent.

The following is a report on the examination of three German prisoners of the 3 Bombing Squadron (Kahgol 3), captured after being shot down during the last major air raid on England by the Gotha bombers on 19 May 1918.

Machines of the 3rd Bomber Squadron carried out the raid on England, on the night of 19 May. There was apparently nothing unusual about the method of attack, as machines left the aerodromes at five-minute intervals and attacked this country independently. The machines that were brought down came from the following flights:

St Osyth	15th Flight	two prisoners
East Ham	18th Flight	crew killed
Harty Ferry	15th Flight	crew killed (shot down by Major Brand, 112 Sqdn)
Frinsted	17th Flight	one prisoner (shot down by Turner/Barwise, 141 Sqdn)
Dover	18th Flight	crew killed

The prisoners spoken to were Vizefeldwebel Max Gummelt and Vizefeldwebel Rudolf Huhnsdorf, both of the 15th Flight, and Unteroffizer Herman Tasche, 17th Flight. The machine of the 15th Flight that landed at St Osyth had lost its way.

The Observer thought they were still south of the Thames when they ran into cloud, actually near Clacton. They accordingly dived down through the clouds at 600ft; having seen land, the pilot switched on again, his right engine choked and he made an emergency landing. The bombs had been released sometime before and fell into the sea. The machine of the 17th Flight made its landfall north of the Thames, but evidently further north than was intended. They reached London and bombed it. On the return journey, they were attacked first by one of our scouts. According to the prisoner they sustained no injuries from this attack. Shortly afterwards they were again attacked by a two-seater which remained for sometime below their tail. The prisoners believed that the left engine was hit and were obliged to land.

Both these machines were driven off their intended course north. It was not possible to ascertain the total number of machines that took part in this raid. According to the prisoners six machines of the 16th Flight were ready to start from Oostacker. Between five and seven machines of the 17th Flight were stated as having started. According to prisoners' statements, the distribution of the 3rd Bombing Squadron was as follows:

13th/14th Flights	Mariakerke
15th/16th Flights	Oostacker
HQ & 17th Flights	Gontrode

The Giant aeroplanes, which were formerly at St Denis Westrem, were said to have been stationed at Scheldewindeke. The establishment of the 3rd Bombing Squadron had not been changed; there were six flights with seven machines. On 19 May the 15th Flight had six Gotha

This Handley Page 0/400, a visitor to Throwley Airfield, appears to have the name 'Clayton' painted on its nose beneath the gunner's cockpit. An unusual sight on such a small airfield, it may have been experiencing engine trouble and so attracted many onlookers. (C.F. Wooley)

GV machines and one Albatross C12, which was used in raids behind their lines. The 16th Flight had five machines ready to start but the prisoners could not say whether they had any others being assembled. Crashed machines were difficult to replace; it took from one to three weeks for a new machine to arrive after its requisition. Their strength, which was unusually high, they attributed to the fact that so few raids on England had recently been attempted. Raids behind our lines in France were less costly.

Since the end of 1917 the squadron had carried out raids behind their lines and had not been reserved for attacks on England. Boulogne, Calais, Dunkirk and St Omer were stated to be the four most frequent objectives. The squadron had not attacked England for a while because the weather had been uncertain and because they had been fully occupied by the short flights to other areas, for which the weather was quite good enough. It is thought probable that the return of Hauptmann Brandenburg as squadron leader was partly responsible for this policy. It is known that he was far more cautious with regard to weather conditions than Hauptmann Kliene; no change of tactics seems to have been contemplated. When over England, all machines flew as high as possible. They were said to be able to reach at least 3,000m when loaded for England and none could exceed 4,500m. The prisoners were anxious to know the number and positions of balloon aprons in use. They had been warned of the existence of aprons to the east of London both north and south of the Thames. Information regarding the exact position, extent and height of the balloons was known only by the German aircraft's Observer. After raids on England balloon aprons were reported in every part of London by different machines and it was believed that the policy was to place them irregularly over London and change their positions frequently. This was sufficient to keep all machines flying at their maximum height.

Left: Maj. C.J. Quintin–Brand, later to be Air Vice Marshal Sir Quintin–Brand KBE, DSO MC, DFC, poses for the camera in the beautiful gardens of Bells Forstal Farm, the officers' mess located close to the airfield. From 1939 to 1941 he was commander of No.10 Fighter Group RAF. Today the house looks much the same as it did in 1918. (R.A. Brown).

Below: Maj. C.J. Quintin–Brand seated in his Sopwith Camel D6423, in which he intercepted and destroyed Gotha 979 of Bombengeschwader 3 Staffel 15. Surrounded by members of the squadron, who are obviously delighted with his success, this was to be the only German bomber shot down by 112 (Home Defence) Squadron Throwley.

Brand's Camel was named 'Makhabane II' after the Basuto warrior. The Gotha which crashed in flames at Harty Ferry, near Faversham, was one of thirty-eight aircraft which formed the last major bombing raid against England on 18/19 May 1918.

Brand got so close to the doomed bomber that his fellow officers noticed that his moustache had been singed by the flames from the stricken aircraft. (E.F. Cheesman)

An illustration indicating the area of Kent which 112 Squadron had to patrol from September 1918. Also shown is the flight path of the Gotha shot down by Maj. C.J. Quintin-Brand on the night of 18/19 May 1918. (A.J. Moor)

Page 53.

	Name.	Abode.	When buried.	Age.	By whom the Ceremony was performed.
109	Heinz Heeligers Killed in Aerial Battle during raid Sunday May 19th 1918. No. 417.	Germany	May 22nd 1918	–	Ca B. Allen Chaplain R.N. Rich. G. Harding Vicar
75	Robert Milne Collingwood Lieut No. 418.	R.A.F. Eastchurch	July 23rd 1918		Ca B. Allen Chaplain R.N. J.T. Phillips C.F.
81	Thomas Frederick Hector Lieut No. 419.	Lieut R.A.F. Eastchurch	Aug 10th 1918		Ca B. Allen Chaplain R.N. R.G. Harding Vicar
82	Leslie Archer Philips No. 420.	R.A.F. East Church	Sept 19th 1918	21 Years	Ca B. Allen Chaplain R.N. R.G. Harding Vicar
106 / 45	Bessie Alice Owers for 22 years School Mistress No.	Leysdown	Oct 15th 1916	59 years	Richard Edward Harding Vicar
	Unknown man Kate Lowe found on the seashore in the parish of Warden No. 413.	Leysdown	Sept 7th 1917 July 12th 1917	44 yrs	Rich. Edward Harding Vicar
74	Harwood James Arnold. Lieut R.N.A.S. accidentally killed fall from aeroplane No. 414.	Leysdown. R.N.A.S Camp.	March 22nd 1918	28 Years	Ca B. Allen Chaplain R.N. Rich. G. Harding Vicar
120	Unknown German presumed H. Bottcher officer killed in Aerial battle during raid Sunday May 19th 1918. No. 415.	Germany.	May 22nd 1918	–	Ca B. Allen Chaplain R.N. Rich. G. Harding Vicar
110	Unknown German presumed Mechanic or N.C.O. killed in Aerial battle during raid Sunday May 19 1918. No. 416.	Germany	May 22nd 1918	–	Ca B. Allen Chaplain R.N. Rich. G. Harding Vicar

The German crew of Gotha 979, Bombengeschwader 3, Staffel 15 were originally buried at Leysdown church, Isle of Sheppey. This is a copy of the original register. (St Clements Leysdown)

46

Above and below: The three crew members, Lt R. Bartikowski, Vizefeldwebel F. Bloch and Vizefeldwebel H. Heiligers, were later reburied in the German Section of Cannock Chase Cemetery, Cambridgeshire. (War Graves Commission)

Another German bomber which did not return home on the night of 19/20 May was Gotha
G V/925/16, which crashed after descending through cloud to check its position, mistaking Blackwater
Estuary for the Thames. An engine choked, and despite jettisoning its bombs to gain height it was too
late. The aircraft was named *Pommern*, possibly after Pomerania in Germany, where the crew came from.
One crew member, Lt R. Rist, was killed. This was the fourth aircraft lost during this particular air raid.
(Imperial War Museum)

Sopwith Camel F1, serial number D6473, was flown by Capt. T.M.B Newton of 112 (Home Defence)
Squadron, based at Throwley Airfield in 1918. (Mike Bailey/Red Lion Press)

A Sopwith Snipe E7337, possibly of 112 Squadron at Throwley. The pilot on the left of the group is 2nd Lt F.B. Barager. (R.A. Brown)

By 1916 the technique of night flying was by no means perfected. Pilots were flying aircraft when they were still untrained in the necessary skills. Despite this handicap pilots were undeterred and still took every opportunity to try and intercept the enemy. By September 1915 eighty-nine flights had been made, during which twenty aircraft were damaged or destroyed taking off or landing, killing three pilots and injuring eight. However, because of the increase in Zeppelin raids, the War Office created a special wing to unify the Defence Units and form new squadrons. These units were equipped with the BE2c, which at the time was considered the best aircraft to combat the Zeppelin, despite the fact that it did not perform well at high altitude.

The first training course in night flying began in 1916 at Hounslow; the instruction included five night flights and armament instruction. It is interesting to note that by early 1916 there had been a total of thirty-six raids by the Germans. Most of these were carried out by single-seat aircraft but the War Office seemed more concerned with the Zeppelin raids, which was reflected by the poor armament of the Home Defence equipment.

In 1916 pilots were expected to attack the airships with two 20lb Hales bombs and two 16lb incendiary bombs, which was rather unlikely as the Zeppelin could fly 10,000ft higher than their own aircraft. As a result of this problem many ideas were put forward, such as hand grenades being trailed on a 500ft cable.

Other suggestions were flame-throwers and even freezing the clouds to use as landing grounds for aircraft! Some practical ideas emerged, such as Le Prieur rockets and explosive bullets. The big difficulty for the pilots was simply being able to use the daytime gun sights, which at night were not much use. This was resolved by Sgt A. Sutton in 1917, when he invented a gun sight which was illuminated, later being replaced by the Neame Sight which as well as being illuminated had the additional feature of a graduated ring sight, enabling the pilot to estimate the target range.

The problem of gun-flash blinding pilots was solved by placing the guns on the upper wing, and later a shield was fitted to machine guns. By the autumn of 1917 training of night fighter pilots had improved and in June 1918 they had to have completed twenty-five solo hours, including four night flights; they were also tested in navigation cross-country flights, wearing darkened goggles to simulate night flying, gunnery skills and wireless transmission. Once training was completed, the pilot gained his wings, an event which was followed by further training with an operational squadron and another wireless course, which took place at Penshurst, Kent. He was then promoted to First Class Operations Officer and posted to a Home Defence unit.

The Flare Party at Throwley consisted of an NCO and an airman from each flight. They were assisted by an aircraft and Patrol Guard and normally paraded at 7.00 p.m. outside the Transport Sheds. Their duties were various, including placing out the flares on the airfield at dusk every evening, lighting the 'blinker' rockets when flying commenced and placing landing lights on the airfield. When night flying was ordered, they had to fire off 'Recall Rockets', checking that the flare tins and lamps were filled ready for use.

After the flares had been laid out the airmen remained in the guardroom until they were needed, to ensure that any orders given in connection with lighting or changing flares were carried out quickly. If there were any obstructions, such as a crashed aircraft or the unlikely event of bomb damage, white hurricane lamps were lit around them until the obstruction was removed or damage to the airfield repaired. To avoid any confusion for pilots landing aircraft, it was forbidden to carry portable lamps around after the flares had been lit. All airmen assigned to this unpopular duty had to sleep in the guardroom until ordered otherwise.

The Landing Ground at Pluckley was used for Ground Firing practice. This consisted of targets being put out and red flags and 'Danger' notices being put up at each end of the footpath, and any livestock kept in the field had to be cleared off the area. Pilots fired a red warning light before firing and a white one on completion. When two or more were firing the targets were not patched up until the last pilot fired a white flare. Responsibility for these activities lay with Major C.S. Tuswell, the Officer Commanding the GDU (Ground Defence Unit), based at Stede Court HQ at Harrietsham. The Emergency Airfields in the area were, on occasion, inspected by a pilot from Throwley. Assigned to this duty in March 1917 was one such officer, Lt Stanley Preston, 112 Squadron.

These inspections, usually lasting no more than an hour, were carried out to check the equipment supplied to the RDC, the unit based at the landing ground, was complete and that the airstrip was safe to use. The north-eastern corner of the site, Park Wood, had a steep slope and was rather dangerous. Preston, in his report, recommended that pilots deciding to land there should not circle round flares preparatory to landing at a height of less than 500ft.

An unusual photograph of an Avro 504 of 188 (Night Training) Squadron RAF, seen here flying over the tented area situated close to Bells Forstal Farm at Throwley. (I. McKay)

FRINSTED VILLAGE.

FRINSTED VILLAGE.
Drawing of original sketch made by Lt H. Preston on 12 September 1918 of Frinsted 2nd Class Landing Ground, near Harrietsham. It would appear that Preston was conducting a survey of Landing Grounds in both Kent and around the Sussex border; his report on Frinsted reads as follows:

The wire fence indicated is hardly visible from the air in daylight and the grass field on the other side seems part of the Landing Ground. On landing yesterday from the NE I very nearly did so on the wrong side of the fence. About a month ago a Sopwith Pup was written–off against the fence and quite recently a BE2e landing from the SW only succeeded in evading it by putting on engine power and hopping over into the next field.

Lt H. Preston was nearly killed himself when, as an Observer, he crashed in an FE2b at Gainborough, the pilot, 2nd Lt H.P Solomon, was killed. The Gotha bomber shot down by Lt E.E. Turner and Lt H.B. Barwise crashed close to Frinsted. The crew were buried on the north boundary of St Dunstan's church. (A.J. Moor)

The remains of the second Gotha bomber shot down on the night of 19/20 May 1918. Although ultimately destroyed by Lt E.E. Turner and his Observer (Lt H.B. Barwise of 141 Squadron, Biggin Hill), the aircraft had been sighted by Lt W.G. Scotcher of 112 Squadron, Throwley, and intercepted by Maj. Sowrey of 143 Squadron from Detling. The stricken bomber crashed close to the village of Frinsted and almost on the 2nd Class Airfield close by. (Mrs L. Mallion)

A section of wooden spar recovered from the wreckage of a Sopwith Camel that crashed in Eastwood. It was recovered from the crash by a Mr Manuel; a schoolboy in 1918, he kept his treasure in his garden shed until the 1980s when he gave it to the author. (A.J. Moor)

More of the wreckage; Mr Manuel, who, with his wife, managed the village shop and post office at Throwley for some years, had fond memories of the pilots and the airfield. The pilot is believed to have been Lt L.W.F. Hopgood, a Canadian who was buried at Throwley church. (A.J. Moor)

Another pilot buried at Throwley church is 2nd Lt J.T. Mitchell, killed on 24 January 1918. It is believed that he span his aircraft into Hockley Wood. The wreckage was not found until it was seen from the air. (A.J. Moor)

The grave of Lt E.W.F. Hopgood in the churchyard at Throwley; he was killed on 14 October 1918 when his aircraft span into the ground from a height of 4,000ft. (A.J. Moor)

A rear view of 'Madge', the Sopwith Pup flown by Capt. T.M.B. Newton. Note the stripes painted on the tail plane and those around the aircraft's fuselage. (E.F. Cheesman)

Capt. T.M.B. Newton seated in his Sopwith Pup 'Madge'; note the number '6' on the side of his aircraft. This is the first of two aircraft he christened with this name. The step used by the pilot to climb into the cockpit can be seen by the roundel. (E.F. Cheesman)

five

The epic flight of Quintin-Brand and background of pilots and airmen transferred to Throwley home defence airfield

Perhaps Quentin Brand will be best remembered for his epic flight to the Cape, accompanied by Lt-Col Pierre van Ryneveldt. The aircraft chosen for the attempt was a Vickers Vimy, painted silver, as its name 'Silver Queen' suggests.

They took off from Brooklands Airfield on 4 February 1920, encountering poor weather over the Mediterranean at night, the wind blowing at 50mph. The pilots missed Crete and reached the African coast an hour and a half behind scheduled time. They were both exhausted after struggling with the weather for nearly eleven hours, and on landing at Sollum they damaged the tailskid, which they managed to repair with parts from a Ford car. The 'Silver Queen' took off from Cairo in darkness on 10 February, hoping to reach Khartoum, which was a 1,044-mile flight.

More than half the distance had been covered when the Vickers Vimy developed problems. One of the engine's radiators was leaking, and as a result they made a forced landing at night. The aircraft was badly damaged but fortunately both the pilots and the engines survived. They landed at Korosko, on the Nile.

Lt-Col van Ryneveldt, with Brand, returned to Cairo with the engines, which were then fitted to another Vickers Vimy, 'Silver Queen II'. By 22 February the aircraft was ready and the following evening they reached Khartoum. Leaking radiators was a common problem with aircraft that attempted to fly to the Cape.

On 26 February 'Silver Queen II' arrived at Mwanza and three days later passed over Tabora, overtaking the aircraft sponsored by *The Times*, which had crashed at Tabora on 27 February. Had Brand been able to he would have picked up the pilot, Dr Chalmers-Mitchell, and taken him with them to the Cape.

'Silver Queen II' crashed on take off from Bulawayo having flown 3,880 miles in thirteen days. Determined to continue their flight, van Ryneweldt and Brand battled on in a DH9, which had been flown to them from Cape Town. They completed the flight in this aircraft, suitably named 'Voortrekker' (Pioneer), on 20 March 1920. The epic flight had taken only four weeks, including eleven days waiting at Bulawayo.

Brand and his fellow pilot were given a great reception in acknowledgement of their endurance and courage. The Union Government voted them a sum of £5,000 as reward. The route taken by Brand and van Ryneveldt was retraced years later by one of England's greatest pioneer pilots, Alan J. Cobham.

They received a telegram from King George V and both were knighted. In May they were honoured at a Banquet at the Savoy Hotel, London, and their health toasted by the Secretary of State for Air, Winston Churchill. Air Vice Marshal Sir Quintin Brand KBE, DSO, MC, DFC, was Director General of Aviation, Egypt, from 1932 to 1936, and Director of Repair and Maintenance Air Ministry from 1937 to 1939. From 1939 until 1941 he was Commander of No.10 Fighter Group, RAF. Brand died at Umtali, Rhodesia, on 7 March 1968 at the age of seventy-four. He was born at Beaconsfield near Kimberley on 25 May 1893 and educated at the Marist Brothers, Johannesburg. There is a statue of Brand and van Ryneveldt in the Main Hall at Jan Smuts Airport, Johannesburg.

Captain Gilbert Murlis-Green DSO.MC began his service life when he joined the Suffolk Regiment in 1914, transferring to the REC in 1915. He flew as an observer with No.5 Squadron, based in France. It was not long, however, before he was selected for pilot training, then in 1916 he flew with No.17 Squadron in Salonica, initially flying a BE2d, later flying a BE12. It was not long before he was awarded the MC, and on 13 December 1916 he was awarded the Bar to his MC, when he engaged and shot down a German twin-seater. In mid-March he was promoted to captain and had added two more enemy aircraft to his score. His next victim was a twin-engined Friedrichshafen, quickly followed by another of the same type the next day.

Shortly after being awarded the DSO, Captain Gurlis-Green destroyed another twin-seater, flying a French Spad which he had borrowed. He was then posted back to England and took command of 44 Squadron (Home Defence), which was equipped with the Sopwith Camel night fighter. On 18 December 1918 he became the first pilot to shoot down a German Gotha GIII over England at night. Murlis-Green was then posted to 151 Squadron in France in a night fighting role; returning to England he became CO of 112 (Home Defence) Squadron at Throwley on 9 July 1918, where he remained until October 1918. To add to his decorations he received the French and Belgian Croix de Guerre and the Karageorge (Serbian Order of the White Eagle). Remaining in the RAF he was later promoted to Group Captain in 1934.

Captain Stanley Cockerell was borne in Osterley Park, Middlesex; after qualifying as a sergeant pilot in the RFC he was posted to 24 Squadron in France in 1916. That October he was wounded in action. On recovering he was commissioned and returning to the squadron he shot down three German aircraft. On going back to England he was promoted to captain and posted to 112 Squadron at Throwley, from where he went to 151 Squadron (Night Fighters) in France. Then on 2 August 1918 he shot down a Gotha over Guizencourt which at the time was landing at night; this was his seventh victory. One or two of the pilots assigned to 112 Squadron were possibly considered eccentric, among them Captain Baker who was Officer Commanding 'B' Flight. He was well known for the cut of his riding breeches and always appeared to be bored. However, he had one passion: the breeding of cream-coloured bull terriers. This peculiar enthusiasm could well explain why several pilots in photographs taken at Throwley Airfield have dogs in their arms! He is remembered for often going out in his Camel, named 'Tootsie', on night-flying exercises, accompanied by one of his favourites. Another officer, Captain Newton 'CO' C Flight, always used to wear a ladies' silk stocking over his flying helmet.

Above: Maj. Q.C. Brand, CO of 112 Squadron, seated at the controls of the first Sopwith Camel delivered to the squadron. He is pictured here on his return from what is believed to be the first Camel sortie undertaken by the squadron. (E.F. Cheesman)

Maj. C.J. Quintin-Brand and Lt Col Pierre van Ryneveldt check over their Vickers Vimy 'Silver Queen' registered G-UABA, a standard Vimy bomber. The aircraft is seen here on the Compass Swinging Base at Brooklands Airfield shortly before the start of their epic flight to the Cape on 4 February 1920. (Vickers Ltd)

Opposite below: Sopwith Camel F1639 of 112 Squadron being checked by a mechanic shortly after being ferried from Norwich by Flt F.C. Broome in 1918. (R.A. Brown)

Another view of Garnons-Williams aircraft with more personnel discussing the amount of repair work to be done. In the background hangars can be seen and other machines are lined up ready for take-off. (E.F. Cheesman)

Officers of 112 Squadron standing close to one of the wooden hangars belonging to 188 (Training) Squadron, Throwley, early 1918. From left to right: Garnons-Williams, Bateman (Adjudant), Goodyear, Beck, Arkell and Chandler. (E.F. Cheesman)

Sopwith Pup B1803 'Madge', flown by Capt. Garnons-Williams. The badge on the side of the aircraft is that of his old regiment, the South Wales & Borderers. (E.F. Cheesman)

Capt. Newton at the controls of a replacement aircraft. Pilots often used the same name on new aircraft, a common practice at the time and a tradition carried on by pilots during the Second World War. (E.F. Cheesman)

Two Avro 504 aircraft of 188 (Training) Squadron collided on the airfield at Throwley. Wearing overalls is Lt A.C.S. Irwin, accompanied by a young lady visitor to the airfield. In the background is Bells Forstal Farm and the tented accommodation of 188 Squadron. There also appears to be a landing strip laid out with white tape, possibly used in some exercise or entertainment. (A.C.S. Irwin)

This aircraft, although a Sopwith Camel, does not belong to 112-Squadron and may only be visiting Throwley. The gentleman approaching the aircraft appears to be wearing civilian clothes.
(E.F. Cheesman)

Above: Mechanics of 112 Squadron working on the undercarriage of B2159, one of the unit's Sopwith Pups; the type was very popular with pilots. (E.F. Cheesman)

Right: Capt. A.A. Garnons-Williams of 112 Squadron, caught by the camera just before climbing into a BE12a. Note the smart leather flying coat and goggles. Sadly Capt. Garnons-Williams was killed in a flying accident. (E.F. Cheesman)

Left: The three officers are Williams, Cockerell and Newton, all of 112 Squadron. It is interesting to note that each pilot is wearing a different style of uniform. (E.F. Cheesman)

Below: A copy made by the Air Ministry Information Division of an original photograph given by Mr J. Tucker, showing a Sopwith Camel of 112 Squadron. Capt. Baker CO 'B' Flight and A.C. Tucker pose for the camera. Note the faint numeral '1' on the fin and the diagonal bar in front of the roundel, the metal part of the cowling remains brilliantly polished. In the background to the left are aircraft of 188 Squadron and to the right is Bells Forstal Farm. (J. Tucker)

Above: A Sopwith Pup of 112 Squadron with a Monosoupape engine. The pilots are Capt. T.M.B. Newton and Lt Davies. It was quite common for pilots to name their aircraft after girl's names; in this case the machine is called 'Madge'. (A.C.S. Irwin)

Below: Sopwith Camel D6664, flown by Lt Wykes, was damaged in an unfortunate crash landing. The pilot was unhurt. (A.C.S. Irwin)

Avove: Lt H. Preston by his Sopwith Pup; in the background are hangars while visible on the side of the fuselage is the plane's squadron number '4'. What appears to be the shape of Australia has also been painted on the fuselage. (E.F. Cheesman)

Right: Lt S. Cockerell appears very comfortable in his leather flying jacket and long over trousers. The aircraft is his Sopwith Pup B1769 and its identification number '1' is clearly visible on the side of the aircraft. (E.F. Cheesman)

Right: Capt. T.M.B. Newton is wearing his own style of flying gear which would have been needed on operations flying in open cockpit fighter aircraft. The material chosen for this outfit appears to be animal fur of unknown origin. (E.F. Cheesman)

Below: The aircraft in this early 1918 view across the airfield is a Sopwith Pup, behind which are two camouflaged Bessoneau hangars. To the left are the wooden hangars and the air sock is just visible above them. (E.F. Cheesman)

Above: Capt. Newton's Sopwith Pup 'Madge' B2178, standing close to one of the wooden hangars. In the background are other aircraft of 112 Squadron. (E.F. Cheesman)

Below: Three members of 112 Squadron. On the left stands an unknown officer, who is not a pilot; in the centre is Lt J.S. Poole, who is wearing a black armband; and to his right stands Lt A.J. Arkell. (E.F. Cheesman)

Above: Lt S. Cockerell and Lt Gilbertson taking a stroll and sharing a joke on a sunny day in 1918. Cockerell was responsible for shooting down a Gotha bomber over France on 2 August 1918 when he was flying with 151 (Night Fighter) Squadron. (E.F. Cheesman)

Below: An airframe fitter surveys the damage to a battered Sopwith Pup flown by Lt A.A. Garnons-Williams after a collision on take-off with another aircraft at Throwley Airfield during 1918. Note the number '5' painted on the side of the fuselage. (E.F. Cheesman)

A group photograph of 112 Squadron Officers, probably taken in the grounds of Bells Forstal Farm. Back row, from left to right: Meredith, Gilbertson, Baker, Garnons-Williams, Cox, Brand, Newton, Preston, Irwin. Front row, from left to right: Morris, Beck, Broome, Dodson. (E.F. Cheesman)

Sopwith Pups of 'C' Flight 112 Squadron line up at Throwley in 1918. To the left of the wooden hangar of 188 Squadron behind the aircraft are the Bessoneau hangars of 112 Squadron. (E.F. Cheesman)

Pilots of 112 (Home Defence) Squadron in front of Bells Forstal Farm in September or October 1917, a few months after their arrival at Throwley. The officers' mess provided comfortable accommodation and was not far down the lane from the airfield. Standing in the back row, second left, is 2nd Lt L.E. Chandler. Seated third left is 2nd Lt S. Cockerell; fifth from left is Maj. G. Allen; and second from the end is Capt. T.M.B. Newton. (A.C.S. Irwin)

This group photograph was taken in the gardens of Bells Forstal Farm in June 1918. Back row, from left to right: –?–, Capt. A.B. Yuille, Lt G.N. Blennerhassett, Lt W.G. Scotcher, 2nd Lt F.B. Barager, Lt F.C. Broome, Lt Frampton. Seated: –?–, Capt. Baker, –?–, Maj. Quintin-Brand, Capt. T.M.B Newton, Lt Collier, Lt A.C.S. Irwin. Front row, from left to right: –?–, –?–, –?–, Lt W. Aitken, Lt Wykes, –?–, –?–. (A.C.S. Irwin)

Major C.O. Usborne, a French Canadian lumberjack who also just happened to be an Indianapolis racing driver, was very proud of his red car, which was nicknamed 'The Crimson Rambler'. He was often seen driving at break-neck speed around the airfield to relieve his boredom! Shortly after arriving at Throwley he took over command of 112 Squadron from Capt. Murlis-Green DSO, MC, on the day the Armistice was signed. Several pilots and airmen who were stationed at Throwley Airfield, as at any base during wartime, met and married into local families.

The following details are taken from Throwley Parish Registers and reflect the social life outside the camp during the years the RFC and RAF were living and billeted in the area. On 8 July 1916 Clive Reginald Parkhurst, twenty-two years old, married a local girl from the village, Nellie Rhoda Mack, who was twenty-six. Clive's father George was by trade an antique furnisher and Nellie's father a steward to Lord Harris. One year later the couple had their first child, Roland Clive Parkhurst, who was baptised on 22 March 1917. Tragically Roland Clive Parkhurst, who like his father joined the RAF, was later killed when his aircraft crashed into a hillside in Hampshire.

Corporal Arthur William Reeve RFC, from Hove in Sussex, was married to Mary Kate Cobb of Throwley on 22 May 1915. Mary was the daughter of Stephen Cobb, a labourer, and Elsie Cobb. On 9 April 1916 Eileen Mary was baptised at Throwley church. Percival Thomas Pengilly, the son of Llewellin Richard Pengilly, first class airman, and Margaret Annie, was baptised on 8 September 1918.

Also living in the area was 2nd Lt C.J. Cross, a pilot with 112 Squadron, and his wife Nina. Their son George Clive Inkerman was also baptised at Throwley church.

six

How Throwley played its role as a
home defence airfield during the first
'Battle of Britain', and the
closure of the airfield

The German bomber raid of 19/20 May 1918 was to be the last involving the squadrons based at Throwley Home Defence Airfield. The last raid on England took place on the night of 5/6 August 1918, and the enemy attacked with a force of five Naval Zeppelins. In fact it ended in the loss of one of their latest Zeppelin types and the death of all its crew. The bomber raids did not end because of England's much improved Home Defence system, nor because the raids on England had become too costly for the Germans, both in lost lives and aircraft. Rather, flushed with the success of their 'terror' raids, they decided to turn their attention to the Western Front, where they considered the bombers could be better employed.

The Zeppelin and bomber raids on England could not have won Germany the war, but they certainly terrified the civilian population and accelerated the need for a more efficient Home Defence system, both in the air and on the ground. The total number of civilians killed during the air raids was 1,414, with 3,416 injured.

The raiders were difficult to intercept, which is reflected by the fact that only one Gotha bomber was destroyed by action from Throwley. There were, of course, several other RFC and RNAS bases taking on the enemy. Their squadrons took to the skies over the south-east of England to try and intercept the incoming Zeppelins, Giant and Gotha bombers and there were indeed successful interceptions. There are many documents and books describing, in depth, the aerial victories and losses during the defence of England between 1916 to 1918. It is not an exaggeration to compare the events of aerial bombardment in the First World War to that of the Blitz and it is no accident that this period has been labelled the 'First Battle of Britain'.

When the Armistice eventually came in 1919, there were some 355 aircraft which formed 6th Brigade, including nine night-training squadrons. From the German point of view, this had meant that there were many pilots, ground crew and a lot of equipment, which had been diverted to combat the aerial threat.

After the First World War one of the pilots of 112 Squadron, Murlis-Green, based at Throwley, wrote of his experiences as a Home Defence pilot:

On a dark night with no moon, the exhaust flames of a stationary engine machine will usually be seen before the outline of the machine itself, but on a clear moonlight night the outline of the machine is generally first seen. After patrolling for an hour or so in the dark without seeing anything there is a tendency, when a hostile is at last seen, to dive straight at it firing both guns. This method seldom leads to success as the machine-guns, even when shielded, usually impairs the pilot's sight to such an extent that after the first few rounds have been fired he loses the target.

The method found most successful up to now is as follows. Once you have seen your objective you must not take your eyes off him until he is destroyed or you wish to break off the fight. Turn your machine quickly into the same direction as he is going and get behind and slightly below him. If you have a 45 degree mounting use it.

If your guns fire in line of flight close up until almost colliding, throttle back and open fire. There are two reasons why it is important not to fire until extremely close range has been reached. Firstly, it is difficult to distinguish friend from foe at night, as of course crosses cannot be distinguished from circles, so that one has to rely entirely upon silhouettes. Secondly, range is very deceptive at night.

A document by the 6th Brigade stated that night-fighters, assisted by searchlights was the way forward, a comment that all the pilots trained in night-fighting at Throwley and other airfields created for Home Defence would have agreed with.

Of the units based at Throwley, 112 Squadron remained at the airfield until a short period after the Armistice, when they were disbanded. However, most of the more experienced pilots from each flight of the Home Defence squadrons, Nos 44, 78, and 112 Squadron, were transferred to Hainault Farm, Essex, on 12 June 1918, to form 151 (Night Fighting) Squadron.

Ironically, in August 1918 the Government felt there may still have been a risk of further German air raids, and decided that the number of Home Defence squadrons should be raised to twenty. By the end of war on 11 November 1918, this requirement fell to fifteen, having never exceeded sixteen.

As for 188 Squadron, which had been formed at Throwley on 20 December 1917 to train pilots in night flying, it was disbanded at the airfield in March 1918, and was never reformed. Some squadrons were later reformed in the Second World War, such as 112, which distinguished itself abroad in this second incarnation and remained in existence until the 1950s.

Activities at Throwley had slowed down after the Armistice, and the wooden hangar was dismantled. The new brick hangar under construction was never completed. Trusses of these structures were sold and transported by road to a garage a few miles away at Sittingbourne. Sadly, although relocated, the garage and the historic building has long since gone, to be replaced eventually by yet another homeware store.

Armistice Day was a day of jubilation at the airfield. To celebrate the long-awaited occasion, Major Usborne jumped into his car and roared off around the airfield with a Union Jack on the front of his car! Predictably it wasn't very long before the flag wrapped itself around his head, and both he and the 'The Crimson Rambler' went straight into a ditch. The same day Faversham police were called out to the airfield to investigate reports of drunken airmen who were threatening to burn down the hangars with Very lights. There is no evidence to suggest that any damage to the buildings had occurred, although most of the remaining airmen at Throwley would have approved such an action.

As well as these impromptu incidents, several parties of a kind were held at the 'Regimental Institute', a sort of NAAFI canteen. This was a building to the right of the lane, close to the hangars, which is a bridle path today. Between the wars the locals at Throwley reclaimed the building for their village hall. Many of the local residents took part in the Armistice Day festivities, of 1918, which should have helped the airmen meet the local girls, evidenced by many of them settling in the area!

Apart from the old Guardroom, which has been saved from destruction because it was converted into a bungalow, there are now no other buildings on the airfield site. However, if you are in the area, you may walk along the bridle path, which used to be the entrance to the airfield, and still find much evidence of the RFC buildings which were constructed at various stages in the airfield's short history. I believe that some years ago empty bullet cases were found in the area of the firing butts. Finally, perhaps the most poignant reminder of the airfield's existence are the two graves of Lt E.W.F. Hopgood and 2nd Lt J.T. Mitchell, who were buried with full military honours in the peaceful village church at Throwley Forstal.

And so it was that in October 1919 the airfield was transferred to the Ministry of Munitions, the site to be used for ammunition storage. Shortly after this it was reclaimed for agricultural use.

Hidden in the undergrowth at the southern end of the airfield are remains of firing butts and there are likely to be some empty shell cases hidden in the area. (A.J. Moor)

The same location, showing the firing butts from another angle. This building is indicated on the Airfield Layout (page 9). (A.J. Moor)

This photograph of the camp canteen was taken shortly before being demolished due to hurricane damage in 1987. It is believed that the building was used for social occasions. Its location was to the right of the lane which led onto the site and it can be seen on the Airfield Layout (page 9). (A.J. Moor)

Looking across the empty meadow which was once Throwley Airfield. In 1918 the Bessoneau hangars of 112 Squadron would have obscured this view. (A.J. Moor)

Looking back along the lane to the Guardroom. This photograph was taken in the 1980s before the restoration of the building. (A.J. Moor)

A closer view of the guardroom and the veranda on which those on duty enjoyed a relatively peaceful watch. (A.J. Moor)

Above: A view looking south along the lane which starts by the guardroom and was the entrance to the airfield. To the left is the area upon which Throwley Airfield was situated, to the right Dodds Willows, where airfield buildings were located. (A.J. Moor)

Left: A stroll around Dodds Willows soon reveals the foundations of buildings. Situated in the right-hand corner of this area are the remains of the semi-underground Ammunition & Pyrotechnic Stores. These are more evident during the summer months when the ground is very dry. (A.J. Moor)

Above: Also evident are
the structural remains
belonging to the airfield
buildings, which were
probably used as workshops
and storage facilities.
(A.J. Moor)

Right: Another view of
the same location on the
airfield site, which does
not appear on the original
Throwley site drawing.
They may have been
erected at a later date.
(A.J. Moor)

The remains of the underground Pyrotechnic and Ammunition store, which is to be found in Dodds Willows Woods. (A.J. Moor)

On closer inspection the entrance to the store is clearly visible. There were many buildings of various types hidden in this wooded area. (A.J. Moor)

Parts of the wooden hangar en route from Throwley to W.J. Pullen's garage, its new home in West Street, Sittingbourne. The camera catches the contractors who dismantled the hangar and transported the trusses to the east of Snips Hill on the Canterbury Road. (Sittingbourne Library)

The hangar roof trusses arrive safely at Sittingbourne. The traction engine moves along West Street at the junction of Park Street, not far from the site of the intended garage. Perhaps onlookers are unaware of the origin of the strange cargo, which once echoed to the noise of Le Rhone engines. (Sittingbourne Library)

Shortly after the war the wooden hangar at Throwley was dismantled, but it lived on. W.J. Pullen, who was the owner of a new garage in West Street, Sittingbourne, bought the roof trusses. The garage, which was situated not far from the junction between Park Street and West Street, remained in business for years. (Sittingbourne Library)

In July 1940 the airfield at Detling was given a site at Cadman's Farm, close to the Throwley Airfield, for use as an ELG or Emergency Landing Ground. There is some doubt as to whether any aircraft did attempt to land there; however, there is a rumour that a Hurricane forced landed on the field, but that is another story.

Today the hedgerow which protected the airfield has been dug out, to allow for maximum farming. It allows the visitor a clear view of the field from which young pilots took off in their efforts to protect England. Little did they know that some twenty years later there would be another war, and another Battle of Britain.

Kent's aviation history is littered with airfield sites from both wars; most of these have long since gone, but let us hope that the brief history of Throwley and other airfields will live on.

Appendix 1

Orders from 6th Brigade following Armistice

From: General Officer Commanding 6 Brigade RAF 24.11.1918
To: Officer Commanding 112 Squadron RAF
Horse Guards Parade, Whitehall SW1.
In view of the cessation of hostilities, and the conditions of the Armistice, as regards the surrender by the enemy of his aircraft. The following alterations to the existing regulations and procedure as regards a state of readiness are notified for information and action.

1.
The Day and Night Dismiss will no longer be sent out from these Headquarters. In so far as operations are concerned, three pilots (one of who must be either the Squadron Commander or a Flight Commander) will be detailed nightly until further notice to remain on duty to provide a first patrol should this be required.

2.
As regards 51 and 75 Squadron, 1 pilot per Flight will be told off each night as an Operations Pilot.

3.
The roster of Officers in charge of Operations Rooms forwarded by squadrons nightly will be discontinued. Squadron Commanders need no longer report to these Headquarters their temporary absence from the aerodrome, under the terms of 6 Brigade letter 24/3/1915 dated 7/10/1918.

4.
No further weather reports will be circulated from these Headquarters. The morning weather reports rendered to these Headquarters from Hadleigh, Rochford and Bekesbourne will be discontinued.

5.
Times will be synchronised at 10am and 6pm daily.

Pilots and groundcrew of 'C' Flight 112 Squadron outside their hangar. The aircraft in the background is a Sopwith Camel, flown by the C.O., which sported 'strut-streamers'. Only three officers' identities are known: seated, front row, fifth from left: Lt A.C.S. Irwin, Capt. T.M.B. Newton, 2nd Lt Turton. (H.H. Russell)

6.

Should it at any time be necessary to revert to the state of readiness which has been in force up to the present date, a telegram will be sent out from these HQ's containing the message 'Resume conditions of Readiness'. On receipt of which the orders contained in this letter will be cancelled.

7.

Notification of flights and reports of aircraft will be made in accordance with LLF.C.R 9677 dated 12.11.1918.

8.

Night flights for training of Searchlights will be continued and henceforth, ordinary Searchlight practice (without Aircraft) will be limited to Mondays, Wednesdays and Fridays, but will not be carried out on those days if the weather is unsuitable. During December the normal hours for searchlight practice will be 1700 to 1730.

Lt. Colonel M. Nichelson
For Brigadier General, Commanding – 6th Brigade Royal Air Force
Distribution: 47, 49, 50, 53 Wings....31, 75, 37, 61, 112, 143, 50, 39, 44, 78, 141, 153 Sqdns.

Above: Sopwith Camel 'Pixie II' standing just inside one of the Bessoneau hangars. A night landing flare is clearly visible under the starboard wing. (A.B. Yuille)

Right: Some pilots had their own insignia designs painted on the aircraft they flew. This damaged photograph shows A.C.S. Irwin standing by his Sopwith Camel, 'The Odd One', which displays its personalised markings, a Pawn Broker's sign. Many pilots had their own pets and Irwin is holding one of his dogs, 'Sporty Boy'. (A.C.S. Irwin)

Maj. G. Allen (centre), who took command of 112 Squadron on 30 July 1917, enjoying a pause from flying duties with fellow officers. Standing to the left of Allen are Preston, Newton and Poole, to the right are Thompson, Cockerell and Chandler. The aircraft is a Sopwith Pup. (E.F. Cheesman)

A group of 112 Squadron pilots. From left to right: Beck, Morris, Goodyear, Arkell, Sutton and Cockerel; in the background ground crew attend to one of the squadron's Sopwith Pups. (E.F. Cheesman)

An unidentified pilot stands by a BE12a; note the Vickers machine gun mounted on top of the fuselage in front of the cockpit. The pilot may well be visiting the squadron on official business but is more likely to be making a social visit. (E.F. Cheesman)

Appendix 2

Structure of No.53 Wing – Kent

No.53 Wing – KENT.
Formed at Harrietsham 11 March 1918. CO Lt.Col. A.A.B. Thomson Headquarters Stede Court Harrietsham.
No.50 Squadron.

COs: Major M.G. Christie	15 May 1916
Major A.T. Watson	23 February 1917
Major A.de B. Brandon	16 October 1917
Major W. Sowrey	17 August 1918

BASES:

Dover	Harrietsham (HQ)	Bekesbourne	Detling	Throwley

AIRCRAFT

BE2c	BE2a	BE12	BE12b	Armstrong Whitworth FK8	SE5a	Sopwith Camel

No.112 Squadron.

COs: Major G. Allen	30 July 1917
Major B.F. Moore	24 November 1917
Capt. C.A. Ridley	1 December 1917
Major C.J.Q. Brand	15 February 1918
Major G.W. Murlis-Green	9 July 1918
Major C.O. Usborne	6 October 1918

BASE:
Throwley

AIRCRAFT:

Sopwith Pup	Sopwith Camel

No.143 Squadron.

COs: Major F. Sowrey	14 February 1918

BASE:
Detling

AIRCRAFT:
Armstrong Whitworth FK8   SE5a   Sopwith Camel

Appendix 3

Squadrons based at Throwley 1917–18

No.50 Squadron was formed on 15 May 1916 at Dover as a Home Defence unit.

It was equipped with BE variants and carried out defensive patrols from airfields in Kent until the end of the war.

In February 1918 it received Sopwith Camels to combat German bombers based in Belgium and was later disbanded on 13 June 1919, being re-formed in May 1937.

BASES:

Dover 15/5/1916	Harrietsham 10/1916	Detling	Throwley	Bekesbourne

AIRCRAFT:

BE2c	BE12	FK8	RE8	Pup – May 1916–February 1918

Camel: February 1918–November 1918
SE5a: November 1918–June 1919

MOTTO:
'From defence to attack'.

No.112 Squadron was formed on 30 July 1917 as a Home Defence unit at Throwley for the defence of the London area.

Day and night patrols were flown against enemy bombers operating from bases in Belgium until the end of the war. The squadron was disbanded on 13 June 1918 and re-formed on 16 May 1939.

BASES:
Throwley: 30 July 1917–13 June 1919

AIRCRAFT:

Sopwith Pup: July 1917–1918	Sopwith Camel: 1918–July 1919

MOTTO:
'Swift in destruction'.

No.143 was formed at Throwley on 1 February 1918 as part of the 53rd Home Defence Wing for the defence of London against German bombers in Belgium. Based in northern Kent, it was well placed to intercept enemy formations flying up the Thames Estuary, but the German raids ceased by the summer of 1918 and were not resumed. In 1919, Snipes began to replace the Camels but the squadron was disbanded on 31 October to be re-formed eventually on 15 June 1941.

BASES:

Throwley 1 February 1918   Detling 3/1918

AIRCRAFT:

Sopwith Camel: 1918–1919   SE5a – 1918/1918   Sopwith Snipe: 1919/October 1919

MOTTO:

'To conquer to live'.

No.188 was formed at Throwley on 20 December 1917 as a training unit for night flying squadrons. Initially training was on Avro's 504K but in June 1918 the forming of squadrons of Camel of Night Fighter resulted in No.188 being given the task of training pilots on the Camel. In March 1919 the squadron was disbanded and was not re-formed.

BASES:

Throwley: 20 December 1917–1 March 1919

AIRCRAFT:

Avro 504K: December 1917/ March 1919   Sopwith Camel: June 1918/March 1919
Sopwith Pup: June 1918/March 1919

MOTTO:

None Given.

Appendix 4

Nominal role of officers & NCO pilots at Throwley 1917–19

Capt.	C.J.Q. Brand DSO, MC	13.2.1918	09.07.1918	CO
Capt.	G. Allen Connaught Rangers	30.07.1917	21.11.1917	CO
Capt.	B.F. Moore	21.11.1917	03.12.1917	CO
Capt.	C.A. Ridley DSO, MC	03.12.1917	13.02.1917	CO
Capt.	G.W. Murlis-Green DSO, MC	09.07.1918	05.10.1918	CO
Capt.	C.O. Usborne	05.10.1918	13.06.1918	CO
Lieut.	A.C.S. Irwin .10.1917	20.05.1919		'C' Flt.Com.
Lieut.	N.E. Chandler	–	–	(NZ)
Lieut.	S. Cockerell	–	–	–
Lieut.	O.M. Sutton	–	–	–
Lieut.	A.B. Yuille DFC	30.03.1918	14.06.1918	–
Lieut.	G.N. Blennerhassett MC	–	–	–
Lieut.	T. Broome DFC	–	–	–
Lieut.	W. Aitken	–	–	–
Lieut.	R.T. Robins	–	–	Admin.
Lieut.	C. Olliver	–	–	Wireless
Capt.	T.J.C. Martyn DFC, MC	30.05.1919	–	Act.Adj. Flt/Com.
Sec/Lieut.	A.F. Nethey	–	–	Equip. Officer
Lieut.	D.F. Lawson	–	–	'A' Flt.Cdr.
Lieut.	C.B. Norwood	–	15.03.1919	–
Lieut.	B.J. Kirchner	–	22.03.1919	–
Sec/Lieut.	E.J. Jordan	–	19.03.1919	Admin.
Flt/Cadet	J.I. Blackburn	–	–	–
Flt/Cadet	T.R. Mace	–	03.09.1919	–
Capt.	C.J. Chabot	–	17.04.1919	Ex.50/143 Sqd.
Flt/Cadet	A.B. Robertson	–	–	–

Lieut.	R.E. Horsfield	–	01.05.1919	(Notts. Derby)
Lieut.	E.W. Carmichael	–	30.04.1919	–
Lieut.	H.A. Morley	–	06.05.1919	–
Lieut.	A.E. Gates	–	06.05.1919	–
Lieut.	G. Cameron	–	06.05.1919	–
Capt.	H.S. Preston	06.05.19	–	–
Lieut.	G.S.L. Hayward	–	18.05.1919	–
Lieut.	J.G. Blanc	–	18.05.1919	–
Lieut.	L.A.A. Bernard	–	–	–
Capt.	T.M.B. Newton	–	–	'C' Flt. Com.
Sec/Lieut.	Turton	–	–	–
Lieut.	W.G. Scotcher	–	–	–
Lieut.	Frampton	–	–	–
Capt.	B.E. Baker	–	–	'B' Flt. Com.
Lieut.	J.T. Collier	–	–	–
Sec/Lieut.	E.G. Hill	–	20.05.1919	–
Lieut.	F.J. Horrell	–	20.05.1919	Aviation Ins.
Sec/Lieut.	E. Hazell	–	20.05.1919	–
Lieut.	G.J. Wilde	–	20.05.1919	–
Lieut.	F.B. Barager	–	20.05.1919	(Can)
Lieut.	W. Partridge	–	20.05.1919	(Can)
Sec/Lieut.	C. Edwards	–	20.05.1919	Aviation Ins.
Lieut.	E.A. Halford	–	20.05.1919	Observer
Lieut.	E.T. Rogers	–	20.05.1919	–
Lieut.	D. Wills	–	–	–
Lieut.	W.J. Corney	–	–	Att.143 Sqdn.
Sec/Lieut.	G.J. Cross	–	–	–
Lieut.	Wykes	–	–	–
Lieut.	M. Davies	–	–	–
Lieut.	C.F. Wolley-Dod	–	–	–
Capt.	A.A. Garnons-Williams	–	–	K/ACC

Appendix 5

Flying accidents – Throwley 1917–18

FLYING ACCIDENTS – THROWLEY 1917–18
31 August 1917
Lt S.H. Pratt 112 Squadron
Injured during Gunnery Practice Herne Bay, Kent

15 September 1917
Lt R.W. Le Gallays 112 Squadron
Killed flying Sopwith Pup A638

24 January 1918
Lt J.T. Mitchell 112 Squadron
Killed when aircraft crashed in Hockley Wood

3 March 1918
Lt L.B. Jull 112 Squadron
Killed flying Sopwith Pup B5296

29 September 1918
G.C. Malcolm 188 Squadron
A.S. Talbot 188 Squadron
Both killed flying Avro 504K – B3111

14 October 1918
Lt E.W.F. Hopgood 112 Squadron
Killed when aircraft spun into ground

Appendix 6

Aircraft and their pilots

AIRCRAFT FLOWN BY PILOTS AT THROWLEY

DATE	FLIGHT	PILOT
16/17 February 1917 (Night)	No Squadron 'B' Flight BEI2 6493	Lt R.E. Butler
16/17 March 1917 (Night)	No.50 Squadron 'B' Flight BE2c 699	2nd Lt A.J. Arkell
	BEI2a A6313	Capt.R.G.H. Murray
23/24 May 1917 (Night)	No.50 Squadron 'B' Flight BE2c 2699	2nd Lt A.J. Arkell
	B12 – 6185	Capt.T.R Irons
	B12 – 6493	Lt H.T.O. Windsor
25 May 1917 (Daylight)	No.50 Squadron 'B' Flight BEI2 6493	Lt H.T.O. Windsor
	RE8 – A3836	Capt.T.R. Irons
5 June 1917 (Daylight)	No.50 Squadron 'B' Flight AW.Fk8 B229	Capt. C.R. Rowden
	RE8 – A3840	2nd Lt A.J. Arkell
13 June 1917 (Daylight)	No.50 Squadron 'B' Flight BEI2 6185	2nd Lt F.V. Bryant
	RE8 A3836	2nd Lt A.J. Arkell.
	RE8 A3840	2nd Lt N.F. Perris
	AW.Fk.8 B229	Capt.C. Rowden
4 July 1917 (Daylight)	No.50 Squadron 'B' Flight Sopwith Pup B1711	2nd Lt N.E. Chandler
	Sopwith Pup A638	Lt R.W. Le Callais
	Sopwith Pup B1769	2nd Lt S. Cockerell
	Sopwith Pup A6153	N.F. Perris
	AW.Fk8 B224	2nd Lt W.R. Oulton
	AW.Fk.8 B238	2nd Lt F.V. Bryant
	AW.Fk.8 B247	2nd.Lt F.A.D. Grace
	Vickers ES.1 7759	2nd Lt I.M Davies
7 July (Daylight)	No.50 Squadron 'B' Flight Sopwith Pup B1711	2nd Lt N.E.Chandler
	AW.Fk.8 B247	2nd Lt F.A.D. Grace
12 August 1917 (Daylight)	No.112 Squadron	

DATE	FLIGHT	PILOT
	Sopwith Pup A638	Lt R.W. Le Callais
	Sopwith Pup B1711	2nd Lt N.E. Chandler
	Sopwith Pup B1763	2nd Lt I.M. Davies
	Sopwith Pup B2158	2nd Lt A.J. Arkell
	Sopwith Pup B1769	2nd Lt S. Cockerell
19/20 May 1918	No.112 Squadron (Night) Sopwith Camel D6469	Lt W.G. Scotcher
	D6635	Lt F.B. Barager
	D6435	Lt F.B. Barager
	D6437	Lt W. Aitken
	D6473	Capt. J.T. Collier
	D6465	Lt G.N. Blennerhassett
	D6423	Maj. C.J.Q. Brand
	D6435	Lt F.B. Barager
	D6429	Lt D.F. Lawson
	B9301	Lt E.P. Mackay
	D6473	Capt. T.M.B. Newton
	D6682	Lt F.C. Broome
	D6415	Lt A.C.S. Irwin

Appendix 7

A survey of airfields in Kent – undertaken by 50 Wing

A SURVEY OF AIRFIELDS IN KENT UNDERTAKEN BY No.50 WING.

KINGSHILL (West Mailing) 2nd Class Landing Ground

This ground is 1 mile S of West Mailing, it is 270ft above sea level and is 650 yards long by 350 yards.

The ground is flat with no slopes and is bound by low hedges and woods and a wire fence on the south sides.

The surface is smooth with a slight dip at the eastern end.

The obstacles are a Workhouse 500 yards NW and Oast Houses 350 yards S. Ground signals are placed near the Guard Hut.

Good landings may be effected from the NW and SE by night and from all points by day.

THROWLEY (Faversham) 'B' Flight 1st Class Landing Ground

This splendid ground is 5 miles S of Faversham and is 400ft above sea level,

800 yards long by 500 yards wide. The nearest railway station is Faversham, 5 miles away.

The ground is flat and bound by wire or low hedges.

The surface is very good.

The obstacles are the Hangars in the northern corner and farm buildings on the eastern side.

Very safe landings may be effected in any direction by night or by day.

BEKESBOURNE (Canterbury) 'A' Flight 1st Class Landing Ground

This ground is 3 miles South East of Canterbury, with Bekesbourne Railway Station ½ mile away. The ground is 170ft above sea level and 1,000 yards long by 450 yards wide.

The ground has a dip across the centre and slopes at the E end.

The surface is good.

The obstacles are the Hangers at the Western end and a Windmill 500 yards S.

Boundaries: Low hedges or fences.

Good landings may be effected in any direction by night or by day.

MARDEN (Maidstone) 2nd Class Landing Ground

This ground is 7 miles S of Maidstone, the nearest Railway Station is Marden 1 mile away. The ground is 90ft above sea level, 900 yards long by 350 yards wide.

The ground is flat and bound by low hedges and a fruit plantation to the E.

The surface is good.

A Bessoneau Hangar is erected at the SE end.

Ground signals are put out near the hangar.

Good landings may be effected from the E and W by night or all directions by day.

HARTY (Isle of Sheppey) 3rd Class Landing Ground

This ground is situated 1 mile N of the River Swale on the SE corner of the Isle Of Sheppey, the nearest Railway Station is Harty Halt while the ground itself is 76ft above sea level and 500 yards long by 250 yards wide.

The ground is flat but somewhat soft.

Work will be in progress during the next few weeks.

There is no circle at present.

The south end of the ground can be landed on.

ALL HALLOWS (Sheerness) 3rd Class Landing Ground

This ground is 6 miles W of Sheerness with the river Medway lying in between. The ground is 130ft above sea level and 400 yards long by 170 yards wide.

The ground slopes down slightly towards the E.

The surface is rough and covered with weeds.

The only obstacle is a Cottage outside the NE corner.

The ground is bound on the N and W by ditches with corn crops on the S and E.

Ground signals are putout near the Guard Hut to the NE.

Landings may be effected from the E and W by night and by day.

BROOMFIELD (Herne Bay) 3rd Class Landing Ground

This ground is 2 miles SE of Herne Bay town and the Railway Station. It is 115ft above sea level and 400 yards long by 300 yards wide.

The ground is flat.

The surface is smooth.

The obstacles are farm buildings to the SW and a Ventilation Post in the SE corner.

There is a wire fence on the NW approach but no other boundaries.

Ground signals are put out at the SW corner.

Landings may be effected from the NW and SE by night and all directions by day.

BROADSALTS (Sandwich) 2nd Class Landing Ground

This ground is 1 mile NE of Sandwich town, it is 10ft above sea level and is 700 yards long by 400 yards wide.

The ground is flat and bound by ditches.

The surface is good.

The obstacles are a Wireless Station to the E and a Factory with its Chimneys to the N. Ground signals are put out near the Farm Buildings to the SE.

Good landings may be effected from the SW and NE by night and all directions by day.

SOUTH ASH (Wrotham) 2nd Class Landing Grounds

The ground is 3 miles north of Wrotham and is 500ft above sea level. It is 600 yards long by 300 yards wide.

The ground slopes to the E and is bound by low hedges.

The surface is fairly smooth.

There are obstacles approaching the ground but they are at some distance.

Ground signals are placed near the Guard Hut on the W side of the ground.

Good landings can be effected from the SE or NE by night and from the E by day.

A Distinguishing Flare is set out as this ground is 500ft above sea level.

RYE (Sussex) 3rd Class Landing Ground

This location is 1 mile E of Rye town and Railway Station, it is 10ft above sea level and is 600 yards long
   by 250 yards wide.

The ground is flat with no slopes and is bound by low hedges except on the W side.

The surface is smooth and sown with clover.

There are no obstacles.

The Ground signals are placed near the Guard Hut at the NE corner.

Landings can be effected from the N and S by night and by day.

The ground is somewhat soft in the winter months.

HIGH HALDEN (Tenterden) 3rd Class Landing Ground

This ground is ½ mile E of Tenterden village and railway station, it is 170ft above sea level and is 700 yards
   long by 250 yards wide.

The ground slopes down its length slightly towards the east.

It is bound by low hedges, there is a pit marked by flags on the southern side of the ground.

The surface is smooth.

The obstacles are Tenterden village to the NE and buildings and trees to the SE. The ground signals are
   placed near the Guard Hut on the NE side.

A landing can be effected from the SE by night and from the NE by day.

SOLE STREET (Crundale) 3rd Class Landing Ground

This ground is 3 miles SE of Chilham, lies 480ft above sea level and is 300 yards long by 300 yards wide.
   The nearest Railway Station is Chilham.

The ground is flat with no slopes and has no boundary hedges on the SE or NW sides.

The surface is smooth.

The obstacles are buildings on the northern boundary and a sloping bank at the SE corner.

Ground signals are placed near the Guard hut at the N side of the ground. A landing can be effected from
   the SE by night and any direction by day.

PETT (Hastings) 3rd Class Landing Ground

This ground is 1 mile from the coast and is to be found 5 miles E of Hastings. The nearest Railway Station
   is at Winchelsea, the ground itself lies 50ft above sea level and is 300 yards wide.

The ground slopes considerably towards the north and is bound by hedges.

The surface is fairly smooth.

There is no circle on this ground.

There are no obstacles approaching the ground.

Ground signals are placed near the Guard Hut on the northern side of the ground.

A lighthouse has been erected.

FRINSTED (Harrietsham) 2nd Class Landing Ground

This ground is 4 miles S of Sittingbourne and the nearest Railway Station is at Harrietsham. The ground
   is 530ft above sea level and is 600 yards long by 350 yards wide.

The ground is flat and bound by low hedges.

The surface is good.

Ground signals are placed near the Guard Hut towards the NE corner.

Landings can be effected from the NE, SW and E by night and from any direction by day.

There is a wire fence on the northern boundary.

A Distinguishing Flare is set out as this ground is over 500ft above sea level.

DETLING (Maidstone) 'C' flight Station 1st Class Landing Ground

This ground is 4 miles NE of Maidstone, it is 600ft above sea level and is 800 yards long by 500 yards wide.

The ground slopes towards the NE, it is bound by low hedges and woods. The bare patch towards the western side of the ground should if possible be avoided and men are sometimes at work on this.

The surface is smooth.

The obstacles are the Hangars and buildings towards the SE corner of the ground. The ground signals are placed near the buildings.

Landings can be effected from the N and E by night and from all points by day.

PLUCKLEY (Ashford) 2nd Class Landing Ground.

This ground is ½ mile W of Pluckley village and is 170ft above sea level. It is 750 yards long by 350 wide.

The nearest Railway Station is Pluckley.

The ground slopes towards the N and S and is bound by low hedges.

The surface is rough and somewhat soft.

Pluckley village standing high on the east proves an obstacle.

The ground signals are placed near the Guard Hut at the southern side of the ground.

A landing may be effected from the SW by night and from all points by day.

SWINGFIELD (Denton) 2nd Class Landing Ground.

This ground is 5 miles N of Folkestone and is located 480ft above sea level. It is 700 yards long by 450 yards wide and the nearest Railway Station is Lydden Halt.

The ground is flat with no slopes and is bound by low hedges. The surface is fairly rough.

The only obstacle is a small bunch of high trees around a farmhouse at the southern corner.

Ground signals are placed near the Guard Hut at the southern corner. Landings can be effected from the NSE and NW by night and from all points by day. Care should be exercised in landing near the centre of the ground, which is the worst part of the surface. There is a bank crossing in each direction.

NOTE:

Pilots are reminded that sheep and cattle are being grazed on most landing grounds and that therefore they should circle round to make sure that they are cleared before landing.

Pett should not be landed on in the day time.

Appendix 8

German bomber raids on England 1917–18

DATE	FORCE	TARGETS	AIRCRAFT LOST
25/05/1917	21–23 Gothas	Folkestone	1 Gotha over Channel
–	–	Shomeclife Camp	1 Gotha crashed
05/06/1917	22–23 Gothas	Sheerness	1 Gotha shot down
–	–	Shoeburyness	–
13/06/1917	17–20 Gothas	London	1 British NC forced landed
–	–	Margate	–
04/07/1917	18–25 Gothas	Harwich	1 British A/C forced landed
–	–	Naval Air Station	–
–	–	Felixstowe	–
07/07/1917	22–24 Gothas	London	1 Gotha shot down
–	–	–	4 Gothas shot down
–	–	–	2 British A/C shot down
–	–	–	1 British Ai/C forced
22/07/1917	21–23 Gothas	Harwich	1 Gotha crashed on landing
–	–	Felixstowe	–
12/08/1917	11–13 Gothas	Southend	1 Gotha shot down
–	–	Shoeburyness	4 Gothas crashed on landing
–	–	Margate	–
22/08/1917	10–15 Gothas	Margate	3 Gothas shot down
–	–	Ramsgate	–
–	–	Dover	–
3–4/09/1917	4–5 Gothas	Chatham RN Docks	None
–	–	Sheerness	–
–	–	Margate	–
4–5/09/1917	9–11 Gothas	London	1 Gotha missing
–	–	Margate	–
–	–	Dover	–
24/09/1917	13–16 Gothas	London	1 Gotha crashed on return
–	–	Dover	1 British A/C crashed
–	–	Leybourne Camp	–

Date	Force	Location	Result
25/09/1917	14–15 Gothas	London	1 Gotha missing
–	–	East Kent	2 British NC crashed
28/09/1917	23/25 Gothas	Suffolk–Kent–Essex	3 Gothas shot down
–	2 Giants	Coastal areas	6 Gothas crashed on landing
–	–	–	1 British A/C crashed
29/09/1917	4–7 Gothas	London	1 Gotha shot down
–	3 Giants	Sheerness	1 Gotha forced down in Holland
30/09/1917	10/11 Gothas	London	None
–	1 Single Engine A/C	Margate	–
–	–	Dover	–
1–2/10/1917	11–18 Gothas	London	No report existing
–	–	Kent	–
–	–	Essex	–
29/10/1917	1–3 Gothas	Essex Coast	1 British A/C crashed
31/10/1917	22 Gothas	London	5 Gothas crash-landed
–	–	Ramsgate	2 British A/C crashed
–	–	Dover	–
06/12/1917	16–19 Gothas	London	2 Gothas brought down by gunfire
–	2 Giants	Sheerness	1 Gotha missing
–	–	Margate	1 Gotha crash-landed
–	–	Dover	–
18/12/1917	13–15 Gothas	London	1 Gotha shot down
–	1 Giant	Margate	1 Gotha crashed on return
–	–	–	6 Gothas crashed on landing
22/12/1917	2 Giants	Kent Coast	None
28–29/01/1918	7–13 Gothas	London	1 Gotha shot down
–	1 Giant	Sheerness	4 Gothas crashed on landing
–	–	Margate	1 British A/C forced down
–	–	Ramsgate	–
29–30/01/1918	3–4 Giants	London	None
–	–	Essex coast	–
16/02/1918	5 Giants	London	None
–	–	Dover	–
17/02/1918	1 Giant	London	1 British A/C crashed
7–8/03/1918	5–6 Giants	London	2 Giants crash-landed return fit.
–	–	Heme Bay	2 British A/C collided crashed
19–20/05/1918	28–38 Gothas	London	1 Gotha forced down England
–	3 Giants	Faversham	5 Gothas shot down
–	2 Single engine A/C	Dover	1 Gotha crashed on return flight

Appendix 9

Air-raid reports (Throwley 1917–18)
Compiled by Intelligence Section GHQ Home Forces.

AIRSHIP RAID 16/17 MARCH 1917
This was carried out over Kent and Sussex and was undertaken by five airships (L35, L39, L40, L41 and L42), the last mentioned did not leave the European Coast. Searchlights were unable to pierce the clouds so no anti-aircraft guns were used but L39 was brought down by the batteries at Compiegne.

Throwley   BE12a (A6313)   11.57–12.15   Captain Murray
Took off from Frinsted and landed at Throqwley. Heavy cloud at 1,500ft below.
Took off again at 2.05 and landed one hour later at Bekesbourne.
Throwley   BE2c   10.15–11.45   2nd Lt.Arkell
Landed at Marden having patrolled at 4,000 to 9,000ft.

AIRSHIP RAID 23/24 MAY 1917
Mostly over East Anglia No.50 Home Defence squadron launched 7 aircraft from Bekesbourne, Detling and Throwley between 11.22 and 4.25.
Reports concern only very low clouds and rain.
The aeroplane raids of 25 May and 13 June mark an entirely new phase of German aerial attacks against this country.
Previous air raids had either taken the form of night raids carried out by aeroplanes or seaplanes. On a few occasions a group of the smaller aircraft reached these shores but made off again without much delay.

AIRSHIP RAID 6 JUNE 1917
During the raid of 6 June on London, No.50 Home Defence Squadron (Bekesbourne, Detling,Throwley) sent up 8 aircraft between 6.01 and 8.11.
Three pilots saw enemy machines which were too high and too fast to be attacked.

AIRSHIP RAID 13 JUNE 1917

During the raid of 13 June on London, No.50 Home Defence Squadron sent up 12 Aircraft between 11am and 1.30pm. There were no reports of sightings of hostile aircraft.

AIRCRAFT RAID 4 JULY 1917

In this month no airships appeared but three separate aircraft raids were carried out by a squadron of aircraft of the Gotha type.

During the raid of 4 July No.50 Home Defence, now based at Harrietsham sent up 4 Sopwith Scouts, 3 Armstong Whitworth and a Vickers Bullet from 7.40 to 9.21, nothing to report.

AIRCRAFT RAID 7 JULY 1917

During the raid of 7 July No.50 Home Defence at Throwley sent up one Armstrong Whitworth 9.32 which engaged enemy planes off Harwich on their return and brought down one in the sea, landing at 1.00. Three other AW's took off at the same time but landed at 12.22 having sighted nothing.

Throwley Sopwith Pup (B1711)   9.25–11.27   Lt.N.E.Chandler

The above pilot was ordered to patrol at 9.25am ascended at 9.29am and descended at 11.27am. Course followed was Throwley to Joyce Green to Croydon.

The patrol was carried out at a mean height of 16,000ft.

'I was flying between Joyce Green and Croydon at 15,000ft when I saw a lot or Ack-Ack bursting over London so at once proceeded in that direction and climbed to 17,000ft and got above a formation of about 20 hostile aircraft dived on the rear machine and fired a short burst which failed to bring the hostile aircraft down so I climbed up to 17,000ft and dived again.

I had to keep pumping the petrol pressure owing to my pump being seized. After a short burst my gun stopped and I was unable to correct it. The hostile aircraft were by this time flying NE so I returned to Throwley and landed. All the time I was under Ack-Ack fire.

My goggles got smothered in oil which made it very hard to see'.

AIRCRAFT RAID 22 JULY 1917

During the raid of 2 July 'B' Flight 50 Honie Defence Throwley sent up SAW's At 8.25 which landed at 10.30 after patrolling between 11,000–12,000ft and seeing nothing.

AIRCRAFT RAID 12 AUGUST 1917

Throwley now has its own squadron No.112. At 5.24 they sent up 7 Sopwith Pups and another at 5.40pm which had been delayed due to starting trouble.

One aircraft came down at 6.15 with gun trouble and later took off again. Most had nothing to report but one, having come straight down again to correct gun trouble, took off again at 5.35 and sighted 8 enemy machines in formation and intercepted them near the coast. After firing 50 rounds into the rearmost machine the gun again jammed and he had to return.

AIRCRAFT RAID 22 AUGUST 1917

During the raid of 22 August three machines of 50hp led by Captain Truran engaged the enemy formation off North Foreland but ineffectively.

Eleven Sopwith Scouts took off from Throwley at 10.17 landing again at 10.17

Landing again between 11.35 and 12.16pm with nothing to report.

By September 1917 the German night raids were becoming a problem as not only were the Germans sending Gotha bombers on raids, but on 21/22 August the airships made a return.

However, 50 Squadron was not scrambled as the Germans were heading for Hull.

Records seem to make no individual mention of 112 Squadron but the symbol (T) for Throwley crops up in the Patrol Route details given for 50 Squadron.

AIRCRAFT RAID 7/8 MARCH 1918

During the raid on 7/8 March 1918 (T) sent up two machines from 11.32 to 1.13. They appear to have flown to Frinstead and back again to Throwley and Faversham but no enemy aircraft were seen.

Appendix 10

Squadron orders issued by COs of 112 Squadron/6th Brigade

SQUADRON ORDERS No.90 By Major C.O. Usborne AFC
Commanding Officer No.112 Squadron Royal Air Force
Throwley Nr. Faversham 15th April 1919

Part 1.
1. DUTIES.

Orderley Officer	Tomorrow 16 Inst.	LLG.S.L Hayward
–	next for duty.	2nd Lt. H.A Morley
Officer of the Watch	Tomorrow 16 Inst.	Lt.E.T Rogers
–	next for duty.	Lt.J.G Blane
NCO I Guard	Tomorrow 16th.Inst.	L/ACM S.Baxter
–	next for duty.	L/ACM H.Kitchingham
Orderley SGT.	–	Cpl.S.F Capell
Orderley Flight	–	"C" Flight

2. PARADES.

Working Parades	0800 & 1345
Pay Parade	1200

3. LEAVE.
The undermentioned officer is granted leave of absence from 12.4.1919 to
21.4.1919 (10 Days)
Capt.A.C.S Irwin   Capt. (Flying) 'A'
(Authority 53rd Wing Orders No.89 dated 14.4.1919

NOTICE.
It is announced for information that the last day for receiving completed application forms under the
Reconstruction Schemes for situations in the Home Civil Defence, including Class 1 Clerkships, Junior
(or Intermediate) appointments and Officer- Ships of Customs & Excise, is Wednesday 30 June 1920 and
that no applications received after that date can be considered.

Part 2.

1. EXTENSION OF SERVICE.
Permitted to extend his service to complete two years Air Force Service: 2701.Ch/Tech.E.S Hiles Fitter
MT 7/2 DW. 'A'. (Extract No.53 Wing Orders No.89 dated 14.4.1919)

2. CIVILIAN SUBORDINATES - STRENGTH INCREASE.
Mr.H. Pritchard   Clerk (Gen.)   Taken on strength at 53/6 per week of 48 hrs,
                                          overtime up to 12 hours @ 1/42 of the weekly
                                          rate, with effect from 12.

3. LEAVE
The undermentioned airman is granted leave with ration allowance from
16.4.1919 to 22.4.1919 inclusive. — 25790 L/ACM R.Lillie Blacksmith
                        (Signed) Lt.D.Mills
                        Acting Adj. 112 Squadron Royal Air Force

SQUADRON ORDERS. No.102 By Major C.O Usborne A.F.C
Commanding No.112 Squadron. Royal Air Force

Part 1.
1. DUTIES.

Orderly Officer	Tomorrow 2nd Inst.	2/Lt.E.Hazell
—	next for duty	Lt.W.J Corney
Officer of the watch	Tomorrow 2nd Inst.	2/Lt.H.A Morley
—	next for duty	Lt.E.T Rogers
N.C.O I/C Guard	Tomorrow 2nd Inst.	L/ACM J.Tucker
—	next for duty	Cpl.A.Porter
Orderly SGT.	—	Cpl.S.F Capell
Flight	—	"B" Flight

2. PARADES.

- Working Parades	0800 & 1345
Pay Parade	1200

3. STRENGTH.
The undermentioned officer having completed his 26 days leave, pending demobilization, is struck off
strength with effect from 30/4/1919.
Lt. E.W Carmichael — Lt.Flying

The undermentioned officer having been posted to 3rd Battalion.Notts &
Derby Regiment is struck of strength with effect from 1/5/1919.

1. STRENGTH INCREASE — CIVILIAN SUBORDINATES.
Mr.W.H Jordan   Driver   60/-week of 72 hours
                                                   With effect from 1/5/1919
                        (Signed) Lt,D.Wills
                        Acting Adjutant No.112 Squadron RAF

114

EQUIPMENT
Nil

(Signed) 2nd Lt. Nothey
E.O Stores No.112 Squadron RAF

CENTRAL REGISTRY
3 May 1919
HQ South East Area RAF.

SQUADRON ORDERS No.129 By Major G.Allen
Commanding Officer No.112 Squadron Royal Air Force Throwley Nr.Faversham 3 1919

Part 1.
1. DUTIES.

Orderley Officer	Tomorrow 4th Inst	Lt.R.T Robbins
–	next for duty.	Lt.C.W Oliver
NCO I/C Guard	Tomorrow 4th.Inst	LIACM.H. Kitchingham
–	next for duty	LIACM W.William

2. PARADES.
Working Parades   0800 & 1345

3. AIR MINISTRY WEEKLY ORDERS.
The attention of Officers Commanding Units and "Q" Staff is directed to
A.Cs 548,649 and 652 of 1919.
(Ext.B.O No.127 dated 31.5.1919)
(Ext.B.O No 129 dated 2.6.1919)

4. LEAVE.
The undermentioned officer is granted 12 days leave in accordance with
AM Letter C.572191D.4.Z dated 24.3.1919
Lt.M.J Corney   Flying Officer

PART 2.
NIL

(Signed) Capt.T.J.C Martyn
No.112 Squadron Royal Air Force

EQUIPMENT
1. L.T.V HIC s STRUCK OF CHARGE.
The following vehicle having been despatched by road to HQ 1O.MTRD
Wormwood Scrubs, is struck off charge with effect from 2.6.1919
Workshop Trailer   Chassis No.107

(Signed) 2nd Lt.A.F Nothey
EC Stores No.112 Squadron Royal Air Force

A typical scene on a Home Defence airfield; the aircraft, a Sopwith Camel, has been painted over in preparation for its new role as a Night Fighter. The normally highly polished engine cowling has also been painted over. Note the streamers on the wing struts which denote that the Flight Commander flies the aircraft. The structure to the left of the aircraft is a Bessoneau hangar that was used extensively on this type of airfield.

Appendix 11

Aircraft types flown at Throwley 1917–18

SOPWITH PUP

Considered to be the most popular aircraft flown by pilots of both the RNAS and the RFC throughout the First World War. Having few vices, it was able to maintain its height and had sensitive controls, being fully aerobatic at 15,000ft, a great factor in the days of low-powered aircraft, which were inclined to hang on their propellers at extreme heights. The Pup, which came into service in 1916, was a direct descendant of the Sopwith Tabloid single-seater scout, which appeared in 1913.

This aircraft was not armed and the Pup was able to take advantage of the interrupter gear in order to fit a forward-firing Vickers machine gun. The Pup was originally ordered by the RNAS and these machines, together with some Sopwith 11/2 Srutters, pioneered deck landings on the converted cruiser HMS *Furious*. The RFC began using the Pup in December 1916 shortly after the introduction by the Germans of the Albatros Scouts, which won back superiority. At the time the Pup was the only British aircraft, able to match the performance of the Albatros. It was powered by a 50hp Le Rhone or the 100hp Gnome Monosoupape engines.

SOPWITH CAMEL
The successor to the Sopwith Pup, very popular with pilots, the Sopwith Camel F1 was welcome on the Western Front for its increased performance.

It became a great favourite with the scout or fighter pilots of the period and has the distinction of shooting down the greatest number of enemy aircraft of any one type of Allied aircraft. From July 1917 when 70 Squadron was the first Camel-equipped squadron to go into action, until the end of the war, F1 Camels accounted for 980 aircraft. It was described as the most manoeuvrable aircraft ever to be built, but it had drawbacks for the fledgling pilot and it had to be treated with both knowledge and respect. Over 4,000 had been manufactured by the end of the war and it could be described as the Spitfire of the First World War.

The F2.1 Camel, built to the order of the RNAS, was equally successful and 500 of these were in existence at the time of the Armistice. The F1 was powered by 1bhp Le Rhone or the 130hp Clerget and the F2, 150hp Gnome Monosoupape or the 150hp Bentley BR1 engines.

Opposite: This illustration depicts a Sopwith Camel F1/3 in the markings of a Night Fighter of the period. Of interest is the location of the 'Holts' flare bracket. (M. Holbrook)

Top view

Cut out this section from Triplane cowling

Bottom view

White in all roundels smeared out with black paint

Colour scheme. Top surfaces dark khaki/green PC10. Undersides natural dope, overpainted with darker colour to effect night camouflage

Elevator control from sprue

Extended handgrip, port Lewis gun only

Rudder stripes smeared out. (Note blue fin, red and white rudder, based on photographic evidence. Most aircraft had national markings on rudder only.)

Foster mounts, 2 off needed

Elevator horns from plastic card

Grey tips to propeller blades

Control horns from plastic card

White bands overpainted black

Holts flare bracket

Gun sight from sprue

Twin Lewis guns on Foster mount

Engine and cowling from Revell Triplane

Flare

Camel F1/3 night fighter
B2402 of No 44 Squadron
(This is a Ruston Proctor-built aircraft)

Note toe-in on wheels

1:48 scale
Drawings by Martin Holbrook

119

BE2c

The BE2c was developed by the Royal Aircraft Factory at Farnborough, from the BE2 which was designed by Geoffrey de Havilland who was working at the time at the factory. Despite the fact that the BE2c was extremely stable in flight, it was not suitable as a fighter; however, it still went into mass production which was rather unfortunate for the RFC as this type, along with its derivatives, was responsible for many RFC casualties.

The early BE2s were fitted with a 70hp Renault engine and later models were fitted with the 90hp RAF, the 90hp Curtis OX5 and the 150hp Hispano-Suiza power units. It was armed with a single Lewis Gun and could carry bombs. By the end of 1918 there were more than 1,300 BE2cs and BE2d machines in service with Home Defence units, and many training units in Eygpt, Palestine, Salonika and East Africa.

The photograph is of a BE.2c of the Royal Naval Air Service, taken at Eastchurch, Isle of Sheppey. This particular aircraft had a long career, being based at Eastchurch, Yarmouth and Cranwell.

BE12

This aircraft was in service in the RFC and RAF throughout the second part of the First World War. It was developed to combat the threat of the Fokker monoplane of 1916, although it was just a modified version of the BE2c.

The front cockpit was taken out to make the aircraft a single-seater type and it entered service on the Western Front in August 1916. However, it was very slow and did not manoeuvre well so its role was changed to bombing. There were 100 to 150 produced for Home Defence squadrons in 1917 with the 200hp Hispano-Suiza engine and it was fitted with twin Vickers guns over the top wing. After the German raids on England in 1918, some of these aircraft were allocated to anti-submarine duties. The aircraft could also carry two 112lb bombs fitted to its underwing.

AVRO 504

It was the 504 which was used as the basis of the special Gosport System of flying training development towards the end of the war by Major R.R. Smith Barry. Some 274 of these aircraft were fitted as single-seaters and with one fixed machine gun above the centre section they were in service with Home Defence units for use against the Zeppelins and Gothas.

There were many different modifications incorporated in the design, which ranged during the war from 504A to 504K, each fitted with a different type of type of engine.

Some 8,340 aircraft were manufactured during the war of which 5,446 were delivered to the RFC, mainly for training purposes.

After the war it was possible to buy an Avro 504 for as little as £5.00 and many pilots who found their services no longer needed purchased such machines and toured the countryside, offering 'Joy Rides' for a few bob.

BRISTOL M1C

Of the 125 built of this type only a quarter of this number actually went into service, mostly in the Middle East. The main reason for limiting this aircraft's production was its landing speed, which was nearly 50mph! However, it is more likely that the War Office decided its fate as they were against the introduction of monoplanes.

With a top speed of 132mph news of its performance soon reached pilots on the Western Front, who were eager to receive the M1s which would have given them the air supremacy over the German machines. But the War Office did not authorise its service in France. The M1C was powered by a Le Rhone rotary engine. Being a monoplane it gave the fighter pilot much improved vision and was used for low-level strafing of infantry. It was armed with a single fixed forward-firing Vickers machine gun. Sadly this aircraft was never given the chance to prove its capability and most probably appeared at Throwley to impress the spectators.

ARMSTRONG WHITWORTH FK.8

Another aircraft which made an appearance at Throwley was the FK8; also used by 50 Squadron, this twin seater was developed for armed reconnaissance. It was nicknamed 'Big Ack' to distinguish it from the FK3 which became known as 'Little Ack'. An unusual feature of the FK8 was the dual controls in the rear cockpit which enabled the Observer to take control should the pilot be injured. The Observer cockpit could also carry a small load of bombs, a total of 1,500 were built by the end of October 1918, there still 694 in RAF Service. The FK was armed with one forward-firing Vickers gun and one free-firing Lewis gun.

S.E.5a

The SE5a and the Sopwith Camel could be referred to as the Hurricane and Spitfire of the First World War. The SE5 and SE5a were designed at the Royal Aircraft Factory and like their predecessors were extremely stable. They were less manoeuvrable than the Camel but had a higher speed and a better gun platform, a comparison often made between the Hurricane and Spitfire. The SE5a was powered by the Hispano-Suizas engine 200, 220, 240hp engines and the 200hp Wolseley Viper. This aircraft was favoured by many fighter pilots of the period, such as Mannock and McCudden.

It was armed with one Vickers gun fixed forward and a Lewis gun on top of the wing centre sections. This type was produced in large numbers; nearly 3,000 had been produced by the end of the war.

SE5a. Lt L. Lucas of No.50 Squadron seated in his SE5a D5995 at Bekesbourne, near Canterbury. 'B' Flight of 50 Squadron was on detachment to Throwley, Bekesbourne and Detling airfields. He was one of the pilots on patrol on the night of 19/20 May 1918 but did not engage any Gotha bombers. (E.F. Cheesman)

VICKERS FB19

In 1915 after being seen by the RFC the original designs the ES1 and ES2 prototypes were turned down. This aircraft which was redesigned as the FB19 reappeared again in 1916. It had been fitted with a new engine, the 100hp Gnome Mono engine, and improved the maximum speed of its previous engine which could only give a speed of 100mph. It was armed with a single Vickers machine gun. This aircraft was only used by Home Defence units or training units, there being only thirty-six built. One of these, 7759, was flown by Lt I.M. Davies, 50 Squadron, during a daylight raid by Gotha bombers on 4 July 1917.

FB.19 Mk.2 at Joyce Green, near Dartford.

RE8

This aircraft was produced in great numbers but was not very popular with pilots. Despite this it went on to become a standard RFC/RAF aircraft and the planes were affectionately called 'Harry Tates', using Cockney slang. By October 1918 they were in service with no less than 19 Squadrons which for a time included 50 Squadron 'B' Flight, Throwley. Production was delayed due to a shortage of materials and trouble with the RAF engine, which gave a maximum speed of 102mph. The RE8 was not very agile and therefore difficult to land; it was armed with a fixed forward-firing Vickers gun and two free-firing Lewis machine guns, and could also carry up to 260lb of bombs.

SOPWITH SNIPE

Developed to follow the successful Camel, the Sopwith F.I Snipe with its 230hp engine represented the last of the Sopwith scouts fitted with rotary engines. It remained in service with the RAF for many years after the war, when its period of service of only three months was cut short by the Armistice in 1918. It was easier to handle than the Camel and it must have been the best single-engine scout of the Allied air force.

Of the Sopwith scouts, the simply constructed, slab-sided fuselage had been abandoned the Snipe and replaced by a more complex structure of plywood bulkheads and stringers. This gave the machine a greatly improved and much more modern appearance than the earlier models. The Snipe was a transition to the single-seater biplane fighters of the late 1920s and early 1930s. Of the 264 Snipes built before the war, only ninety-seven saw service on the Western Front.

Sopwith Snipe E7337, possibly of 112 Squadron. The pilot on the left is Lt F.B. Barager, a Canadian who was posted from Throwley on 20 May 1919. (R.A. Brown)

GOTHA BOMBER

Towards the end of 1916 it was obvious to the German High Command that the Zeppelin airships were too vulnerable to continue their raids on England. As a result of this conclusion a number of heavy bombers were developed to take over the role from the airships. The most successful of these was the twin-engined Gotha aircraft; it was to become a household name in England.

The earlier Gotha G.I was fitted with 160hp Mercedes engines with a wing span of only 71ft. It was not until the G.IV and G.V models that the span was increased to 77ft and the power units replaced by the 260hp Mercedes engines. The design of the G.V is said to be the result of the capture of a Handley Page 0/400, which was delivered intact to the Germans in February 1917 due to an error in navigation when being delivered to France. The Gotha was armed with one free Parabellum machine gun in the front and rear cockpit, and one fixed Parabellum under the fuselage firing to the rear. It carried racks for twelve bombs inside the fuselage and two externally, giving a maximum payload of 9,001lb, and had a crew of three.

A Gotha V bomber, possibly of Bombengeschwader 3. Note the camouflage design, which was printed on the fabric. The colour of the polygon pattern varied from green, brown and purple on the upper surfaces to black and various shades of blue on the sides and undersurfaces.

Other titles published by Tempus

The Home Front Civilian Life in World War One
PETER G. COOKSLEY

The well-known history of the First World War is one of trenches and bloodshed, but this was the first truly global war and had far-reaching effects worldwide. Here Peter Cooksley looks at the effects of war on Britain's civilian population, who endured air raids and rationing during a time of unprecedented upheaval. Illustrated with contemporary photos and ephemera, this is the story of those left at home.

0 7524 3688 3

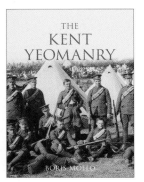

The Kent Yeomanry
BORRIS MOLLO

As the armies of the new French Republic swept through Europe, Pitt called for a cavalry force to defend our shores. Kent's response was to form yeomanries in the east and west. This book tells the proud story of these yeomanries through photographs taken at home and abroad, from the 1860s to the present day.

0 7524 3575 6

Firefighting in Kent
ROGER C. MARDON AND JOHN A. MEAKIN

Organised firefighting came with the Romans when they landed in Kent in AD43, since when the county has been at the forefront of developments in this area. Using over 200 old photographs, this book chronicles the history of firefighting in Kent looking at fires, brigades, engines and architecture.

0 7524 3260 1

If you are interested in purchasing other books published by Tempus,
or in case you have difficulty finding any Tempus books in your local bookshop,
you can also place orders directly through our website

www.tempus-publishing.com

Civilian refugees walking east, past Red Army troops heading
west to the front to counter the German advances. July 1941.
© akg-images / Universal Images Group / Sovfoto

Also by Vasily Grossman in English translation

Life and Fate
Everything Flows
The Road and Other Stories
An Armenian Sketchbook
Stalingrad

By Vasily Grossman, and edited and translated by
Antony Beevor and Lyuba Vinogradova

A Writer at War: Vasily Grossman and the Red Army 1941–1945

Vasily Grossman

THE PEOPLE IMMORTAL

Translated by Robert and Elizabeth Chandler

Original Russian text edited by Julia Volohova

With an Introduction and Afterword by
Robert Chandler and Julia Volohova

MACLEHOSE PRESS
QUERCUS · LONDON

First published in serial form in 1942 as Народ бессмертен

First published in this edition in Great Britain in 2022 by

MacLehose Press
An imprint of Quercus Editions Limited
Carmelite House
50 Victoria Embankment
London EC4Y 0DZ

An Hachette UK company

A CIP catalogue record for this book is available from the British Library.

ISBN (HB) 978 1 52941 473 8
ISBN (TPB) 978 1 52941 474 5
ISBN (Ebook) 978 1 52941 476 9

10 9 8 7 6 5 4 3 2 1

Designed and typeset in Quadraat by Libanus Press, Marlborough
Printed and bound in Great Britain by Clays Ltd, Elcograf S.p.A.

Contents

Names of Ukrainian and Belarusian Towns and Cities

The transliteration of Ukrainian and Belarusian names is a sensitive issue. If I were writing in my own name, or translating a contemporary writer, I would call the Ukrainian capital "Kyiv" and its second city "Kharkiv". Grossman, however, used the conventional Russian spellings of his time – "Kiev" and "Kharkov". These were the standard spellings during the war years and – in most cases – for the next fifty years. Retaining these spellings is to stay true both to history and to Grossman himself – a Ukrainian Soviet Jew who wrote in Russian, and to whom war between Russia and Ukraine would have been inconceivable.

Here below are the names used by Grossman, followed by the contemporary equivalents in the relevant language:

Bielostok – Białystok
Bobruisk – Babruisk
Berdichev – Berdychiv
Chernigov – Chernihiv
Chertkov – Chortkiv
Dnepropetrovsk – Dnipro (since 2016)
Glukhov – Hlukhiv
Gomel – Homyel
Lvov – Lviv
Marchikhina Buda – Marchykhyna Buda
Mozyr – Mazyr
Proskurov – Proskuriv (until 1954), Khmelnytskiy (since 1954)
Shepetovka – Shepetivka
Stanislavov – Ivano-Frankisvsk (since 1962)
Vilna – Vilnius
Vinnitsa – Vinnytsia
Voroshilovgrad (1935–58 and 1970–89) – Luhansk (before 1935; 1970–89; 1989 to present day)

List of Characters

(not including characters mentioned only a single time)

MILITARY SOVIET

Yeromin, Viktor Andreyevich	Lieutenant General, Front C-in-C
Cherednichenko	Divisional Commissar, Member of the Front Military Soviet
Ilya Ivanovich	Major General, the chief of staff
Piotr Yefimovich	Colonel, Head of Operations Section, deputy to chief of staff
Murzikhin	Orderly
Orlovsky	Battalion Commissar, Secretary to the Soviet
Samarin	Major General, commander of an army group

VILLAGE OF MARCHIKHINA BUDA

Cherednichenko, Maria Timofeyevna (her name evokes that of Matriona Timofeyevna, one of the peasant heroines of Nekrasov's long narrative poem *Who is Happy in Russia*)

Lionya	Maria Timofeyevna's grandson
Grishchenko	kolkhoz chairman
Kotenko, Sergey Ivanov	an anti-Soviet peasant
Vasily Karpovich	a cowherd

REGIMENTAL HQ

Petrov	Colonel, divisional commander
Mertsalov	Major, regimental commander
Kudakov, Semion Germogenovich	Mertsalov's chief of staff
Kochetkov	Major, commander of first battalion
Babadjanian	Captain, commander of second battalion

Myshansky	Lieutenant, deputy chief of staff
Kozlov	Senior Lieutenant, commander of a reconnaissance platoon
Bogariov, Sergey Alexandrovich	Battalion Commissar
Kosiuk	Lieutenant, commander of a machine-gun company

HOWITZER UNIT

Rumiantsev, Vasily (Vasya)	Captain, commanding officer of the unit
Nevtulov, Sergey (Seriozha)	commissar of the unit
Klenovkin	Lieutenant

BABADJANIAN'S BATTALION

Ignatiev, Semion	soldier in First Rifle Company
Granny Bogachikha	an old woman from Ignatiev's village, a mentor to him
Pesochina, Marusya	Ignatiev's betrothed
Vera	a beautiful young refugee in Gomel
Sedov	formerly a Moscow fitter, a friend of Ignatiev
Rodimtsev, Ivan	a collective farmer from Riazan; friend of Ignatiev
Zhaveliov	soldier in First Rifle Company

Introduction

In the early hours of 22 June 1941 Hitler invaded the Soviet Union. Stalin had refused to believe more than eighty intelligence warnings of Hitler's intentions, and Soviet forces were taken by surprise. Over two thousand Soviet aircraft were destroyed within twenty-four hours. During the following months the Germans repeatedly encircled entire Soviet armies. By the end of the year, they had reached the outskirts of Moscow and more than three million Soviet soldiers had been captured or killed.

Before the German invasion, Grossman appears to have been depressed. He was overweight and, though only in his mid-thirties, he walked with a stick. In spite of this – and his poor eyesight – he volunteered to serve in the ranks. Had he been accepted – like several of his colleagues who volunteered for writers' militia companies – he would probably have been killed within the next two or three months. Assigned instead to *Red Star*, the Red Army's daily newspaper, he soon became one of the best-known Soviet war correspondents, admired not only for his powerful stories and articles but also for his personal courage. *Red Star* was as important during the war years as *Pravda* and *Izvestia*, the official newspapers of the Communist Party and the Supreme Soviet; many of the best writers of the time wrote for it and it enjoyed a wide readership among both soldiers and civilians. Its circulation at the beginning of the war was approximately three hundred thousand – and most copies, especially at the front, were read by a large number of people.

David Ortenberg, *Red Star*'s chief editor, was clearly aware of Grossman's gifts. In April 1942 he gave him permission to go on leave for two months in order to work on a short novel about a Soviet military unit that breaks out of German encirclement. Grossman then joined his family in Chistopol, a town in Tatarstan to which a number of Soviet writers, including Boris Pasternak, had been evacuated.

Grossman was appalled by the falsity of the many stories and articles being published at this time about the heroism of the Red Army. On 17 June he wrote to his father: "I'm close to the end – just two chapters left. I'll finish by the 20th and it seems I'll leave [for Moscow – R.C.] on 21–22nd. I read my work aloud to people and receive much excited praise. People are very, very enthusiastic. But this, of course, is not because my story is so very good, but because what my poor fellow writers are now writing is so bad. Have you read Panfiorov's story in *Pravda*? Naturally, after something like that, anything half-decent seems excellent." Grossman makes similar criticisms in his wartime notebooks. In a September 1941 entry he quotes a sentence from the editorial of another military newspaper, "The severely battered enemy continued his cowardly advance."[1] In the following entry he dismisses the work of another bad journalist by repeating a joke he had heard from his colleagues: "Ivan Pupkin killed five Germans with a spoon."[2]

The People Immortal – the first Soviet novel about the war –

was serialized in *Red Star* in July and August, to general acclaim. Grossman went on to cover all the main battles of the war, from the defence of Moscow to the fall of Berlin, and his articles were valued by ordinary soldiers and generals alike. Groups of front-line soldiers would gather to listen while one of them read aloud from a single copy of *Red Star*; the writer Viktor Nekrasov, who fought at Stalingrad as a young man, remembers how "the papers with [Grossman's] and Ehrenburg's articles were read and reread by us until they were in tatters."[3]

Grossman's articles were republished countless times – in a variety of military newspapers, in booklets published all over the Soviet Union, and sometimes in *Pravda*. *The Years of War* – a large volume, first published in 1945, that includes a revised version of *The People Immortal*, Grossman's long article about Treblinka, two short stories and twenty-one of his *Red Star* articles – was translated into a number of languages including English, French, Dutch and German. As a separate volume, *The People Immortal* was published in Danish, Welsh and most of the languages of Soviet-occupied Eastern Europe.

★

Vasily Grossman's three war novels are recognizably the work of the same writer; all display his sharp psychological insights and his gift for descriptive passages that appeal to all our different senses. Nevertheless, the goals he set himself in these novels are very different.

His best-known work, *Life and Fate*, is not only a novel but also an exercise in moral and political philosophy, asking whether or not it is possible for someone to behave ethically even when subjected to overwhelming violence. The earlier *Stalingrad*, mostly written between 1945 and 1947, is primarily a work of commemoration, a tribute to all who died during the war. *The People Immortal*, set during the catastrophic defeats of the war's first months, is Grossman's contribution to the Soviet war effort. Grossman successfully meets two conflicting demands. On the one hand, the novel is optimistic and morale-boosting. On the other hand, it includes much that was controversial – Grossman makes several cogent criticisms of how the war is being fought.

The plot is simple and – at least in its general outline – conventional. What immediately grips the reader is the vividness of the details. As in the two Stalingrad novels, the minutiae of army life – the soldiers' jokes, the layout of their foxholes and trenches, their thoughts when faced by German Panzers – are conveyed clearly and succinctly. Grossman's descriptions of the natural world are no less convincing. His account of a detachment of peasant recruits marching at night through fields of grain not only allows us to hear, see and sense the entire scene but also allows us an unexpected insight into what this night march might mean to the men themselves: "Marching through the still unharvested fields, they could recognize the different grains – oats, wheat, barley or buckwheat – by the swish of falling seeds, by the creak of straw underfoot and by the rustle of the stalks that clung to their tunics. And this trampling of the tender body of the ungathered harvest, this sad, invisible, rain-like patter of the falling seeds, spoke more eloquently about the war, brought home its true nature more clearly to many hearts than did the great fires blazing on the horizon, the red stitches of tracer bullets creeping towards the stars, the bluish pillars of searchlight beams sweeping across the sky or the distant rumble of exploding bombs."

Grossman's character sketches are simple but deft. Among the most memorable are Lionya, an eleven-year-old boy, determined to hang on to his toy black revolver as he trudges for several days behind German lines, confident that he will be able to find his commissar father; Lionya's defiant grandmother, who is shot after slapping a German officer in the face; Bruchmüller, a respected and experienced German artillery colonel who admits to being troubled by his lack of understanding of the Russian character; and Semion Ignatiev, a womanizer and gifted storyteller who turns out to be the one of the bravest and most resourceful of the rank-and-file soldiers.

Several chapters are devoted to life in Belorussia under the Germans. Grossman shows us this world from several perspectives: from that of young Lionya; from that of two older girls who look on everything they see around them as a mad dream that simply cannot continue much longer; from that of Kotenko, a bitterly anti-Soviet peasant who initially welcomes the Germans; and from that of Ignatiev, who is enraged by the sight of German officers and soldiers eating, drinking and enjoying themselves in a village just like his own.

Grossman spent most of the war years close to the front line and he had an unusual gift for winning the confidence of both ordinary soldiers and senior commanders. People spoke freely to him and this enabled him to create a picture of wartime life that accorded with their own experience. This edition includes not only the text of the novel itself (along with many previously unpublished passages from Grossman's manuscript), but also a variety of background material, including cards and letters taken from German prisoners-of-war, appreciative letters sent to Grossman by Soviet commissars and commanders, extracts from Grossman's wartime notebooks, and a page of notes Grossman wrote after reading Tacitus – the greatest historian of the Roman Empire.

The additional material helps us to understand that this novel, at the time, was far more controversial than one might first imagine. As in nearly all his work, throughout the three decades of his professional career, Grossman was writing on the boundary of what was permissible. It is not surprising that some of his more unorthodox thoughts were deleted by his editors. It is, rather, astonishing how many criticisms of conventional military thinking he managed to introduce into the Soviet Union's most important military newspaper.

It is particularly striking how often two of his most positive fig-ures – Captain Babadjanian and Battalion Commissar Bogariov – act and speak in defiance of the important Order no. 270, issued by the Stavka (the Soviet Supreme Command) on 16 August 1941. Not only do Babadjanian and Bogariov act far too independently, risking accusations of insubordination, but they also show unacceptable leniency, merely reprimanding subordinates who – according to this order – should be shot on the spot.

The text of the last part of this shockingly brutal order follows this introduction. It serves not only to bring out the boldness of Grossman's thinking but also to illustrate the desperation of Stalin's attempt to check the Red Army's headlong flight.

Robert Chandler and Julia Volohova, September 2021

Order no. 270, issued by the Stavka (the Soviet Supreme Command) on 16 August 1941

This concludes as follows:

In the ranks of the Red Army, can we tolerate cowards who desert to the enemy and surrender, or commanders so cowardly that, at the slightest hitch, they tear off their badges of rank and desert to the rear? No! If we give free rein to such cowards and deserters, they will promptly bring about the disintegration of our army and the destruction of our Motherland. Cowards and deserters must be destroyed.

Can a commander be called a commander if he hides in a slit trench during a battle, if he does not keep his eyes on the battlefield, if he does not observe the course of the battle from the front line – yet still sees himself as a battalion or regimental commander? No! Such a man is not a battalion or regimental commander but an impostor. Should we give free rein to such impostors, they will soon make the army into nothing more than a massive bureaucracy. [...]

I ORDER:
1. That commanders and political officers who, during combat, tear off their badges of rank and desert to the rear or surrender to the enemy are to be considered malicious deserters, their families also subject to arrest as relatives of a man who has violated his oath and betrayed his Motherland.

All higher commanders and commissars are required to shoot on the spot any such deserters from among command personnel.

2. Units and sub-units encircled by the enemy are to fight selflessly to the last, to take care of their equipment like the apple of their eye and to break through to our main forces from behind the enemy front line, defeating the Fascist dogs.

Should his unit be surrounded, every Red Army man, regardless of rank or position, is required to demand from a higher commander that he fight to the last in order to break through to our main forces, and should such a commander or Red Army unit prefer to surrender rather than strike a blow against the enemy, all possible means, both ground and air, should be used to destroy them. The families of Red Army men who allow themselves to be taken prisoner are to be deprived of all state benefits and assistance.

3. Divisional commanders and commissars are required to immediately remove from their posts any battalion or regimental commander who hides in a slit trench during a battle and is afraid to direct the course of the fighting from the battlefield. Such men should be demoted as impostors, transferred to the ranks, and, if necessary, shot on the spot. They should be replaced by brave and courageous men from the junior command staff or from the ranks of Red Army soldiers who have distinguished themselves.

This Order to be read aloud in all infantry companies, cavalry troops, artillery batteries, aircraft squadrons, command posts and HQs.
Stavka of the Red Army Supreme Command
Chairman of the State Defence Committee I. STALIN
Deputy Chairman of the State Defence Committee V. MOLOTOV
Marshal S. BUDYONNY
Marshal S. TIMOSHENKO
Marshal B. SHAPOSHNIKOV
Army General G. ZHUKOV

Timeline

12 December 1905: Birth of Vasily Grossman in Berdichev, Ukraine.

8–16 March 1917: "The February Revolution" – a spontaneous revolution that topples the Romanov monarchy.

7 November 1917: "The October Revolution" – the Bolshevik Party seizes power in a coup.

November 1917–October 1922: Russian Civil War. Grossman and his mother spend most of these years in Kiev, which changes hands many times.

1923: Grossman moves to Moscow to study chemistry. He becomes increasingly interested in literature, politics and the arts.

1928: Grossman's first publications as a journalist.

Winter 1929–30: "Total Collectivization" of Soviet agriculture.

1934: Grossman's first publications as a novelist and writer of short stories.

1937: Height of the "Great Terror". Hundreds of thousands of members of the Soviet elite – Party members, politicians, NKVD and military officers – are arrested and executed or sent to labour camps.

1 September 1939: Germany invades Poland. This is generally accepted as marking the beginning of the Second World War.

22 June 1941: Launch of Operation Barbarossa. German forces invade the Soviet Union. This is the date that most Russians see as marking the beginning of the war, which they usually refer to not as "the Second World War" but as "the Great Patriotic War".

28 June 1941: German forces capture Minsk, the capital of Belorussia.

7 July 1941: German forces occupy Berdichev, where Grossman was born and where his mother, Yekaterina Savelievna, is still living.

9 July 1941: German forces capture 290,000 Soviet troops near Minsk.

27 July 1941: German forces complete the encirclement of Smolensk.

28 July 1941: David Ortenberg, the editor of Red Star, appoints Grossman as a special correspondent.

5 August 1941: Grossman leaves Moscow by train. Two days later, he arrives in Gomel, 560 kilometres south-west of Moscow, the location of General Yeromenko's Western Front HQ. A few days later, Gomel falls to the Germans.

16 August 1941: Order no. 270 published by the Stavka. This is almost as draconian as the better-known "Not a Step Back Order" of July 1942. Anyone considered to be a deserter is to be shot. Their families, too, will be subjected to draconian penalties.

30 August–8 September 1941: The historical Lieutenant Colonel Babadjanian takes part in the Yelnya offensive, the first Soviet victory during the war. Though it fails to prevent the fall of Smolensk, it provides a boost to Soviet morale.

15 September 1941: Yekaterina Savelievna is murdered, along with approximately 18,000 other Jews from the Berdichev ghetto.

16 September 1941: The Soviet Southern Front is encircled near Kiev and more than half a million soldiers are taken prisoner.

2–21 October 1941: Battle of Briansk. The 50th Army and two other Soviet armies are encircled. General Mikhail Petrov and Regimental Commissar Nikolay Shliapin, the commander and senior commissar of the 50th Army, either take their own lives or are killed in action.

10 April 1942: David Ortenberg, the editor of Red Star, gives Grossman two months' leave to work on a novel.

11 June 1942: Grossman delivers a complete manuscript of *The People Immortal*, which Ortenberg promises to publish without cuts.

19 July–12 August 1942: First publication of *The People Immortal*, serialized over 18 issues of *Red Star*.

28 July 1942: Stalin issues his Order no. 227, generally known as *Ni shagu nazad!* (Not a Step Back!). This order, which became the main slogan of the Soviet press during the following months, is often confused with Stavka Order no. 270 of 16 August 1941 (Stalin's personal orders are numbered separately from orders issued by the Stavka as a whole).

14 September 1942: The Germans reach the centre of Stalingrad.

31 January 1943: Friedrich Paulus, Commander of the German Sixth Army, surrenders to the Red Army at Stalingrad.

5 July–23 August 1943: Battle of Kursk, the largest tank battle in history. The real Hamazasp Babadjanian took part in this battle, as a lieutenant colonel in command of a light armoured brigade.

1943: First English-language publication of *The People Immortal* (Moscow: Foreign Languages Publishing House), tr. Elizabeth Donnelly and Rose Prokofiev.

8–9 May 1945: Last German forces surrender. End of World War Two.

August 1952: First Russian publication of *For a Just Cause*, the first of Grossman's two Stalingrad novels.

14 September 1964: Death of Vasily Grossman.

1980: First publication, in Switzerland, of a Russian-language edition of *Life and Fate*, the second of Grossman's Stalingrad novels.

2020: First publication in any language, under the title *Stalingrad*, of an expanded version of *For a Just Cause*. Unlike any previous edition, this English translation incorporates passages from Grossman's manuscripts and typescripts that he was unable to publish during his lifetime.

THE PEOPLE IMMORTAL

I

AUGUST

One summer evening in 1941, heavy artillery was moving towards Gomel. The guns were so huge that even the blasé cart drivers, who thought there was nothing they hadn't already seen, kept glancing with curiosity at the colossal steel barrels. Dust hung in the air, the gunners' eyes were inflamed, and their faces and uniforms were grey. Most of the men were riding on their guns; only a few were walking. One man was drinking water from his steel helmet; drops were dripping down his chin and his wet teeth glistened. For a moment, you might have thought he was laughing – but his face was tired and preoccupied.

Then came a long shout from the lieutenant walking at the head of the column:

"A-a-a-i-r-cr-a-a-a-ft!"

Above the small oak wood were two planes, flying swiftly towards the road. The men watched anxiously.

"Donkeys!"4

"No, they're German. Junkers or Heinkels."5

And, as always at such moments, someone came out with the standard front-line witticism, "They're ours all right. Where's my helmet?"

The planes were flying at right angles to the road – which meant they were ours. German planes usually banked when they spotted a column, so that they could fly in line with the road and drop small bombs or strafe the column with machine-gun fire.

Powerful road tractors were hauling the guns down the main street of a village. Cows were lowing and dogs were barking in a variety of voices. Women and old greybeards were sitting on the earth banks around whitewashed huts. Small front gardens were filled with curly golden coneflowers and red peonies that flamed in the sunset. Amid all this, the huge guns moving through the quiet of the evening seemed strange and out of place.

A small bridge, not used to such burdens, was letting out groans. Beside it, a car was waiting for the guns to pass. The driver, accustomed to delays like this, was smoking a hand-rolled cigarette, smiling as he watched the gunner drink from his helmet. The battalion commissar[6] sitting beside him kept looking ahead, hoping that the tail of the column might now be in sight.

"Comrade Bogariov," the driver said with a strong Ukrainian accent, "perhaps we should stop here for the night. It'll be dark soon."

The commissar shook his head.

"We must hurry," he said. "I have to get to HQ."

"Like it or not, we can't drive down roads like this in the dark. We'll be spending the night in the forest."

The commissar laughed. "Wanting a drink of milk, are you?"

"I wouldn't say no – and some fried potatoes would be good too!"

"Or even some goose," said the commissar.

"That too!" the driver replied cheerily.

"Three hours from now we must be at HQ – no matter how dark it gets or how bad the roads."

Soon they were able to drive onto the bridge. Flaxen-haired village children ran tirelessly after the jeep, their bare feet almost soundless in the dust, as if they were running through water.

"Here!" they shouted. "For you! Cucumbers, tomatoes, pears!" And they tossed cucumbers and hard, unripe pears through a half-open window.

Bogariov waved at the children and felt a chill pass through his heart. For him, there was always something bitter-sweet about the sight of village children saying farewell to the Red Army as it retreated.

Before the war, Sergey Alexandrovich Bogariov had been a professor in the Faculty of Marxism in one of the main Moscow higher education institutes. Research work was important to him and he tried to devote as few hours as possible to giving lectures. His main concern was a study he had begun about two years before. The directors of the Marx–Engels Institute[7] were very interested in his work and he had twice been called to the Communist Party's Central Committee to discuss some of his preliminary conclusions. His topic was the theoretical foundations of the collective principles of industrial and agricultural labour in Russia. His wife, Yelizaveta Vlasievna, had often been angry with him for not giving enough time to his family: he had usually left home at nine in the morning and seldom returned before eleven o'clock in the evening. And when he finally sat down to dinner, he would take a manuscript from his briefcase and start reading. His wife would ask if he was enjoying his food and whether she'd put enough salt on the fried eggs – and he would reply at random. This would both anger her and make her laugh. Then he would say, "You know, Liza, I had a wonderful day. I read several amazing letters from Marx to Lafargue.[8] They were in some old archive and they've only recently been discovered." He would go on to tell her all about these letters, and she would listen, involuntarily carried away by his excitement. She loved him and was proud of him. She knew how respected and valued he was by his colleagues and with what admiration they spoke of his purity and integrity.

She also found something touching about his lack of practical competence, his inability to manage small everyday matters. In summer, when the school year came to an end and they went for a month to Teberda, in the Northern Caucasus, it was she who was responsible for everything from taxis and porters to train tickets and vouchers for the house of recreation. Sergey Alexandrovich, though well able to display iron strength and determination in his work and in arguments over some matter of principle, was utterly helpless when it came to these simpler matters.[9]

And now Sergey Alexandrovich Bogariov was deputy head of the Front Political Administration department responsible for work among the enemy troops.[10] Now and then he would remember the cool vaults of the institute's manuscript repository, a desk heaped with papers, a shaded lamp, the creak of the stepladder a librarian was moving from one bookshelf to another. Sometimes odd sentences from his unfinished study would come to mind and he would return to the questions that had so passionately engaged him throughout his life.

★

The car speeds along the road. There is dust everywhere: dark brick dust, yellow dust, fine grey dust. Men's faces look like the faces of corpses. These clouds of dust hanging over every road near the front line have been raised by hundreds of thousands of Red Army boots, by truck wheels and tank tracks, by road tractors and artillery, by the small hooves of pigs and sheep, by collective-farm horses and huge herds of cows, by collective-farm tractors, by the creaking carts of refugees, by the bast sandals of collective-farm foremen and the little shoes of girls leaving Bobruisk, Mozyr, Zhlobin, Shepetovka and Berdichev.[11] Dust hangs over Ukraine and Belorussia; it swirls over the Soviet earth. At night, the dark August sky reddens from the sinister glow of burning villages. The heavy rumble of exploding bombs rolls through birch groves, over quivering aspens and through dark forests of oak and pine. Green and red tracer bullets riddle the sky's heavy velvet. Anti-aircraft shells burst like small white sparks. Heinkels loaded with high-explosive bombs drone through the dark, their engines seeming to say, *B-b-bomber, b-b-bomber.* Old men, women and children in villages and hamlets wave the retreating soldiers on their way, offering them curd cheese, pies, cucumbers and glasses of milk. The old women weep and weep, searching amid thousands of grim, dusty, exhausted faces for the face of a son. And they hold out the little white bundles with their gifts of food, "Take this, love. You are all my own sons. Every one of you has a place in my heart."

Sergey Alexandrovich Bogariov has been on these roads for fifty days now. Now and then he asks himself, "Do I still need my old life – my thoughts, my joys and disappointments, all those pages I wrote, all my hard work that seemed as precious as gold?"[12]

Hordes of Germans are advancing from the west. Their tanks are daubed with antlered deer heads, with green and red dragons, with wolf maws and fox tails, with skulls and crossbones. Every

German soldier has in his pocket photographs of conquered Paris, devastated Warsaw, shameful Verdun, burned-down Belgrade and occupied Brussels, Amsterdam, Oslo, Narvik, Athens and Gdynia. In every officer's wallet are photographs of German women and girls with fringes and curls, lounging at home in striped pyjamas. Every officer wears some kind of amulet: a gold trinket, a string of coral, a tiny stuffed animal with yellow bead eyes. Every officer carries in his pocket a German–Russian military phrasebook full of such clear, straightforward phrases as "Hands up!", "Halt, don't move!", "Where's your gun?", "Surrender!" Every German soldier has learned a few words of Russian or Ukrainian: *mleko* (milk); *kleb* (bread); *yaiki* (eggs); *koko* (Cluck-cluck!); and the curt *Davay, davay!* (Come on – hand it over!). All these officers and soldiers are confident of Nazi Germany's greatness and invincibility. They defeated Denmark in half a day, Poland in seventeen days, France in thirty-five days, Greece in eight days and Holland in five – and they have no doubt that within seventy days they can reduce Ukraine, Belorussia and Russia to slavery.[13]

And tens of millions of people rose to meet them – from the bright Oka and the broad Volga, from the stern, yellow Kama and the cold, foaming Irtysh, from the steppes of Kazakhstan, from the Donbas and Kerch, from Astrakhan and Voronezh. Tens of millions of loyal workers dug deep anti-tank ditches, trenches, pits and dugouts. Thousands of trees ceased to sound in the wind and lay down quietly across highways and peaceful back roads; barbed wire twined and tangled around the yards of factories; iron bristled into anti-tank barriers in the squares and streets of our lovely green towns.

Bogariov sometimes felt surprised how quickly and easily, in only a few hours, he had been able to put aside his former life; he was glad to find he could still make good judgments, even in difficult situations, and that he was capable of acting decisively. And most important of all, he could sense that he was still himself. Here, in the war, he had held on to his integrity and his inner world, and people trusted and respected him and were aware of his inner strength – just as they had in the past, when he took part in philosophical debates at the institute. He rejoiced in his unshakeable faith and often said to himself, "No, it's not for nothing that I studied Marxist philosophy. Revolutionary dialectics has proved a good schooling for this war, which has seen the collapse of Europe's oldest cultures."[14] All the same, he was not satisfied with his work; he felt he was too distant from the soldiers themselves, from the heart of the war, and he wanted to exchange his work in the Political Administration for a more strictly military role.

He often had to interrogate German prisoners – mostly non-commissioned officers – and he had noticed that, during these sessions, his burning hatred for Fascism, which gave him no rest day and night, yielded to a sense of contempt and disgust. Nearly all these men turned out to be cowards. They quickly and willingly described their armaments and gave him the numbers of their units. They made out that they were workers, that they had Communist sympathies and had been imprisoned on account of their revolutionary ideals. With one voice they repeated, "Hitler kaput, kaput," although it was obvious they did not believe this for one moment.

There was something astonishingly wretched about both their own letters and the letters they received from home. Most of the former were taken up by sentimental descriptions of landscapes and excited accounts of cooking pork, goose and chicken and of how much honey and sour cream they had been eating. As for the letters from home, these differed little from invoices: "I received your parcel with silk, eau de cologne and lady's' underwear. Thank you. In one of your next parcels, you should send a warm sweater for your grandfather, a few skeins of wool, some children's boots, etc., etc."[15]

Only occasionally did Bogariov come across real Nazis, with the courage even in captivity to affirm their loyalty to Hitler and their faith in the supremacy of the German race and its mission to enslave the rest of the world. He usually questioned such men at length. They had never read anything – not even Nazi brochures and novels – and they had not heard of Goethe and Beethoven, or even of such pillars of German statehood as Bismarck or such famous military figures as Moltke, Schlieffen and Frederick the Great.[16] The only name they knew was that of the secretary of their district branch of the National Socialist Party and they believed that the Germans were the highest of people and that the Führer, Goering and the wise Goebbels were the highest of Germans. And that this vile, ignorant, lie-based sense of their own superiority gave them the right to trample on other people's bread and to shed the holy blood of children.

Bogariov carefully studied orders from the German High Command and was struck by the extraordinary organizational ability they revealed. The Germans looted, burned and bombed in a methodical and orderly fashion; they could organize the collection of empty tin cans in a bivouac and they could elaborate a plan for the advance of a huge column, taking into account thousands of details, and then execute this plan according to schedule and with mathematical accuracy. In their capacity for mechanical obedience, in their readiness to march on mindlessly, in the ability of millions of soldiers to execute huge and complex manoeuvres with iron discipline – in all this there was something base, something foreign to the free spirit of man. Rather than being a cultivation of reason, this was a harnessing of instincts, a form of organization similar to that of ants and herd animals.

Among this mass of German letters and documents, Bogariov had come across only two letters in which he could sense genuine feeling, free of vulgarity, or any true movement of thought – letters full of shame and sorrow with regard to the appalling crimes being committed by the German people. One was from a young woman to a soldier; the other was one that a soldier had been about to send home. And once he had interrogated an elderly officer, a former teacher of literature, who had also turned out to be a thoughtful man with a genuine hatred of Nazism.

"Hitler," he had said, "is not a creator of national values. He's a usurper. He has plundered the German nation's industrial culture and zeal for work. He's like an ignorant gangster who has stolen a magnificent car built by a brilliant scientist."

"Never," Bogariov said to himself, "will these men defeat our country. The more meticulously they calculate trifles and details, the more mathematically they execute their manoeuvres – the harder they find it to grasp anything of importance and the more terrible the catastrophe that awaits them. They plan every smallest detail but they think in only two dimensions. They are methodical artisans. They are people governed by instinct and the very lowest utilitarianism – and as such, they do not understand and never can understand the laws of historical movement in the war they have started."

The jeep sped on amid the cool of dark forests, across little bridges over winding streams, through misty valleys, past quiet ponds that reflected the blazing stars of the vast August sky. The driver said quietly, "Comrade Battalion Commissar, remember that soldier drinking from his helmet – the one sitting on his gun? I suddenly had a strange feeling, as if he's my brother. That must be why I noticed him!"

2

MILITARY SOVIET

Shortly before the meeting of the military soviet,[17] Divisional Commissar Cherednichenko went for a stroll in the park. He was walking slowly, stopping now and then to refill his short-stemmed pipe. After passing the old palace with the tall gloomy tower and the stopped clock, he went down to the pond. The branches hanging over the water were like a luxurious green mane and the swans gleamed in the morning sun. They were moving very slowly, their necks tensely coiled – as if the water were taut and dense and they were struggling to make their way through it. For a while Cherednichenko just stood there and watched, deep in thought. Then a middle-aged major with a dark beard came down the avenue from the signals office. Cherednichenko recognized him – he was from the operations department and had already reported to him a couple of times. As the major approached, he said in a loud voice, "May I have a word with you, Comrade Cherednichenko?"

"Of course," said Cherednichenko, still watching the swans. Alarmed by the major's voice, the swans were now making for the opposite bank.

"We've just received a report from the commander of the 72nd infantry division."

"That's Makarov, isn't it?"

"Yes, Makarov. This is of the utmost importance, Comrade Member of the Military Soviet. Yesterday, at about twenty-three hundred, large formations of enemy tanks and motor infantry began to move forward. Prisoners have testified that these belong to three separate divisions of Guderian's tank army and that their direction of movement is Unecha – Novgorod – Seversk."[18]

The major looked at the swans and added, "Panzer divisions, incomplete – according to prisoners."

"Yes," said Cherednichenko, "I heard during the night."

The major looked questioningly at his lined face and long narrow eyes. Against Cherednichenko's dark, weather-beaten face, marked by the winds and frosts of the Russian–German War and the steppe campaigns of the Civil War, his eyes seemed unexpectedly bright. His expression was calm and thoughtful.

"May I be dismissed, Comrade Member of the Military Soviet?" asked the major.

"Give me the latest operations bulletin from the central sector."

"The report valid until zero four hundred hours—"

"Zero four hundred," Cherednichenko interrupted, "or perhaps zero three fifty-seven?"

"Very likely, Comrade Member of the Military Soviet," the major replied with a smile. "But the bulletin contained nothing important. The enemy was not especially active in the remaining sectors. Only to the west of the river crossing, where he occupied the village of Marchikhina Buda, suffering losses of up to one and a half battalions."

"What village?" said Cherednichenko, looking at the major intently.

"Marchikhina Buda."

"You're certain?" Cherednichenko asked sternly.

"Absolutely."

The major paused for a moment and, smiling, went on a little apologetically, "They're fine swans. Prince Paskevich-Yerivansky[19] used to breed them, same as in our village we used to breed geese. But two were killed during yesterday's air raid. Their chicks survived."

Cherednichenko drew once more on his pipe, then let out a cloud of smoke.

"May I be dismissed?" said the major.

Cherednichenko nodded. The major clicked his heels and set off back to the operations department. He passed Cherednichenko's orderly, who was standing beneath an old maple, Mauser at his side. Cherednichenko stood without moving for a long time, looking at the swans and at the bright patches of light on the pond's green surface. Then, in a low, hoarse voice, he said, "Lionya, Mama, will I ever see you again?" – and coughed the dry cough of a soldier.

He began to walk back to the palace, at his usual slow pace. His orderly, still waiting beneath the maple, asked, "Comrade Divisional Commissar, shall I send a car for your mother and son?"

"No," Cherednichenko replied curtly. Seeing the surprise on his orderly's face, he added, "Marchikhina Buda was taken by the Germans during the night."

*

The military soviet met in a high, vaulted room, with tall, narrow windows draped with door curtains. In the half-light, the red tasselled cloth on the long table looked black. Fifteen minutes before the meeting was due to begin, the secretary walked noiselessly across the carpet and asked the orderly in a whisper, "Murzikhin, have you brought the commander his apples?"

"Yes," the orderly replied at once, "I ordered them the same as always, along with Narzan water and cigarettes. Ah, here they come!"

Another orderly appeared, carrying a plate of green apples and several bottles of mineral water.

"Over there, on the little table!" said the secretary.

"Think I don't know?" the orderly replied.

Next to come in was Ilya Ivanovich, the chief of staff, a general with a tired, dissatisfied look on his face. He was followed by a colonel, Piotr Yefimovich, head of the operations section, who was holding a roll of maps. The general was plump and pale, the colonel thin, tall and ruddy – yet somehow they looked strangely alike.

The general asked the orderly, who was standing to attention, "Where's the commander?"

"On the telephone, Comrade Major General."

"Is there a connection?"

"It was restored twenty minutes ago."

"See, Piotr Yefimovich!" said the chief of staff, "and your much-praised signals officer said he wouldn't be able to put us through until noon!"

"Well, so much the better, Ilya Ivanovich," the colonel replied – and with the familiarity expected of a subordinate at such moments, he added, "When are you going to get some sleep? This is the third night you've stayed up."

"Well, it's not easy to think about sleep at a time like this," said the chief of staff. He went over to the little table and took an apple. The colonel was spreading out his maps on the large table. He too reached for an apple. The orderly and the secretary, who was standing by the bookcase, exchanged smiles.

"Yes, here we are," said the chief of staff, bending over the map and staring at the thick blue arrow that showed a German tank column moving deep into the red semicircle of our defence. He frowned, bit into the apple, grimaced and said, "Too damned sour!"

The colonel took a bite of his own apple and said, "Yes – pure vinegar, I beg to report." He turned to the orderly and asked crossly, "Can you really not find any better apples than these for the military soviet? This is outrageous!"

The chief of staff laughed. "No accounting for tastes, Piotr Yefimovich. This is what the commander ordered, he adores sour apples."

They bent down over the table and went on talking quietly. The colonel said, "They're threatening our main communication line. It's only too clear what they're up to. They're outflanking us on the left."

"Hmm," said the chief of staff. "Better to call it the potential threat of an outflanking movement."

They put their nibbled apples down on the table and, simultaneously, sprang to attention. Yeromin, the Front C-in-C, had come in.[20] He was tall and lean, with greying, close-cropped hair. Unlike everyone else, he walked not on the carpet but on the polished parquet, and his boots clattered noisily.

"Good morning, comrades, good morning," he said. After a

quick look at the chief of staff, he asked, "What's up with you, Ilya Ivanovich? You're looking worn out!"

Usually, the chief of staff addressed Yeromin by name and patronymic – Viktor Andreyevich. Now, though, just before an important meeting of the military soviet, he answered in a loud voice, "I feel excellent, Comrade Lieutenant General. Permission to report?"

"Certainly," said Yeromin. "And here comes the divisional commissar."

Cherednichenko gave a silent nod as he came in. He sat down at the far corner of the table.

"Just a minute," said Yeromin. He flung open the window. "I told you to open the windows," he said sternly to the secretary.

The situation the chief of staff then reported was extremely serious. German spearheads were attempting flanking movements, threatening to encircle our forces. Our forces were withdrawing to new lines of defence. These retreats were accompanied by fierce fighting. The Soviet artillery thundered away day and night; hundreds of thousands of heavy shells howled towards the enemy. Every day our divisions launched counter-attacks. Every river crossing, every ridge, every bottleneck on the roads, every clearing between bog and forest – all saw long and bloody battles. Nevertheless, the enemy was advancing and we were retreating. The enemy captured cities and vast swathes of land. Every day, the Nazi radio and press reported yet more victories. Nazi propaganda exulted. We too had our share of people unable to see beyond the undeniable fact that the Germans were advancing while our own troops retreated. And these people considered the war lost; they despaired of the future and were overwhelmed by anxiety. They did not understand the harsh, complex laws of the most terrible war the world has ever known. They did not sense the molecular processes taking place in the vast organisms of the warring countries. They did not sense how the musculature of our defence was strengthening and growing more resilient, while that of the advancing enemy grew weaker and more anaemic from day to day. The *Völkischer Beobachter*[21] carried huge headlines in red; jubilant speeches were given in Fascist clubs; wives got ready to welcome their husbands, thinking they'd be back in only a few weeks' time. But after meetings at German HQs, some of the older generals held quiet, troubled conversations with one another, falling silent when approached by optimistic young believers in National Socialist strategies. As for the Germans who were taken prisoner, and who were almost suffocating in the fierce August sun, they were clearly astonished when Battalion Commissar Bogariov questioned them about their quartermasters' supplies of winter uniforms. Fascism's strategists thought only in two dimensions; these stupid, self-righteous masters of brilliant detail were blind to the coordinate of time, one of the main terms of the vast battle of peoples being fought throughout Belorussia and Ukraine.[22]

The chief of staff, who was now reporting, the colonel who was his deputy, the secretary, Cherednichenko and Yeromin himself – all could see the heavy blue arrow pointing deep into the body of the Soviet lands. To the colonel, the arrow seemed terrible, swift and indefatigable in its movement across the ruled paper. The C-in-C, Lieutenant General Yeromin, knew more than the others about reserve divisions and regiments, about formations still deep in the rear but now being brought forward. He had an excellent sense of the contours of battles, a physical awareness of the folds of the terrain, the unsteadiness of the Germans' pontoon bridges, the depth of the fast-flowing streams and the precarious sponginess of the bogs where he would meet the German tanks. His war – unlike that of the HQ and operations department staff – was not being fought only on the grid of a map. He fought on Russian soil, with its forests, its morning mists, its uncertain twilight, its fields of tall wheat and dense uncut hemp, its hay-stacks and granaries, its small villages on steep riverbanks, its deep ravines overgrown with scrub. He could feel the length of main roads and winding back roads; he had a physical sense of the dust, of the winds and rains, of small blown-up railway halts and the torn-up track at important junctions. And the blue arrow with its point like a fishhook did not alarm him. He was a cool-headed general who knew and loved his country, who loved to fight and knew how to fight. He wanted only one thing – to take the offensive. But he was retreating, and this was a source of torment to him.

Ilya Ivanovich, the chief of staff – formerly a professor at the Military Academy – was a true military scientist, an expert in both tactics and grand strategy. He was well versed in military history and fond of noting differences and similarities between current operations and other important battles from the previous one hundred and fifty years. He had a lively mind and was never dogmatic. In conversation with his colleagues, he would say, "Comrades, we must remember that what constitutes the heart of modern mobile warfare is close, dynamic cooperation between every branch of the armed forces. Swiftness of movement!" He was impressed by the German generals' ability to plan and execute swift manoeuvres, the mobility of their infantry and the skill with which their air and ground forces had learned to work together. He had a broad understanding of the war, seeing it not only in military terms but also grasping its economic, historical and political aspects. He was both a soldier and an academic, a man of true European culture. One night he dreamed that General Gamelin had come to his HQ office for an oral examination and he had hauled Gamelin over the coals for his obtuseness with regard to the specific features of modern warfare.[23] He was dispirited by the Soviet retreat; he felt as if the blue arrow were piercing his own heart – the heart of a Russian soldier.

Piotr Yefimovich, the colonel who headed the HQ operations section, a brisk, efficient officer with considerable experience and specialist knowledge, thought mainly in terms of military maps. For him, the only reality was the squares of the general staff's large-scale maps and he always knew exactly how many of the open sheets on his desk had been replaced as the Red Army moved east, and which valleys and ravines had been marked by blue or red pencils. For him, the war was fought on maps and conducted by staff officers. And he too was dispirited. He thought it inevitable that our armies would continue to retreat. German motorized infantry was repeatedly threatening to outflank the Soviet armies – and the blue arrows on the map moved east according to mathematical laws of scale and speed. To the colonel, all this was simply a matter of geometry; no other laws were of any account.

The calmest person present was Cherednichenko, the taciturn divisional commissar known as the "Soldiers' Kutuzov".[24] Even in the fiercest moments of fighting there was always an atmosphere of unusual calm around this unflurried, slow-moving man with the thoughtful, rather sad face. People remembered, and often

41

repeated, his laconic witticisms and incisive rebukes and everyone recognized his broad-shouldered, stocky figure. He would often go out for a stroll, puffing quietly on his pipe, or else sit on a bench, deep in thought and slightly frowning – and everyone, commander and soldier alike, felt lighter at heart when they glimpsed this man with the high cheekbones, narrowed eyes and wrinkled forehead.

During the chief of staff's report, Cherednichenko sat with his head bowed, and there was no knowing whether he was listening attentively or thinking about something else altogether. From time to time, he glanced out of the window, then bowed his head again, resting his elbow on the edge of the table. Only once did he get up, go over to the chief of staff and stand beside him for a while to look at the map, swaying a little as he shifted his weight from heel to toe.

After the report, Yeromin asked both the general and the colonel a few questions and glanced now and then at Cherednichenko, waiting for him to join in the discussion. The atmosphere in the room was tense. The colonel kept taking his fountain pen from his tunic pocket, unscrewing the cap, trying the nib on his palm, returning the pen to his pocket, and then going through the whole process again. This did not escape Cherednichenko's notice. Yeromin paced about the room, his heavy tread making the parquet creak. He was frowning – German tanks were threatening the left flank of one of his armies.

"Listen, Viktor Andreyevich," Cherednichenko began unexpectedly, "as a child, you got used to the unripe apples you stole from other people's orchards. And because you still love that taste, we all have to suffer."

Everyone looked at the row of bitten-into apples and laughed.

"You're right," Yeromin replied. "We need ripe apples too."

"Very good, Comrade Lieutenant General," the secretary said with a smile.

"What's going on here?" asked Cherednichenko. He went up to the map and said to the chief of staff, "Is this to be your line of defence?"

"That's right, Comrade Divisional Commissar. Viktor Andreyevich believes that this is where we can most actively and effectively exploit all the means of defence at our disposal."

"Yes," said Yeromin. "And the chief of staff has suggested that the best way to effect this would be to counter-attack near Marchikhina Buda and retake the village. What do you think yourself?"

"Retake Marchikhina Buda?" repeated Cherednichenko – and something in his voice made everyone look at him. He relit his pipe, blew out a cloud of smoke, waved the smoke away with his hand, and looked at the map for some time without a word.

"No, I'm against it," he said. Running the stem of his pipe over the map, he went on to explain why he thought this proposal mistaken.

Yeromin then dictated orders to reinforce the left flank and to regroup Samarin's divisions. He also ordered one of the reserve rifle units to be brought forward against the German tanks.

Cherednichenko signed this order straight after Yeromin and added, "And I'll certainly give them a good commissar."

Just then came the roar of an exploding bomb, quickly followed by a second bomb. There was the sound of hurried anti-aircraft fire and the quiet whine of German bombers. No-one even looked towards the windows. Only the chief of staff said crossly to the colonel, "And in about five minutes' time we'll be hearing the air-raid sirens."

"It's called a delayed reflex," said the colonel.

Cherednichenko then said to the secretary, "Comrade Orlovsky, call Bogariov."

"He's already here, Comrade Divisional Commissar. I was about to report."

"Good," said Cherednichenko. On his way out, he said to Yeromin, "So, we're agreed about the apples?"

"Yes, yes, of course," Yeromin replied. "Apples of every kind."

"Excellent!" said Cherednichenko and walked towards the door, accompanied by the chief of staff and the colonel, who were both smiling. In the doorway, he said casually, "Colonel, you're always fiddling with your pen. Why? How can you go on doubting? You simply mustn't. We've got no choice – we just have to win."

Orlovsky, the secretary of the military soviet, thought he had a good understanding of people, but he was unable to grasp why Cherednichenko was so fond of Bogariov. Cherednichenko was an old soldier who had served in the Russian army for about thirty years. Usually, he had little time for commanders and commissars newly called up from the reserves. Bogariov – a former philosophy lecturer – was a striking exception.

In the company of Bogariov, Cherednichenko was a changed man, anything but taciturn; once he had sat in his office with Bogariov and talked almost the whole night through. Orlovsky had hardly been able to believe it; he had never heard Cherednichenko speak so loudly and animatedly, asking questions, listening and then speaking again. When he went in, they were both looking flushed; it seemed, though, that the two men were not arguing but simply talking about something that really mattered to them.

Now, as he left the hall, Cherednichenko did not give his usual smile when he saw Bogariov spring to attention. Instead, with a stern look, and in a tone Orlovsky had never heard from him before, even during the most solemn parades, he said, "Comrade Bogariov, you have been appointed military commissar to an infantry unit entrusted with an important mission."

"I thank you for your confidence in me," Bogariov replied.

3

A CITY IN TWILIGHT

Semion Ignatiev, a tall, powerfully built young man, was a soldier in the First Rifle Company. Before the war, he had worked on a collective farm in the Tula province. His call-up papers had come at night, while he was asleep in a hayloft – at the very hour that Bogariov received a telephone call with orders to report the following day to the Main Political Administration of the Red Army.

Ignatiev enjoyed reminiscing with his comrades about his last hours in his home village. "Yes, they certainly saw me off in style! My three brothers came from Tula during the night, along with their wives. All three of them work at the machine-gun factory there. And there was the chief mechanic from the tractor station. We drank and sang like there was no tomorrow." Ignatiev remembered this send-off as a cheerful and splendid occasion. At the time, however, he had found it painful even to look at his weeping mother or at his elderly father, who was doing his best to put on a brave face. His father had taken out two George Crosses he'd been awarded in the first German war and held them up to his son, his old hands trembling.[25] "Look, Sima,"[26] he had said, "here are my two silver Georges. There were two gold ones as well, but I put those into a Freedom Bond.[27] Your old sapper father once blew up a bridge along with the best part of a German regiment."

It was all too clear, however, that for all his attempts to be strong, the old man would rather have joined in with the women and wept. Semion was the favourite of his five sons, the jolliest and the most affectionate.

Semion was engaged to be married to Marusya Pesochina, the daughter of the collective-farm chairman. She had been studying accountancy in Odoev and was not expected back until 1 July. Her friends – and her mother still more – had warned her against Semion. To them, he seemed altogether too cheery and frivolous. He loved singing and dancing, and he drank too much. It was inconceivable for a man like him to fall in love at all seriously and stay faithful to a girl for any length of time. In reply, Marusya would just say to her friends, "I don't care, girls. I love him so much that my hands and feet go all cold at the mere sight of him. It frightens me."

When the war began, Marusya asked for two days' leave and walked some thirty kilometres through the night in order to see her sweetheart. She got home at dawn and found that the conscripts had been driven to the station the previous day. Without stopping to rest, she walked another eighteen kilometres to the railway station, the local assembly point. There she was told that the conscripts had already left, in a special troop train. Where the train was going, no-one would tell her. "That is a military secret," an important boss with two squares on his collar tabs had pronounced.[28] At that, Marusya had almost fainted. It had been all she could do to make her way to the apartment of someone she knew, a woman who worked as a cashier in the station luggage office. In the evening, her father had ridden over on a collective-farm horse and taken her back home.

47

Ignatiev soon became famous not only in his company, but also throughout the regiment. He was strong, tireless and cheerful, and a remarkable worker; any tool he took up seemed to dance and play in his hands. And he was endowed with a still more remarkable gift; he worked with such joy and grace that anyone who so much as glanced at him wanted to join in – to take up an axe, a saw or a spade and work as well as he did. He had a good voice, and he had learned many strange old songs from Granny Bogachikha, who lived on the edge of their village. Granny Bogachikha was very unsociable. She allowed no-one into her hut. Sometimes she did not speak a word to anyone for a month. She even preferred to go to the well at night, to avoid meeting other women who might ask her irritating questions. And so, everyone had been astonished at the way she made an exception for Ignatiev – inviting him into her hut, telling him old tales and teaching him songs.

For a while, Ignatiev had worked at the famous Tula factory, along with his brothers, but he had soon gone back to his village. "I need free, open air," he had said. "I need to walk on the earth, just as I need bread and water, but in Tula the land's paved with stone."

He often went for walks in the surrounding countryside – into the forest, or down to the river. He would carry a fishing rod or an old shotgun, but this was mainly for appearance's sake, so that people wouldn't make fun of him. Usually he would walk briskly – then stand still for a while and listen to the birds. He would shake his tousled hair, let out a sigh and walk on further. Or he would climb through the hazel groves to the top of the hill above the river – and sing songs. His eyes were usually as merry as if he were drunk. The villagers would have been sure to dismiss him as an eccentric and laugh at these strolls with a shotgun, except that they couldn't help but respect him for his strength and tremendous capacity for work. He enjoyed practical jokes; he could hold his liquor; he could always come up with some witticism or tell an interesting little story; and he was generous with his tobacco. And so, everyone in his company quickly took a liking to him, and Mordvinov, the sullen sergeant major, once said to him – maybe in admiration, maybe in reproach – "Oh, Ignatiev, you and your Russian soul!"

Ignatiev's two closest friends were Sedov – a locksmith from Moscow – and Rodimtsev, who worked on a collective farm near Riazan. Rodimtsev was thirty-six years old, stocky and with a dark complexion. He already had four children – all girls – and his wife was pregnant. The two men's friendship began with Ignatiev saying, "She's sure to have a boy, no doubt about it." "Seems there's little you don't know!" Rodimtsev had replied with a smile. His dark, stern face looked very beautiful when he smiled.[29]

During the last few weeks, their unit had been held in reserve, on the outskirts of the city. Some of the men had been billeted in abandoned houses. There were a great many such houses, since more than a hundred thousand of the city's one hundred and forty thousand inhabitants had been evacuated to the east. The agricultural machinery factory, a large match factory and a railway-carriage repair works – these had left too.[30] There was a sadness in the air – in the empty streets of the workers' settlement, in the smokeless chimneys of the now silent factory buildings, in the pale-blue kiosks that until recently had been selling ice cream. One of these kiosks had taken on a new role; a military traffic controller with his bunch of different-coloured flags now used it as a shelter from the rain. In the windows of the boarded-up houses there were still withered houseplants – phloxes, hydrangeas now turning brown, and rubber plants with heavy, drooping leaves. Camouflaged army trucks were parked under the trees lining the streets. Khaki armoured cars drove past heaps of golden sand in deserted children's playgrounds; the cars' raucous hoots made them sound like birds of prey. It was these outskirts that had suffered the worst damage from air raids. And everyone driving into the city noticed the burnt-out warehouse building with the huge smoke-blackened sign: "Flammable".

Canteens and barbers, however, continued to operate – as did a small soft-drink factory. Sometimes, after a shower, when the air felt soft and pure, when puddles gleamed merrily and raindrops still glittered brightly on leaves – sometimes people were able to imagine for a moment that no dreadful grief had befallen the country, that there was no enemy waiting only fifty kilometres from their home, and that their ordinary, straightforward life had not come to an end. Girls exchanged looks with soldiers; old men let out sighs and groans as they sat down on benches in little parks and gardens; children played with the heaps of sand placed here and there on the streets in case of incendiary bombs.

Ignatiev liked this green, half-empty city.[31] He did not sense the dreadful sadness that enveloped the few remaining inhabitants. He did not notice the aged, tear-reddened eyes gazing pleadingly into the face of every passing soldier. He did not hear the quiet weeping of the old women; he did not know that hundreds of old men, unable to sleep at night, were standing by windows and looking out into the darkness with tear-filled eyes. They would whisper prayers through pale lips, go over to their daughters, who were crying and calling out in uneasy sleep, or to their grand-children, who were also tossing and turning – and then return to their windows. There they would listen to the vehicles outside and try to guess where in the darkness they were heading.

At ten o'clock the soldiers were alerted. Drivers started their trucks; engines rumbled softly. Civilians went out into their yards and silently watched the soldiers assemble. An old Jewish woman who looked like a skinny little girl, but with a thick warm shawl around her head and shoulders, asked the soldiers, "Comrades, tell us, should we leave or should we stay?"

"Where are you hoping to get to, Granny?" asked Zhaveliov, cheerful as ever. "You must be about ninety, I can't see you walking far."

The old woman nodded mournfully, not disagreeing. She stood by the truck, in the blue light of the headlamp. With the edge of her shawl, she was cleaning away the muck stuck to the truck's mudguard, handling the metal as delicately as if it were a Passover dish. Ignatiev noticed this and his young heart felt a sudden wave of pity. The old woman seemed to sense this; she began to cry.

"What can we do, comrades? What can we do? You're all leaving, aren't you?"

The roar of engines drowned out her weak voice. Heard by no-one, the embodiment of meek sorrow, she continued, "My husband's paralysed. I've three sons in the army. The last joined up yesterday, he's in the militia. Their wives all went with their factory. How can we go, comrades? How can we go anywhere?"[32]

A lieutenant appeared and called Ignatiev over to him.

"Ignatiev, three men are to stay here until morning, to accompany the commissar. You will be one of them."

"Yes, Comrade Lieutenant," Ignatiev answered cheerfully.

Ignatiev wanted to spend the night in the city. He was very taken by Vera, a young refugee now working as a cleaner in the editorial office of a local newspaper. She usually came home from work soon after eleven, and Ignatiev would wait for her out in the yard. She was tall, dark-eyed and full-breasted. Sitting on the bench with her meant a great deal to him. He would sit close beside her – and she would sigh as she told him in her soft Ukrainian voice about her life in Proskurov before the war, how she escaped from the Germans on foot during the night, how she had time to snatch up only a single dress and a bag of baked rusks, leaving her grandparents and her little brother behind, and how fiercely the Germans had bombed the bridge over the Sozh as she and a crowd of other refugees were crossing. All her stories were about the war – about those killed on the roads, about friends who had been dishonoured and tortured, about the deaths of children, about blazing villages. There was always a look of anguish and horror in her black eyes. When Ignatiev tried to embrace her, she would push his arms away with the words, "What's the point? Tomorrow you'll go your way and I'll go mine. You won't remember me and I'll forget you." "So you keep saying," he would reply, "but maybe I won't forget you." "Oh yes, you will. If you'd met me earlier, you'd have heard how I can sing, but now I haven't the heart for it." And she would keep on pushing him away. All the same, Ignatiev very much liked sitting with her, and he kept hoping she would change her mind and not deny him her love. He seldom remembered Marusya Pesochina now, and he felt that it was no great sin for a fighting soldier to have an affair with a beautiful young woman. He only half heard her account of the horrors she had been through. Instead, he just went on gazing at her dark eyes and eyebrows and inhaling the delicate scent of her skin.

One after another, the trucks drove out onto the street. It was difficult, in the darkness, to make out the soldiers' faces, and there was still less chance of recognizing anyone by their voice; they were all sitting there in glum silence. There was a quiet word of command and the trucks moved off towards the Chernigov highway. It took a long time for the whole column to pass the bench where Ignatiev and Vera were sitting. Then everything went quiet, dark and still. Only the white beards of the old men and the white hair of the old women were still visible in the windows.

The sky was full of stars and entirely peaceful. There was only the occasional flash of a shooting star – which to the soldiers seemed like a plane being shot down. For sixteen nights now, the city had been able to sleep peacefully. After two night-time air raids on the station, the Germans had not reappeared in the sky. Some people thought that, having learned about the factories being evacuated, the Germans had called a halt to their bombing. Ignatiev waited until Vera came back and talked her into sitting down beside him.

"I'm very tired, soldier boy," she said.

"Just a little while," he replied. "I'm leaving tomorrow."

She sat down beside him. He gazed into her face. She looked so beautiful and desirable that he couldn't help but let out a sigh. She really was very beautiful indeed.

4

AIR ALERT

Deep in thought, Bogariov sat at his desk. He had not enjoyed the meeting with Mertsalov, his new regimental commander.

Mertsalov had been polite and attentive, but Bogariov had not liked his unfeeling and self-confident tone. He had particularly disliked his parting words to the head accountant: "Every action requires its corresponding document. No action should be undertaken without such a document."

"I don't think that's always the case," Bogariov had put in.

"I too once thought like you," said Mertsalov. "But after you've been with the regiment for a while, Comrade Battalion Commissar, you'll see what I mean."

When Mertsalov talked about his junior commanders, it became apparent that the quality most important to him was orderliness. He repeatedly emphasized such words as "efficient" and "precise", saying of one man that "he executes a task with precise, clocklike timing and immediately files detailed reports". All this was strikingly at odds with what Bogariov had heard from another commissar, who had said, "Your commander's a real hothead. You'll probably find yourself struggling to hold him back!"[33]

Bogariov walked across the room and knocked on the door of the man in whose apartment he was billeted.

"Not yet asleep?" he asked.

"No, no, please come in," an elderly voice quickly replied.

The man was a retired lawyer. Bogariov had already had two or three talks with him, which he had enjoyed. The large room was full of bookcases, with old journals strewn all over the place.

"I've come to say goodbye, Alexey Alexeyevich," said Bogariov. "We're leaving tomorrow morning."

"I'm sorry to hear that," said the old man. "In these grim days, fate has given me someone I can talk to – the kind of companion I've dreamed of for many years. No matter how long I live, I shall remember our evening conversations with gratitude."

"Thank you," said Bogariov. "And here's a small present – a packet of China tea. I know that's something you're fond of!"

They got talking again. The old man said that he too would be leaving in a few days, to go and join his niece in Tashkent.

"I realized I must abandon my books," he said sadly. "A librarian I know in Minsk saw the Germans pour petrol over the Belorussian Academy's books and set fire to them all. People say he's lost his mind."

"Well," said Bogariov, "we must remember that all this book-burning simply bears witness to the helpless superstitiousness of a savage people. After all, thought cannot be destroyed. A force that can overcome the ideas of Marx and Lenin is impossible – just as it is impossible to compel humanity, and not only humanity but also nature itself, to renounce Darwin and Newton, or Copernicus and Mendeleyev. Copernicus's strength lay in the fact that the earth truly does revolve around the sun, and Lenin's strength lies in the fact that his teaching gives expression to the natural laws of life and the development of a great country. To defeat Lenin means to defeat the natural laws of our life. That is not so easy. You can burn Newton's books, but you cannot burn the law of universal gravitation."

"Yes," said the old man. "You're right. The earth keeps on turning."

"It certainly does," Bogariov replied cheerfully. "And how!"

"You know," said the old man, "there's something I have to confess. In 1917 and the year after, I was against the Bolsheviks. I thought they were playing into the hands of the Germans. And now it's as if I'm seeing everything in a new light. Although I fear I still can't tie up all the loose ends. Some things are probably still beyond me."

"Here we see the great dialectic of history," Bogariov said slowly. "Its laws are not so simple, especially for people accustomed to more linear thinking. And even someone as enlightened and clear-headed as Plekhanov[34] was unable to imagine that Russia, twenty-five years after Lenin's revolution, would turn out to be the one deadly enemy of German imperialism. He couldn't see that this revolution had forged a Russian power capable of resisting Hitler."

"Yes, I admit it," said the old lawyer. "I too failed to see that."

"Well, I wish you all the best," said Bogariov.[35]

He shook hands with Alexey Alexeyevich and went back to his room. During the brief period since the beginning of the war he had managed to read some dozen books on military subjects. He had particularly sought out works summarizing the lessons of the great wars of the past. Reading was as necessary to him as eating and drinking. One night he even read a long article in a journal by the light of blazing buildings. His need to read was so natural and organic that reading did not in any way damage his eyes. He had excellent eyesight and never needed glasses.

But that night Bogariov did not read. He wanted to write to his wife, to his mother, and to his closest friends. He fully understood the difficulty and danger of the task assigned to his regiment. Tomorrow would mark the beginning of a new chapter in his life, and he would find it difficult, in the near future, to keep up a correspondence with his loved ones.

"My dearest, my darling," he began, "I've finally got the appointment I dreamed of. Remember what I said before I left home?"

He stopped to think, looking at what he had written. His wife, of course, would be alarmed by this news. She would be unable to sleep at night. Should he be telling her this?

The door opened a little. It was the sergeant major.

"Permission to report, Comrade Battalion Commissar?"

"Please do. What's up?"

"There's one remaining truck, Comrade Commissar, and three soldiers. What are your orders?"

"We leave at zero eight hundred. My jeep's being repaired, so I'll go in the truck. By evening we'll have caught up with the regiment. From now, no-one is to leave the yard. Everyone is to sleep here. And you're to check the jeep yourself."

"Understood, Comrade Battalion Commissar."

The sergeant major seemed to have more to say. Bogariov looked at him questioningly.

"Comrade Battalion Commissar, searchlights are playing up in the sky. There'll be an air-raid warning any minute now."

The sergeant major went out into the yard and quietly called out, "Ignatiev!"

"Present!" Ignatiev replied crossly. He walked over to the sergeant major.

"You're to stay here in the yard. Don't absent yourself for even a minute."

"I shall remain here without interruption," Ignatiev replied.

"What's not being interrupted I don't know, but the commissar's orders are not to absent yourself for even a minute."

"Understood, Comrade Sergeant Major!"

"Now, how are things with the jeep?"

"All in order."

The sergeant major looked at the splendid sky, at the dark, barely visible buildings, and said with a yawn, "Now listen, Ignatiev. Anything unexpected – wake me at once!"

"Understood, Comrade Sergeant Major!" Ignatiev replied, while saying to himself, "What's got into the damned man? Why can't he just go back to sleep and leave us alone?"

He returned to Vera, embraced her and whispered fiercely in her ear, "So who is it you're saving yourself for? The Germans?"

"You are a one!" she replied. And he sensed that, rather than pushing him away, she was now returning his embrace. "But you don't understand a thing," she went on in a whisper. "It's because I'm scared to love you. I could forget some other man, but I won't forget you. Well, now it seems I'll be crying over you too – if I've still got any tears left. But then I'd never have thought there could be so many tears stored up in my heart."

Ignatiev didn't know what to say, nor did she expect any answer from him, and so he began to kiss her.

The distant, broken sound of a locomotive whistle carried through the air. Then a second, and a third.

"An air raid," she said plaintively. "Another air raid."

Somewhere in the distance, they heard quick salvoes of anti-aircraft fire. Searchlight beams crept cautiously across the sky, as if afraid their thin pale-blue bodies might tear against a star, and bursting anti-aircraft shells sparkled brightly high above the city.

5

DEATH OF A CITY

The day will come when the court of great nations will sit in judgment; when the sun will shine down in disgust on Hitler's fox-like face, on his narrow forehead and sunken temples, while a man with fat, sagging cheeks, the boss of the Fascist air force, squirms beside him on the bench of shame.

"Death!" will be the verdict of the old women whose eyes have gone blind from tears.

"Death!" will be the word of the children whose parents have died in blazing buildings.

"Death!" mothers who have lost their children will repeat. "Death, in the name of the holy love of life!"

"Death!" the land desecrated by the Germans will pronounce.

"Death!" we will hear from the ashes where villages, towns and cities have been burned to the ground.

And the German nation, sensing the reproach and contempt that the world now directs at them, will shout, "Death, death!"

"No, not death, but eternal hard labour!" the Poles and Serbs deported as slaves to Germany will call out.

One of the most terrible of the millions of Nazi crimes is the bombing of peaceful towns and cities.

A hundred years from today, a young German will exclaim,

"How can I ever be free of the shame? My great-grandfather was a Fascist pilot."

A hundred years from today, historians will examine with horror the orders that the German High Command drew up so calmly and methodically, with true Germanic precision, and issued to the commanders of air force wings and squadrons. Who wrote these orders? Wild beasts? Lunatics? Or is it possible that this was not the work of living creatures? Could these documents have been signed by the iron fingers of integrating instruments and calculating machines?

There is no punishment or retribution that would atone for even a thousandth part of the guilt of those who issued these orders, or a tenth part of the guilt of those who carried them out. Comrades, no such punishment exists, or ever can exist.

★

The air raid began around midnight. The first high-altitude reconnaissance aircraft dropped flares, along with sticks of incendiary bombs. The stars faded and disappeared as the white globes of these flares, dangling from parachutes, began to blaze in the air. Quietly, thoroughly and meticulously, the dead light illuminated squares, streets and alleyways. The whole sleeping city became visible: the white plaster sculpture of a boy holding a bugle to his lips in front of the Palace of Young Pioneers; the gleaming windows of bookshops; the pink and blue spheres in the windows of pharmacies. The dark foliage of the tall maples in the park sprang into view, each fretted leaf clearly outlined, and the silly young rooks began to caw excitedly, astonished by the sudden arrival of day. Light shone on posters about the latest show in the puppet theatre, on curtained windows with flowerpots, on the colonnade outside the city hospital, on the jolly signboard above a small restaurant, on hundreds of garden benches and windows, and on thousands of small sloping roofs. Round attic windows shone timidly, and stains of amber crept across the polished parquet in the main reading room of the city library.

There the sleeping city lay – a city that was still a home to tens of thousands of women, children and old people, a city that had been slowly growing for nine hundred years, a city where a seminary and a Roman Catholic cathedral had been built three hundred years ago, a city where generations of merry students and skilled craftsmen had studied and worked. Long trains of oxcarts had once made their way through this city and bearded raftsmen had floated past its white houses, crossing themselves as they gazed at the domes of the cathedral. This glorious city had forced the dense, damp forests to retreat. Century after century, famous coppersmiths, cabinetmakers, tanners, bakers, tailors, tinsmiths, painters and stonemasons had worked in this city. And now, on this dark August night, this beautiful ancient city on the bank of a river was lit up by the chemical light of German flares.

Forty twin-engine bombers – Ju-88s and Heinkel-111s – had been ready and waiting since late afternoon. Working as precisely as chemists, uniformed German mechanics had filled the fuel tanks with a light, translucent liquid. Dark-olive high-explosive bombs and silver incendiaries, in a ratio scientifically determined for the most effective destruction of cities, had been hung from the plane's bomb racks. The *Oberst*[36] had studied the precise flight plan prepared by HQ, and the meteorologists had sent in reliable weather reports. The pilots – young and smartly dressed, with fashionable haircuts – had munched their chocolate, smoked a few cigarettes and sent jokey little postcards to their families back home.

The planes whined overhead. They were met by searchlight beams and the stabbing fire of anti-aircraft guns. Soon one plane was in flames; like a broken cardboard toy, it tumbled towards the earth, now enveloped by rags of black flame, now slipping free of them. But the other German airmen could already see the sleeping city, brightly lit by the flares.

Then came the howl of the high-explosive bombs. This did not last long, but there was something indescribably painful about these few seconds, when many tons of death had been released from the planes and not yet touched the earth.

Next came the explosions themselves, making the ground tremble as they reverberated through the town. Shattered glass flew from windows; plaster showered from walls and ceilings; doors and windows flew open. Half-dressed women with small children in their arms ran out towards ditches and trenches. Ignatiev seized Vera's hand and ran with her to a trench beside the fence. The few remaining residents were already gathering there. The old lawyer in whose apartment the commissar had been billeted came slowly out into the yard, carrying a bundle of books fastened with twine. Ignatiev helped him and Vera down into the trench, then started back towards the house. Next came the sound of a falling bomb. Ignatiev dropped to the ground. The whole yard went dark – the air was dense with fine brick dust from a neighbouring building, which had crashed to the ground.

"Gas attack!" shrieked a woman.

"No!" Ignatiev exclaimed angrily. "It's dust. Stay in your trench!"

And he ran to the house. "Sergeant Major," he yelled, "air raid!"

But everyone was already pulling on their boots in the glow from the buildings now beginning to blaze. Aluminium mess tins glittered in the light of the young, still smokeless flames. Ignatiev glanced at his comrades, who were quickly and silently dressing, and then at the mess tins. "Have you got me some grub?" he asked.

"I like that!" said Sedov. "You sit out there with your babe, counting the stars – and we have to take care of your grub!"

"Quick now!" the sergeant major shouted angrily. "Ignatiev, wake the commissar!"

Ignatiev ran up to the floor above. The whole of the old building was creaking and groaning from the rumble of bombs. Doors squeaked as they swung to and fro and plates and dishes clattered alarmingly in cupboards. It was as if this old house, which had seen so much human life, was trembling all over, appalled by the swift and ghastly death of so many of its fellows.

Bogariov was standing by the window and he did not hear Ignatiev come in. A new explosion shook the earth. Plaster thudded to the floor, filling the room with dry dust. Ignatiev sneezed. Bogariov went on gazing out at the city, still not hearing Ignatiev.

"That's what I call a true commissar!" thought Ignatiev. This tall, motionless figure, looking out so intently, was endowed with something strong and magnetic. It was impossible not to admire him.

Bogariov slowly turned round. Gaunt cheeks, dark eyes, compressed lips – all bore witness to the same dogged determination. "Stern as an icon," Ignatiev said to himself.

"Comrade Commissar," he began, "you must get out of here.

Bombs are falling very close. One direct hit and there'll be nothing left of this building."

"What's your name?" asked Bogariov.

"Ignatiev, Comrade Commissar."

"Comrade Ignatiev, tell the sergeant major that my orders are to give every assistance to the civilian population."

"We'll do all we can, Comrade Commissar. But as for putting out the fires, there's not much we can do there. Most of the houses are wooden, and very dry at that. Hundreds are catching fire at a time and there's no-one to put out the flames. Every young civilian has either been evacuated with their factory or else joined the militia. There's only children and old people left."

"Remember this night, Comrade Ignatiev," Bogariov said unexpectedly. "Remember all you can see. This night, and this city. These old people and children. The screams of the women."

"This night would be hard to forget, Comrade Commissar." Ignatiev looked at Bogariov's grim face and added, "Yes, Comrade Commissar. I shall remember it." Then he asked, "May I take that guitar hanging there on the wall? The building's going to burn down anyway, and the men like it when I play to them."

"This building is not on fire," Bogariov said sternly.

Ignatiev glanced at the big guitar, sighed and left the room. Bogariov slipped his papers into his map case, then put on his coat and forage cap and went back to the window.

The city was burning. Curls of red smoke, shot through with sparks, were leaping high into the air. A dark, brick-coloured glow swayed over the marketplace. Thousands of flames – white, orange, cranberry-red, pale-yellow and blue – rose over the city like a vast, shaggy cap. Leaves shrivelled and faded on trees. Pigeons, rooks and crows flew this way and that through the hot air – their homes too were on fire. Corrugated-iron roofs turned incandescent in the heat, rumbling and letting out loud cracks. Smoke poured out of windows filled with flowerpots; milky white or deathly black, pink or ash-grey, it curled and swirled, rose into the air in reddish strands or thin golden streams or burst out in a single huge cloud, as if expelled from the chest of a giant. The smoke then lay over the city like a shroud, spreading out over the river and surrounding valleys; here and there, thick tufts hooked onto trees.

Bogariov went down the stairs. In the fire and smoke, amid exploding bombs and the cries of children, he found calm and courageous people. They were putting out fires, throwing sand on incendiaries, rescuing the aged from flames and carrying things out from burning apartments. Red Army soldiers, firemen, policemen, workers and apprentices in smouldering clothes, with soot-blackened faces, were fighting with all their strength to defend their city. Paying no attention to howling death, they were doing their utmost to save and rescue whatever could still be saved and rescued. In the general chaos, Bogariov at once sensed the presence of these people. Bound by a great brotherhood, they emerged from the smoke and flames, rushed into burning build-ings, joined together to perform great deeds and disappeared again into the fire and smoke, neither telling anyone who they were nor learning the names of those they had saved.

Bogariov saw an incendiary land on the roof of a two-storey building. First, it looked like a firework, sending up showers of white sparks. Then, a patch of dazzling white began to spread across the roof. He dashed up the stairs into the stifling attic, which smelled of smoky clay that brought back some childhood memory, and then groped his way to a dimly lit dormer window. The red-hot of the corrugated-iron roof seared his hands. Sparks like little red flies settled on his clothes, but he quickly made his way over to the bomb and gave it a powerful kick. The bomb landed in a flower bed, briefly lit up the showy heads of asters and dahlias, sank into the crumbly soil and slowly faded from sight.

From up on the roof, Bogariov saw two men in uniform carrying an old man on a camp bed out of the next-door building, which was in flames. He recognized Ignatiev, the soldier who had wanted to take the guitar. His companion, Rodimtsev, was shorter and had broader shoulders. An old Jewish woman quickly said something to them, probably thanking Ignatiev for saving her husband's life. Ignatiev gave a dismissive wave of the hand – and his sweeping, generous, free-and-easy gesture seemed to embody all the richness and good-heartedness of the nation. Just then, the anti-aircraft fire got louder, and it was accompanied by the rattle of machine-guns. A second wave of bombers was attacking the burning city. Once again, they heard the piercing howl of falling bombs. A high-explosive bomb went off just as Bogariov got back down onto the street. The shock wave knocked him to the ground, but he quickly stood up again, shook out his clothes and said to himself in a loud voice, "Still in one piece!"

"Quick! To the trenches!" someone shouted. But by then people were so enraged that they had lost all sense of danger. As for Bogariov, he soon lost not only all sense of danger but also all sense of time, all sense of the sequence and duration of events. Along with everyone else, he helped put out fires, threw sand on incendiaries, rescued people's belongings from the flames, helped stretcher bearers to carry away the injured, went with his men to a maternity hospital that had just caught fire, and carried books out of the blazing public library.[37] Some moments imprinted themselves in his mind for ever. One man had rushed out of a burning building, screaming, "Fire! Fire!" When he saw that there was fire all around him, he had gone silent; he had sat down on the pavement and stayed there without moving. Bogariov also remembered how a delicate fragrance had suddenly spread through the clouds of smoke – a perfumery had caught fire. He remembered a young woman who must have lost her mind after her little daughter had been killed by a bomb splinter. In the light of the flames, in the middle of a deserted square, she had been holding in her arms a small, mangled, bloodstained corpse and calmly singing it a long lullaby.

And there had been a wounded horse, dying on a street corner. In the horse's eyes, which were glazing over yet still living, Bogariov had glimpsed a reflection of the burning city. Like a living mirror of crystal, the horse's dark, tear-filled, tormented pupil had taken in the entire scene: the flames of the burning buildings, the billowing smoke, the glimmering, incandescent ruins and the forest of tall chimneys now growing in place of the buildings that had disappeared in the flames.

Bogariov unexpectedly found himself thinking that he too had taken in the whole of the night-time destruction of this peaceful and ancient city. [38]

With dawn, the fires began to fade. The sun rose on smoking ruins and old people sitting blankly on bundles – amid vases, dishes and old, black-framed portraits hurriedly snatched from the walls. And this sun looking down through slowly cooling smoke at the bodies of dead children was itself deathly pale, poisoned by the dust and fumes. Bogariov went to HQ in case there were any new orders and then started back to his room. The sergeant major intercepted him in the yard.

"How's the jeep?" Bogariov asked.

"OK now." The sergeant major's eyes were red and inflamed.

"We must get going. Call the men."

"There's been an incident here during the night, Comrade Commissar. Just before dawn a bomb fell right next to the trench where people were sheltering. Nearly everyone was badly injured and two were killed: the old man you were billeted with and a young woman, a refugee." He gave a little laugh and added, "Ignatiev had been spending a lot of time with her."

"Where are they now?" asked Bogariov.

"The wounded have been taken away. And the dead are still there – a cart's just come for them."

Bogariov went further into the yard, where a group of people had gathered and were looking at the two dead bodies. The old lawyer's corpse was so mutilated that it was hard to recognize him. Near him were a few battered, blood-spattered books from the bundle he had carried out of his room. Wanting to look around him, he must have half emerged from the shallow trench at the very moment of the explosion; the whole upper half of his body was deformed – his skull smashed and his ribcage shattered.[39] Bogariov looked at the title of the book lying beside him: *Chronicles.* Tacitus.[40] The young refugee woman, on the other hand, looked as if she were still alive; she might just have been sleeping. Her dark complexion disguised her deathly pallor. Her black lashes covered her eyes and she was smiling shyly and a little knowingly, as if ashamed that people were now crowding around her.

The carter had just appeared. Evidently accustomed to dealing with the dead, he took a rough hold of the young woman's legs and shouted crossly, "Hey, you lot, someone give me a hand!"[41]

"Leave her alone!" Ignatiev yelled.

Gently and tenderly, he picked up her body and carried it to the cart. A little girl holding a withered aster carefully laid it on the young woman's breast. Bogariov then helped the carter to move the old man. Everyone else stood there in silence, heads bowed, faces covered in soot, with red-rimmed eyes.

Looking at the young refugee, an old woman murmured, "Lucky girl!"

Bogariov walked on. The people standing around the cart remained silent. There was just one hoarse voice, saying sadly, "We've given up Minsk, Bobruisk, Zhitomir, Shepetovka. How can we stop them? They're fast workers. One night to burn down a city as big as this – and then they just fly back home!"

"Not exactly," said a soldier. "Our boys shot down six of them."

Bogariov did not stay long in the dead lawyer's apartment. He looked around the half-destroyed room for the last time, at the floor now covered with glass, at the overturned furniture and the books thrown from their shelves by the blast. After a moment's thought, he took the guitar from the wall, carried it downstairs and put it in the back of the truck.

Ignatiev was standing beside the truck. Rodimtsev was holding out his mess tin to him. "Here you are, Ignatiev. Meat and white macaroni – I got it for you yesterday."

"I don't want to eat," Ignatiev replied. "I want water. Everything's all hard and dry inside me."

They soon left the city behind them. The summer morning

greeted them with all its solemn, peaceful charm. In the early afternoon they stopped in the forest. There was a clear, narrow stream, rippling gracefully over pebbles and stones. The cool air soothed the men's sore skin, and their eyes were able to rest in the shade of the tall oaks. Bogariov saw a whole family of cep mushrooms in the grass. There they were, with their grey heads and thick white legs – and he remembered the eager passion with which, only a year ago, he and his wife had gathered mushrooms around their dacha. How overjoyed they would have been then if they had chanced on such a mass of ceps! They had not had much luck that year – most days they had come back with only russulas or bovine boletes.

The soldiers washed in the stream.

"Fifteen minutes for lunch," Bogariov said to the sergeant major. He wandered slowly among the trees, both delighted and saddened by the world's carefree beauty and the continual rustle of leaves. Suddenly, he stopped. Pricking up his ears, he looked back towards the truck. Ignatiev was playing the guitar. The others were listening to him as they ate their bread and tinned meat.

6

REGIMENTAL HQ

Divisional command had a generally low opinion of the regiment. Only a few of the soldiers and commanders were experienced professionals. "A mixed bunch, you could say" was how Major Mertsalov, the regimental commander put it to Bogariov. Most of the men were in their early thirties and from collective farms. Mertsalov was a veteran of the Finnish war and a Hero of the Soviet Union.[42] Kudakov, the chief of staff, was in his mid to late forties; he was bald, slow and extremely self-confident.[43] Captain Babadjanian, the commander of the First Battalion, was suffering from toothache when Bogariov arrived; a few hours earlier, after getting very hot, he had taken a huge gulp of icy spring water – and his jaw, he made out, "had yet to recover from the shock". Major Kochetkov, the good-natured and talkative commander of the Second Battalion, kept making little jokes about this. And then there was the deputy chief of staff, the handsome, broad-shouldered Lieutenant Myshansky.

An enemy advance was threatening to encircle several units of one of our infantry corps; to delay this, the regiment had been ordered to strike a sudden blow, with heavy-artillery support, at their flank. Mertsalov began to explain the plan of operations to the battalion commanders and commissars. As he was coming to an end, they were joined by Lieutenant Kozlov, the commander of a reconnaissance platoon, who had been called to report. Round-eyed and freckled, he saluted and clicked his heels with unusual vigour. He gave his report in a loud voice, lending a staccato emphasis to every word, but his round eyes smiled knowingly and with a kind of calm condescension.

Bogariov sat through the entire meeting in silence. He was still overwhelmed by all he had witnessed during the night and he kept shaking his head, as if trying to clear his mind and return to the present moment. Nevertheless, he watched and listened attentively. He was someone who usually trusted his first impressions, yet he was afraid of their persistence and intrusiveness. "Dead husks and shells are the enemy of thought," he would sometimes say to himself, as he struggled to let go of some long-held view. At the beginning of the meeting, the commanders kept looking round at Bogariov, but then they got used to his presence and ceased to notice him.

"You're not saying much about the operation itself," Bogariov said all of a sudden, leaning over towards Mertsalov.

"We've been ordered to attack, so that's what we're doing," Mertsalov replied. "I'm not one for long discussions over a map," he went on. "It's action that matters. In combat everything becomes clear."[44]

With a broad smile, as if his toothache had vanished, Babadjanian turned to Bogariov and said, "I like it, Comrade Commissar. The army retreats. Just think – an entire army retreating! And Babadjanian's battalion is to advance. I like it – I truly do!"

At this point, the commander of a neighbouring howitzer regiment, a sullen lieutenant colonel who was constantly jotting down notes, spoke for the first time. "Very good, comrades. Only I must warn you that we shall not be able to exceed the established norm for the expenditure of shells."

"That goes without saying," said Kudakov. "So the regulations stipulate."

Bogariov noted that this was not the first time that Kudakov had mentioned military regulations.

And then, when Kozlov suggested taking a battery behind the German lines and opening direct fire, the chief of staff replied sharply, "You're talking nonsense. Such an action would be contrary to all regulations. I've never once seen mention of anything of the kind."

And the howitzer lieutenant colonel said gravely, "Yes, comrades. After all, a norm is a norm. No getting away from it!"

To which Babadjanian cheerily retorted, "What's all this about norms? The only norm I know is Victory!"

Everyone laughed.[45] Once they'd got through all the immediate concerns, the conversation turned to questions about the German army. Myshansky spoke at length about a German attack near Lvov.

"They come on in a line, shoulder to shoulder – like a wall at least a kilometre in length. Can you imagine it? And then, about four hundred metres further back, a second line exactly the same. And then a third. All of them with their sub-machine guns, all of them marching on through the tall wheat. Our field artillery mows them down, but they just keep on advancing. They don't shout, they don't shoot, and there's no sign of any of them being drunk. Some keep falling, falling into the wheat, but the rest just march on. Some sight – believe me!"

Then he recounted how he'd seen thousands of German tanks

moving along the Lvov and Proskurov highways, how he'd seen
German paratroopers landing at night in the light of green and
blue flares, how detachments of motorcyclists had shot up one
of our HQs. He spoke of the skill with which German tanks
and aircraft coordinated their operations. He clearly enjoyed
talking about the Soviet retreats of the first days of the war. "And
I certainly took to my heels too!" he admitted. And he seemed to
take no less pleasure in admiring the strength of the Germans.
"What they did to France," he said, "is no joke. Thirty days to
defeat a huge army – that takes organization and military culture!
That takes skilled leadership!"

"Yes," said Mertsalov. "There's no doubting their organization."

"Excuse me, but in my view to create such an army, with such
amazing new weapons, with such strategy and such tactics—"

"Shows real genius?" Bogariov interrupted loudly and angrily.[46]

Myshansky looked at Bogariov and said condescendingly,
"Forgive me, Comrade Commissar, but I'm a front-line soldier.
I'm used to saying what I think! And please forgive me again, but
I'm probably the only man here who's been fighting since Brest,
since the first day of the war. And forgive me a third time – but
to crush the entire French army . . ." And he threw up his hands
in a gesture of helpless despair.[47]

"I shall never forgive you for this. Neither you nor anyone else
who voices such thoughts," Bogariov said curtly. "Understood?"

"But it would be wrong to underestimate them," said Kochetkov. "As I've heard my men say, 'The German may be a coward,
but he knows how to fight.'"

"We're not children," said Bogariov. "And we all understand
that we're dealing with the strongest army in Europe. And I can't

deny that their technical equipment at this stage of the war is superior to ours. We're dealing with the Germans – that's all I need say. But I was listening to you attentively, Comrade Myshansky, and I need to give you a little lecture. This is essential. You must learn to despise Fascism. You must understand that it is the basest, vilest, most reactionary thing on earth. It is a revolting compound of *ersatz* and theft, in the broadest sense of these words. This foul ideology lacks any spark of creativity. We must despise it with every cell of our being – do you understand?

"Please listen to what I say now. Their social ideas are nothing more than obtuse ravings, ridiculed long ago by Chernyshevsky[48] and Engels. As for their military doctrine, this has been taken word for word from the plans of the German General Staff elaborated decades ago by von Schlieffen[49] – all these wedges, flank attacks and so on are the purest plagiarism. The tanks and paratroopers with which the Fascists have astonished the world are no newer. The tanks have been stolen from the British, the paratroopers from us. I am constantly amazed by Fascism's monstrous sterility! Not a single new military tactic! Everything plagiarized. Not one major invention! Everything stolen. Not a single new type of weapon! Everything second-hand. Even their vile antisemitism is the child of Prussian militarism and the Russian autocracy.[50]

"Every realm of German creative thought has been rendered sterile. The Fascists are powerless to create; they cannot write books or compose music or poetry. They are stagnant – they are a swamp. They have brought only one new element to world history and politics: shameless brigandry and organized atrocity!

"We must scorn and despise them. We must mock them for their intellectual poverty. Have I made myself clear, Comrade

Myshansky? This spirit of contempt must permeate the entire Red Army, from top to bottom. It must permeate the entire country. You like to think that, as a front-line soldier, you're telling it like it is, calling a spade a spade – but you have the psychology of a man who has been retreating for a long time. There's a note of grovelling servility in your voice."

Bogariov rose to his full height, looking Myshansky in the eye. "As military commissar of this unit," he pronounced, "I forbid you to utter words that are unworthy of a patriot and do not correspond to the objective truth. Do you understand me?"

★

Babadjanian's battalion was to be first to go into action. The attack was scheduled for 3 a.m. Kozlov, who had twice been out on reconnaissance, had furnished a detailed account of the German dispositions. Their tanks and armoured vehicles were in the central yard, and the men slept in the collective-farm vegetable store, a narrow barrack-like building forty to fifty metres in length. They had made themselves comfortable there, ordering the villagers to bring them whole wagonloads of hay, spreading the hay on the floor and laying lengths of linen and sackcloth on top of it. They slept in their underwear, even taking off their boots, and they lit lamps without blacking out the windows. In the evenings, they sang songs, and the scouts hiding in the vegetable plots could hear everything perfectly – which infuriated them. "They keep singing away," said one of the scouts, "but our men are silent. You never hear them singing." And this was true. At that point in the war our infantry never sang while they were on the march. Nor was there any singing or dancing during halts.

When it got dark, the howitzer unit took up its firing position. Soon after this, the unit's commander and commissar went to their HQ hut and sat down opposite each other at a table. The commissar opened a chessboard and the commander took the chessmen from his map case. They made their first moves, then sat there in thought.

Kochetkov, commander of Mertsalov's second battalion, had come over to join them. He remarked, "I can see you're true gunners. Nearly all you gunners play chess."

Not looking up from the board, the commissar, Sergey Nevtulov, replied, "And as far as I've seen, the infantry all prefer dominoes."

Captain Rumiantsev, the howitzer commander, also keeping his eyes on the board, added, "Very true. And not just any old dominoes, but something complicated like chicken foot." He then pointed to the board and said, "If you do that, Sergey, you're sure to lose. You'll lose your queen, like you did near Mazyr."

The two men bent over the board and went silent. Five minutes later, after Kochetkov had left, Nevtulov said, "Nonsense – I won't lose my queen, or anything else." Still looking at the board, seeming to imagine that Kochetkov was still present, he added: "And cavalrymen like to play cards. Isn't that so, Comrade Kochetkov?"

The signaller sitting by the field telephone burst out laughing, but then frowned, turning the handle of his apparatus, and said severely, "Lima, Lima. Medynsky, is that you? Testing, testing."

Mertsalov was speaking in an undertone to Kudakov. Then

Babadjanian appeared, thin, tall and very agitated. His black eyes shone in the dim light. He spoke quickly and passionately, repeatedly prodding the map.

"This is a chance in a million. Our scouts have reported the exact position of their tanks. If we advance our artillery to this hill, we can fire over open sights. We mustn't let this opportunity slip. Believe me – they're in the palm of our hand! Well and truly, in the palm of our hand!" And he smacked his thin dark hand against the table.

"All in all, not such a bad idea," said Kudakov. "Although, in accord with regulations, we'll need to make a few changes to our infantry dispositions too."

Mertsalov looked at Babadjanian and said, "I agree, and we'll make no other changes. I'm not one for half measures or long discussions."

He went across to the gunners. "Comrade chess players, I have to tear you away from your game. Come over here."

Together they bent down over the map.

"They're clearly hoping to reach the highway – they're already within forty kilometres of it – and then attack our rear."

"Precisely," said Kudakov. "That's why we're carrying out this operation. It's a matter of great concern to the army commander."

"Yesterday the Germans were using loudspeakers," said Rumiantsev. "They were bellowing out in Russian, 'Surrender, Red Army soldiers! Our flamethrower tanks have arrived. Every one of you will be burned to death. But if you surrender, you can go back home.'"

"Damned insolence," said Mertsalov. "Yes, they're cheeky bastards. I haven't taken off my boots for days – while they sleep in their underwear. And they don't even switch off their head-lamps when they're near the front line."

He thought for a moment, then went on, "And as for our commissar and the way he let fly just now!"

"Somewhat extreme," said Kudakov. "He really tore Myshansky to pieces."

"Well, I liked that," said Mertsalov with a laugh. "To be honest, you and Myshansky both get on my nerves. Him with his tall stories, and you with your norms and forms. I'm a plain man myself. I'm a combat officer, and I fear words more than I fear bullets."

He looked at Kudakov and said cheerily, "Our commissar's a good man. We'll be fighting shoulder to shoulder."

7

AT NIGHT

Babadjanian's battalion had taken up its position. The men sat or lay under the trees, in little shelters made from branches with rustling, withered leaves. Between the leaves you could see the stars, and the air was quiet and warm.

Bogariov and Babadjanian were walking together along a path they could barely make out in the dark.

"Halt!" shouted a sentry. "One of you – forward! Others – not a step further!"

"There aren't so many others," said Babadjanian. "A total of one." Laughing, he went up to the sentry and whispered the password. He and Bogariov went on further. They stopped near one of the leafy shelters and listened to the quiet talk of the men inside.

"What do you think?" asked a calm, thoughtful voice. "What will we do with Germany when the war's over? Destroy her? Or let her be?"

"I've no idea," answered a second voice. "We can decide that when the time comes."

"That's the kind of talk I like to hear during a long retreat!" Bogariov said cheerfully.

Babadjanian glanced at the luminous dial of his wristwatch.

★

Ignatiev, Rodimtsev and Sedov were not given much chance to make up for their night without sleep in the burning city. They had lain down briefly but were soon woken by the sergeant major, who told them to go and get their supper. The square red eye of the field-kitchen stove[51] glowed wanly in the dark of the forest. The other men were crowding around it, clinking their mess tins although they were trying not to make too much noise. They had already been told about the impending night attack.

Their spoons knocking together as they shared their mess tin of soup,[52] the three men were talking slowly and quietly. Rodimtsev had already taken part in six attacks. "It's scary the first time," he said. "You don't understand a thing, and that makes it frightening. You've no idea what's coming at you or where it's coming from. New recruits are usually frightened of sub-machine guns, but their fire's always wildly inaccurate. Machine guns are pretty inaccurate too. And you've got time to slip into a ditch or behind a mound and stay there while you decide which spot of cover to make for next. The truly vile weapon – the weapon I hate – is the mortar. The mere thought of mortars scares me to death, I can't deny it. Your only salvation is to keep advancing. Lie down or turn back – and they'll get you in no time."

"That poor Vera," Ignatiev said all of a sudden. "It's as if she's right here in front of me."

"I don't even think about women," said Rodimtsev. "I've lost all feeling for them now. All I care about is my children. Give me a day with them – and I could fight on till the end of this war. No, I'm not like the Germans – I'm no randy goat."

"You don't understand!" said Ignatiev. "It makes me so sad. Why her? So young and gentle. Why did they have to kill *her*?"

"Oh yes!" said Rodimtsev. "You've been ever so sad! Playing your guitar all day in the truck!"

"Guitars are neither here nor there," said Sedov, the locksmith from Moscow. "It's just Semion's way of being. People call it innate character." Looking up at the patches of starry sky glimmering through the dark foliage, he continued more slowly, "Animals and plants fight for existence, but people fight for supremacy."[53]

"That's right, Sedov," said Rodimtsev, who loved difficult, learned words. "Yes, you couldn't have put it better." After a moment of silence, he went on, "At home I used to feel scared when I heard the gate creak. I was afraid to walk in the forest at night – but now I'm not afraid of anything. How come? Have I just got used to things, or has my heart become different? Has the war hardened it? Some men here are scared stiff – but as for me, I don't mind what happens to me now. I'm simply not afraid, and that's all there is to it. I used to be a quiet, peaceful man, a family man. I never imagined anything like this war. I was never a fighter. I didn't get into scraps as a boy. And as a man, I didn't use to pick fights even when I was drunk. More likely I'd start crying – I used to feel awfully sorry for people."

"It's because of all you've seen during these last weeks," said Sedov. "Listen to people's stories, see things like yesterday's fire – and not even the devil can scare you!"

"I don't know," said Rodimtsev. "Some men still do get very frightened. But the battalion commander's certainly dinned one thing into our heads – we must stand our ground. Whatever the cost, we must stand firm."

"Yes, Babadjanian's a strong man," said Sedov.

"He's a good fellow," Rodimtsev went on. "He takes care of his men, he doesn't risk our lives for nothing. And he's always there at our side, he goes through the same dangers that we do. There was one time he was badly ill, and he got caught in a bog. He was stuck there all day, he was coughing up blood. That was before your time, when their Panzers were making for Novograd-Volynsky. I went into the forest to get out of the rain. And there he was, lying on the ground, barely able to move. I went over to him and said, 'Comrade Captain, have a bite. I've got some bread and sausage.' And he didn't even open his eyes, he knew me just by my voice. 'No, Comrade Rodimtsev,' he said. 'Thank you, but I don't feel like eating. There's only one thing I want, and that's a letter from my wife and children. They disappeared the very first day.' And his voice as he said that . . . 'Yes, my brother,' I thought, 'I know what you mean.'"

Ignatiev got to his feet, had a stretch, and grunted.

"Fit as a fiddle," said Rodimtsev.

"What do you mean?" asked Ignatiev, somehow sounding both cross and jovial.

"Simple enough. Our grub's not so bad. And the work's no harder than it was back home. No reason you shouldn't be fit as a fiddle."[54]

"No harder than it was back home!" came a sarcastic voice from the darkness. "Wait till you get a kilo or two of shell splinters slap in the guts. That'll make you wish you were back home all right!"

"A voice!" said Sedov. "A true voice of the forest." Addressing this unknown speaker, he asked, "So, you old sod, seems you're not so keen on being shot at?"

"All right, all right," said the voice. "As long as you enjoy it yourself."

Soon the battalion began to move forward. They marched in silence along the narrow track; there was only the occasional quiet word of command, or a few curses as someone stumbled over a tree root. The forest was tall, black and motionless, as if cast in a single mould; the leaves of the oaks were not even rustling. Now and then, the men came to open clearings where the starry sky – so black as to be almost blue – would spill over their heads. Sometimes they were startled by clear, swift, shooting stars. And then the forest would close around them again. The sandy track gleamed dimly in the dark, while in their minds' eye the sky became a golden starry porridge, stirred by the stout boughs of the oaks. Then the men came out onto a wide plain. Marching through the still unharvested fields, they could recognize the different grains – oats, wheat, barley or buckwheat – by the swish of falling seeds, by the creak of straw underfoot and by the rustle of the stalks that clung to their tunics. And this trampling of the tender body of the ungathered harvest, this sad, invisible, rain-like patter of the falling seeds, spoke more eloquently about the war, brought home its nature more clearly to many hearts than did the great fires blazing on the horizon, the red stitches of tracer bullets creeping towards the stars, the bluish pillars of searchlight beams sweeping across the sky or the distant rumble of exploding bombs. This was a war like no other; the enemy was riding roughshod over the whole life of the nation, smashing crosses in cemeteries where mothers and fathers were buried, burning children's books, wrecking orchards where grandfathers had planted black cherry and Antonovka apple trees, stepping on the throats of old women who liked to tell their grandchildren the tale of the cock with a golden comb, ripping linen shifts from the bodies of breastfeeding mothers, and hanging village coopers, blacksmiths and grumpy old watchmen. Never had Ukraine, Belorussia and Russia seen such things. Never had such things happened on Soviet soil. And so, marching through the night, trampling down their own wheat and buckwheat, the men came to a state farm. There, among the white huts, stood black tanks with long-tailed dragons daubed on their sides. And quiet, kind-hearted Ivan Rodimtsev said, "No, we can show them no mercy."

Even before the first shell burst near the barn where the German infantry and tankmen were sleeping, Babadjanian's first company had crossed a small bog close to the western edge of the village and was lying low in a copse there. A soldier whose name no-one remembered made his way through the barbed wire, slipped between some huts into an orchard, climbed over a fence into the central yard, and made for some hayricks that the Germans had built there the day before. A sentry spotted and challenged him. The soldier silently walked on further. The sentry hesitated, taken aback by the man's fearlessness. By the time the sentry turned his sub-machine gun on him, the soldier was only a few metres from the ricks. After throwing a Molotov cocktail into the hay, he fell to the ground – dead. Red and orange flames immediately lit up the German tanks and armoured cars in the yard. Then, from only six hundred metres away, the howitzers opened fire. The gunners could see the German soldiers dashing out of their long barrack. They were like wingless birds, screaming, rushing this way and that.

"The infantry's late," Rumiantsev said angrily to Nevtulov.

But soon a red rocket gave the signal for the infantry to attack. The gunfire ceased. A moment of silence – and the men sprang to their feet. And then – rolling through the dark copse and the uncut wheat – came a low, drawn-out yell: "U-u-r-a-a!" This was Babadjanian's companies going forward. There was the sound of heavy machine guns and the more diffuse crackle of rifle shots. Babadjanian took the telephone receiver from the signaller. "We've broken into the village," said the commander of his first company. "We're on the outskirts. The enemy's on the run."

Babadjanian went over to Bogariov. Bogariov could see that there were tears in his dark, fiery eyes.

"They're on the run, Comrade Commissar!" Babadjanian said excitedly. "They're on the run!" And then, his voice rising to a shout, "But damn it, we could have cut the bastards off! Mertsalov put Kochetkovsky's battalion in the wrong place! They should have been on the Germans' flank!"

From the observation post they could see German soldiers running from the outskirts towards the centre of the village. Many were only half-dressed, carrying weapons and bundles of clothing. The long barrack and the Panzers in the central yard were ablaze and there was a living tower of smoke and flame rising over the oil tankers. Officers were running about too, yelling at the soldiers and brandishing their revolvers. "The power of surprise!" thought Bogariov.

"Machine guns, machine guns forward!" shouted Mertsalov, running towards the company held in reserve. Along with the machine-gunners, he then entered the village.

The Germans retreated along the road towards the larger village of Marchikhina Buda, nine kilometres to the west. They took with them their dead and wounded and many of their tanks and armoured cars.

Day was already breaking. Bogariov examined the burned-out German vehicles, which smelled of hot paint and oil. He felt the dead metal, which was still warm.

The Red Army soldiers were laughing and grinning. The commanders were cracking jokes. Even the wounded, their lips pale and bloodless, were excitedly discussing the battle.

Bogariov understood very well that this sudden, hastily prepared raid on a state farm was only a minor episode in our long retreat. He could sense in his heart and soul the immensity of the territory we had abandoned and the tragedy of the millions who had fallen under Nazi rule. He knew that we had lost big cities and whole industrial regions. He was aware that in the course of two months we had lost tens of thousands of villages – and had just retaken only one of them. Nevertheless, he felt an immense joy; with his own eyes he had seen half-dressed Germans running every which way like a herd of maddened animals; he had seen their frightened, screaming officers. He had heard the loud, merry talk of his own soldiers; he had seen a commander from distant Armenia weep tears of joy because his battalion had recaptured a village on the border of Ukraine and Belorussia. This was no more than a tiny seed, yet from it would grow the great tree of victory.

Bogariov was probably the only man in the regiment who truly understood the danger to which they were now exposed. Divisional Commissar Cherednichenko's parting words to him had been, "You must hold out! You must hold out to the last!"

He had seen the map at Front HQ and he had a clear idea of the regiment's task. They were to hold the road where it passed the state farm and to do everything in their power to keep the Germans from breaking through to the highway and preventing the rest of the Soviet forces from effecting a safe retreat. He knew that the regiment faced a cruel fate.

The German bombers came over at 7 a.m.

They appeared from behind the forest, seventeen black Ju-87 dive bombers.[55]

"Aircraft!" yelled the sentries.

The bombers broke formation, lined up one behind another, then formed a circle, the leading plane now directly behind the last plane, nose to tail. For about a minute and a half this whole terrifying merry-go-round circled over the state farm while the pilots took stock of what lay beneath them. The soldiers down below rushed from one shelter to another, as if this were a game of hide and seek. "Lie down! Stay still!" the commanders kept shouting. The leading plane went into a dive, closely followed by two more planes. Then came the howl of bombs, then shattering explosions. The air was filled by dust, black smoke and clods of earth. The men tried to press themselves closer against the ground, making the most of every slightest dip. It was as if they were being forced into the earth, compressed by the howl of bombs, the rumble of explosions and the roar of engines as the planes came out of their dives.

Unexpectedly, one of the soldiers raised himself up a little and began to fire at the planes with his sub-machine gun. It was Semion Ignatiev.

"What the hell are you doing?" Myshansky shouted from a slit trench. "Stop! You're giving away our position!"

The soldier went on shooting.

"I order you to stop shooting!" shouted Myshansky. But then a second sub-machine gun began to rattle away somewhere close beside him. "What the hell!" he yelled. He looked around, then fell silent. This second sub-machine-gunner was Commissar Bogariov.

"Well, so much for that!" Kudakov said after the Junkers had flown off. "Fifty bombs in half an hour. And all they did was bust one heavy machine gun and slightly wound two of our men."

"True enough," said Mertsalov. "Still, it's a useful warning. We were over the moon when we retook the state farm. We seemed to think we'd got rid of the Germans for ever. But we haven't – we must prepare our defences."

"But what a swift response!" said Myshansky. "So many planes – and so soon after we'd taken back the farm!"

As for Bogariov, he didn't say anything at all in reply to Kudakov. To himself, though, he said, "No, he's wrong. Those bombers did a great deal of damage. Once again, our men are dropping their voices. Once again, they look troubled and anxious. They've lost something very precious indeed – their self-confidence."

Kudakov turned to Mertsalov. "In my view, the correct course of action would be to move our HQ away from the road and into the forest. The Germans will give us no peace here – and we've fulfilled our mission. We should just leave Babadjanian in position."

"No," said Mertsalov. "We must defend the road."

"Still more damage from those wretched bombs," thought Bogariov. Then he turned to Kudakov and the other commanders. "Comrades," he began, "if the Germans give us no peace here, so much the better. It means we're in their way. Our task is simple and severe – to prevent the Germans from breaking through to the main highway. We must subordinate everything to this task – it may be the last task of our lives."

"That's right, Comrade Bogariov," Mertsalov said brightly. "You and I will fight shoulder to shoulder. And, by God, we'll fight well."[56]

Just then, they were joined by Kozlov. His face seemed to have got thinner and it was covered by that dark film you so often see on someone who has just been in combat. Whether it is soot, smoke or a mixture of sweat and the fine dust raised by shell bursts, there's no knowing. All that can be said for sure is that faces always look thinner, darker and sterner after a battle – while eyes become calmer and more deep.

"Comrade Regimental Commander," Kozlov began, "Zaitsev has returned from reconnaissance. German tanks have appeared in Marchikhina Buda. He reckoned there could have been a hundred of them. Most of them medium, but some heavy tanks too."

Mertsalov looked at his subordinates' frowning faces and said, "See what I mean, comrades! No doubt about it – we're a thorn in their flesh all right!" And he went off towards the central yard.

The soldiers were digging trenches across the road and constructing foxholes for the anti-tank riflemen.

Handsome, cheeky Zhaveliov said quietly to Rodimtsev, "So, Rodimtsev, you were the first to get into the German stores? Is it true there were a thousand watches there?"

"Yes, more than enough for our grandchildren. Enough for all our great-grandchildren too!"

"Take anything as a keepsake?" Zhaveliov asked with a wink.

This took Rodimtsev aback. "What do you mean?" he asked. "I couldn't. Just touching their things makes me feel sick. Anyway, what's the use? I'll be fighting to the death."

He looked around him and said, "But as for Ignatiev – for every spadeful we dig, he digs three. While the two of us dig one trench, he digs two on his own."

"And the son of a bitch is still singing," said Sedov, "after two days without sleep."

Rodimtsev paused for a moment to listen.

"Would you believe it!" he said cheerfully. "Still singing away!"

8

MARCHIKHINA BUDA

Maria Timofeyevna Cherednichenko, the divisional commissar's mother, a seventy-year-old woman with a dark complexion, was getting ready to leave her home village. Her neighbours had wanted her to leave with them during the afternoon, but she had been baking bread for the journey and it wouldn't have been ready in time. The collective-farm chairman was leaving the following morning and she had decided to leave with him. Lionya, her eleven-year-old grandson from Kiev, would be going with them too; he had been staying with her since the end of his school term, three weeks before the Germans invaded. As for her son, she had heard nothing from him at all. She had decided to take Lionya to Voroshilovgrad, to the parents of his late mother, who had died three years previously.

Her son had been trying for several years to persuade her to move in with him; life would have been a great deal easier and more comfortable for her in his large Kiev apartment. She used to go and stay with him every year, but seldom for more than a month. He would take her for drives around the city. She had been twice to the Historical Museum, and she loved the theatre. The other theatregoers would look with interest and respect at the tall, elderly peasant woman, with wrinkled, work-worn hands, sitting in the front row of the stalls. More often than not, her son only joined her just before the last act; he finished work very late. They would walk side by side through the foyer and people would make way for them – the stern, upright old woman with a black shawl over her shoulders and the high-ranking military man with the same stern face and dark complexion. "Mother and son," women would murmur, turning to look at them.

In 1940, Maria Timofeyevna had been ill and unable to visit her son. That July, on his way to take part in a military exercise, he had stopped to spend a couple of days with her. Once again, he had asked her to join him in Kiev; he had lived a lonely life since his wife's death, and he was worried that Lionya might be missing the care and tenderness of a woman. Also, it upset him to see his mother, at the age of seventy, still working on the state farm, fetching water from a distant well and having to chop her own firewood. The two of them had been sitting out in the garden, drinking tea under an apple tree that his father had once planted in his presence. She heard him out in silence, but towards evening she took him to visit his father's grave in the village cemetery and said, "How can I leave this place? This is where I shall die. Forgive me, my son."

And now here she was, getting ready to leave her home village. That evening, she and Lionya had gone to say goodbye to an old woman she knew. But they had found the gate outside her hut wide open. Vasily Karpovich, the old, one-eyed cowherd, was standing there in the yard, with the mistress's little brown dog beside him, looking agitated, its tail between its legs.

"She's gone already," said Vasily Karpovich. "She thought you'd left in the morning."

"No," Lionya replied. "We're going tomorrow. The chairman's lending us a horse."

The setting sun lit up the ripening tomatoes that the old mistress had carefully planted in the window box, the lush flowers running riot in the front garden, and the fruit trees with white-washed trunks and branches so heavily laden they had to be propped up. The latch on the gate had been neatly planed. The vegetables in the kitchen garden were flourishing. There were peas and beans, ripe ears of corn, and yellow pumpkins gleaming among green leaves. There were tall sunflowers, gazing out with round, dark eyes.

Maria went into the abandoned home. Here too everything bore witness to a peaceful life, to the mistress's cleanliness and love of flowers. Curly-petalled roses brightened windowsills; a large dark-leaved rubber plant took up one corner of the room; and on the chest of drawers stood a lemon seedling, along with two flowerpots containing the slim shoots of date palms. And everything in the house – the kitchen table marked by the black circles of hot iron pots, the green washstand with the painted white daisy, the dark paintings on the walls, the cupboard with the dainty little cups no-one ever drank from – everything spoke of the long life that had been lived in this now abandoned hut, about the old grandparents, about the children who had sat at the table to study *Our Nation's Literature*, about peaceful summer and winter evenings. Thousands of such white Ukrainian huts now stood deserted, while the men who had built them, the men who had planted trees all around them, plodded grimly along the dusty roads leading east.

"Grandpa, why did she leave the dog behind?" asked Lionya.

"She didn't want to. But I'll be looking after him myself," said Vasily Karpovich. And he began to cry, making a strange creaking sound that could almost have issued from his old, toil-worn bones.

"What's the good of tears?" asked Maria Timofeyevna.

"What's the good of anything?" the old man replied, with a helpless shrug.

And the heaviness of his hands, with their blackened, work-battered fingernails, expressed how his whole world had crashed down about him.

Maria Timofeyevna rushed back home, and pale, thin little Lionya (he had inherited not his father's strong constitution but his late mother's poor health) was barely able to keep up with her.

"Grandma," he asked, "what do you think? Does a chicken have a backbone?"

"Shush, Lionochka! Shush!"

How bitter it now felt to be walking down this village street! Once she had been driven down it to be married. She had walked the length of it behind the coffins of her father, her mother and her husband. And tomorrow she would be sitting on a cart, looking at it from among bundles of hurriedly thrown together household belongings. She would be leaving the home she had looked after for fifty years, where she had brought up her children and where her quiet, delicate and perceptive grandson had come to stay with her.

And in this village lit by the warm evening sun – in white huts, in orchards and flower gardens – people were saying in whispers that there was no Red Army between them and the river, and that the Germans would arrive soon. And the women gossiped about old Kotenko, who had left for the Donbas at the time of collectivization and returned only several years later. Apparently, he was now telling everyone to hang up more icons – and he had told his old woman to whitewash their hut as if this were Easter. And Gulenskaya, whose late husband had kept a tavern in the days of the tsars, was standing by the well and repeating to everyone, "Seems these Germans will be giving us back our land again, and that they have faith in our Lord!"

The village was seething with rumours. In the evenings, the old men looked fearfully into the pink dust of the sunset, towards where the village cattle used to appear as they came back from their pasture. They'd heard that "the German" would be coming from beyond a distant forest, from oak woods usually teeming with mushrooms. The women sobbed and wept as they dug pits in their orchards and under their homes in order to bury their few possessions – blankets, felt boots, bolts of linen, and bowls and dishes. They too kept glancing to the west. The west, however, remained clear and quiet.

Grishchenko, the collective-farm chairman, went over to old Kotenko to collect four sacks that Kotenko had borrowed the month before.

Kotenko, a tall, broad-shouldered man in his mid-sixties, with a thick beard, was sitting at the table and watching his old woman whitewash the hut.

"Good evening!" said Grishchenko. "I've come for my sacks."

"Getting ready for a journey, are you, Comrade Kolkhoz Chairman?"[57] Kotenko replied.

"I certainly am," said Grishchenko, with an angry look. Kotenko had changed during the last few days. He seemed to have grown taller and, when he spoke to Grishchenko, it was with an edge of mocking condescension.

"Yes," Kotenko replied. "What else can you do? The village soviet chairman has left. Everyone from the kolkhoz office has left. Your accountant has left. There's hardly anyone still here. The postman's left, and so has every one of your foremen." He laughed, then went on. "Not so easy for you, eh? But as for your sacks, there's not much I can do there. My son-in-law used them to take grain to Bely Kolodets, and he won't be back till the day after tomorrow."

Grishchenko nodded and said quietly, "Well, that's that then. But why have you chosen today to whitewash your hut?"

"Why?" said Kotenko. He wanted to speak his mind, but he had grown used over the years to keeping his feelings to himself and he was afraid even now. "Who knows?" he thought. "This fellow might just suddenly shoot me." At the same time, he was drunk with joy. Even though Grishchenko was still present in the village, Kotenko wanted to let himself go, to give voice to all he had mulled over during long winter nights, thoughts and memories he had kept secret even from his old woman.

Once, about forty years ago, he had gone to visit his uncle, who worked as a labourer for a rich Estonian kulak.[58] His memories of that visit had stayed with him throughout his life. He had never forgotten that beautiful, bright house, the cattle yard – with a cement floor that they washed with soap – the steam mill, and the owner, a stout, bearded old man in a fine red cloak, trimmed with fur. Again and again, he had seen in his mind's eye how the owner's brightly painted sleigh, pulled by a young, spirited yet obedient black horse, had drawn up to the porch. He had recalled the owner's fine cloak and his tall, expensive hat, his embroidered mittens and soft, warm felt boots. He had remembered how, as they drove through the forest where labourers were sawing wood, the owner had taken out a bottle, unscrewed its intricate cap and knocked back some vodka infused with brownish-red berries. And this man was no merchant or landed gentleman. He was a peasant, a true peasant – but a rich and powerful peasant.

Ever since then it had been Kotenko's dream to become an equally rich peasant, with splendid russet cows, flocks of sheep and hundreds of large pink pigs – a peasant with dozens of strong, willing labourers in his employ. He had moved ruthlessly, tirelessly and intelligently towards the realization of this dream. By 1915, he had acquired 150 acres of land and had built a steam hulling mill. The Revolution had robbed him of all this. Two of his sons had joined the Red Army and been killed in the Civil War; Kotenko did not allow his wife to hang photographs of them on the wall. Ivan, their youngest son, had not wanted to live with his father and had left home at the age of sixteen. Kotenko had waited and waited. He had hoped and prayed. In 1931 he had gone to the Donbas and had worked for eight years down a mine. But his dream of kulak life did not want to die; it was unable to die.

And now, at last, it seemed he truly could realize this dream.

Year after year he had been tormented by envy of Maria Timofeyevna, the mother of the divisional commissar. He could see that a life of labour after the Revolution had won her the honour and esteem he had hoped to win for himself in the days of the tsars. She was taken to Kiev by car and she gave speeches in the city's main theatre. He was unable to look calmly at her photograph in the district newspaper – she would look back at him with knowing, hostile eyes. It was as if this thin-lipped old woman with a black shawl over her shoulders was mocking him, saying, "No, Kotenko, you haven't lived your life right." And he would be gripped by a sense of hatred and horror when he saw her quietly going out to work in the fields, or when he heard neighbours say, "Timofeyevna's gone to Kiev to stay with her son. A lieutenant came for her in a blue car."

But now Kotenko knew he had not waited in vain. It was he who had been proved right, not Maria Timofeyevna. It was not for nothing that he'd grown a beard just like the Estonian kulak's; it was not for nothing that he had gone on hoping so long.

And so, aware how intently Grishchenko was watching him, he counselled himself, "Patience, patience. You've waited long enough. You can wait one more day!"

And then, with a yawn, he replied to Grishchenko's question. "What do I know? The old woman just took it into her head to whitewash the hut today. And once she's set on something, there's not much can be done about it."

He accompanied Grishchenko to the gate and stood there for a long time, looking down the empty road, his mind racing. "Cherevichenko has built a hut on my land – and that hut will be mine now. If Cherevichenko wants to stay there, he'll have to pay me in gold. The kolkhoz stables were built on my land, so they'll be mine too. And the kolkhoz orchard is on my land, so the apple and cherry trees will belong to me. And the same with the kolkhoz bees – I can prove that the apiary was requisitioned from me during the Revolution."

The road lay calm and deserted. There was no dust, and not even a rustle from the trees. A calm, red, sated sun was sinking into the earth.

"At last," Kotenko said to himself. "After so many years."

9

THE GERMANS

"Will we get away in time, Grandma?"

"Yes, Lionya," Maria Timofeyevna replied. "We'll be all right."

"Grandma, why do we keep on retreating? Are the Germans really stronger than us?"

"Go to sleep, Lionya," said Maria Timofeyevna. "We must leave tomorrow, at break of day. I'll just lie down and rest for an hour. Then I'll get ready. Right now, I can hardly breathe. It's as if there's a great stone on my chest. I want to push it away, but I haven't the strength."

"Grandma, they haven't killed Papa, have they?"

"What do you mean, Lionya! Your papa won't be killed. He's strong."

"Stronger than Hitler?"

"Stronger, Lionya. He was a peasant like your grandpa, and now he's a general. And he's smart as smart can be."

"But he never says anything now. He sits me on his knees and doesn't say a word. There was just one evening we sang songs together."

"Go to sleep, Lionya. Go to sleep."

"Will we take the cow with us?"

Never had Maria Timofeyevna felt so weak as she felt that

day. There was a great deal to do, but she had no strength at all. She felt old and decrepit.

She spread out a cotton blanket on the bench, placed a pillow at the head and lay down. The room was hot from the stove.[59] And the loaves she'd taken out gave off warmth too; they were golden, like the sun, and they smelled sweet and fragrant.

Could this really be the last time she took fresh, hot loaves from the stove? Might she never again eat bread baked from her own wheat?

Her thoughts and memories were all jumbled together. She had lain like this on the stove long ago, on her father's shaggy sheepskin, and watched her mother take out loaves of white bread. "Mashenka, come and eat!" her grandfather would call out to her. And her son? Where was he now? Was he alive? How could she get to him? "Mashenka, Mashenka!" her sister would shout – and she would scamper across the cool clay floor on her thin little bare feet. She mustn't leave any of the photographs, she must take all the pictures down from the wall. The flowers would stay behind. The fruit trees would remain in the ground. And all the graves would remain. She had not gone to the cemetery to say goodbye to them – but she had wanted to. And the cat would stay behind. She'd heard that only cats remain in villages that have been burned to the ground. Dogs go off with their masters, but cats are too attached to their homes and they don't want to leave. But why was it so hot? And so difficult to breathe? And why did her arms feel so heavy? It was as if she had only now truly sensed all the work she had done in the seventy years of her life. Tears were flowing down her cheeks, but her hands were too heavy to move and the tears kept flowing and flowing. She had cried like this when a fox had gone off with the very plumpest goose in their flock. She had come home in the evening, and her mother had said sadly, "Mashenka, where's our goose?"

She had cried, and the tears had flowed down her cheeks, and her stern, always taciturn father, had come up to her, patted her on the head, and said, "Don't cry, daughter, don't cry." And for a moment she might now too have been crying with joy at the touch of her father's rough, affectionate hand on her hair. During this bitter last evening of her life, time had ceased to exist, and her childhood and girlhood, and the first years of her married life, had reappeared in the hut she now had to abandon. She could hear the crying of her babies and the merry, sly whispers of her friends. She saw her strong, young black-haired husband sitting at table with the guests he'd invited, and she could hear the clink of forks and the crunch of cucumbers as firm as apples. It was her grandmother who had taught her how to salt cucumbers. Their guests had begun to sing, and she had joined in with her young voice. She had sensed the admiring looks of the other men and her husband's pride in her. And old Afanasy had nodded affectionately and said, "Maria, Maria!"

She must have fallen asleep. And then she was woken by a noise unlike anything she had ever heard in the village. Lionya had woken too, and he was calling, "Grandma, Grandma, get up! Get up quick! Grandma, please, please don't go on sleeping!" She hurried over to the window, parted the curtain and looked out.

Was it night, or the dawn of some ghastly new day? Everything had turned red, as if the whole village – the squat huts, the orchards and fences, the trunks of birches – had been drenched in bloody water. She heard shouts, sporadic shooting and the drone of engines. The Germans had broken through. The horde was here in the village.

The horde from the west had arrived – with their magnificent, compact radio transmitters, with equipment fabricated from nickel, glass, tungsten and molybdenum, with vehicles on synthetic rubber tyres and powered by multi-cylinder engines.[60] And daubed all over these remarkable vehicles – as if the Nazis felt shamed by what European science and skilled labour had created in spite of them – were bears, wolves, foxes, dragons, skulls and crossbones, and other such symbols of savagery.

Maria Timofeyevna understood that her death had come.

"Lionya," she said, "run over to Vasily Karpovich. He'll get you out of here. He'll take you to join your papa."

She helped her grandson to dress. She no longer felt weak and her eyes were now calm. She knew she had the strength to meet her death with dignity. Her thoughts now moved clearly and fluently, without the least trace of confusion. Instead of his sailor jacket, she gave her grandson a torn old, padded garment she used to wear out in the fields.

"Where's my cap?" he asked.

"It's warm now," she said. "You don't need your cap."

As if suddenly adult, Lionya understood at once why it might be best not to wear a smart cap or a sailor jacket with gold buttons.

"Can I take my gun and my fishhooks?" he asked quietly.

"Of course!" And she handed him his toy black revolver.

Maria Timofeyevna hugged her grandson and kissed him on the lips. "Off you go, Lionya," she said. "Tell your father, his mother bows low before him, to the very earth.[61] And as for you, my boy, remember your old grandmother, don't forget me."

Lionya left the hut just as the Germans were approaching their yard.

"Quick!" she shouted after him. "Through the vegetable garden!"

He ran, and it seemed that her parting words would be lost for ever in his confused child's soul. He did not know that these words would resurface in his memory, never to be forgotten.

Maria Timofeyevna went to meet the Germans, on the threshold of her hut. Standing behind them was old Kotenko. And even at this terrible moment, she was struck by the look in his eyes. He was observing her intently and greedily, searching her face for some sign of fear or confusion, or even a plea for mercy. A tall, thin German with a grimy, sweaty face asked her in Russian, painstakingly articulating each syllable, "Are you the commissar's mother?"

Maria Timofeyevna sensed death's presence. Standing taller than ever, she replied quietly and calmly, "I am his mother."

The German looked at her slowly and thoughtfully, and then at the portrait of Lenin,[62] the stove and the unmade bed. The soldiers with him were also looking around the hut. Maria Timofeyevna, now more alert and observant than ever, noted the businesslike manner with which the soldiers registered the jug of milk on the table, the dish of hard-boiled eggs she'd prepared for the journey, the towels embroidered with red cockerels, the golden loaves of wheaten bread, the salt pork wrapped in a clean cloth, and the ruby glint of the bottle of cherry liqueur on the windowsill.

One of the soldiers said a few quiet words in a genial voice; the others laughed. And once again, with her now almost clairvoyant insight, Maria Timofeyevna understood what was being said.

They were merely joking about the good food that had unexpectedly come their way. And she shuddered, suddenly realizing these men's absolute lack of interest in her. They were in no way concerned, moved or disturbed by the plight of a seventy-year-old woman preparing to meet her death. All that mattered to them was that they were hungry and thirsty – and behind her they could see bread, salt pork, towels and linen. The old woman did not arouse hatred in them, since she was no danger to them. She could just as well have been a cat, or a calf. She was just a useless old woman who chanced to be occupying *Lebensraum* of vital importance to them.

Nothing on earth can be more terrible than such total indifference to a human being. This impending murder was engendered not by hatred or martial passion but from the bookkeeping obsessions of German economists and industrialists. No murder in the world can be viler than these statistical murders, these conscientiously planned annihilations.[63] As the Germans advanced, they recorded their lines of march on maps and noted in their diaries how much honey they had eaten. They wrote about the rains, about bathing in rivers, about moonlit nights and conversations with comrades. Very few wrote even a word about the murders in all the countless villages with difficult and quickly forgotten names. That was something entirely normal and of no particular interest.

"Where is the commissar's son?" asked the officer, with the same painstaking articulation as before.

"Are you at war with children too, you swine?" replied Maria Timofeyevna.

She remained where she fell, on the threshold of her hut. The German tankmen carefully stepped over the pool of dark blood as they walked to and fro, carrying things out and chatting animatedly.

"The bread's still warm."

"If you were a decent fellow, you'd let me take at least one of those five towels. Well? Come on! I haven't got any with cockerels."

★

In the middle of the room was a table covered with a white cloth. On it were honey, cream, Ukrainian homemade sausage filled with salt pork and garlic, and several large dark jugs of milk. A samovar was boiling on a bench.

Sergey Ivanovich Kotenko had put on a black waistcoat, an embroidered shirt made from the finest white linen and a black jacket still glistening from mothballs. He was entertaining German guests – a major in command of a tank detachment, and a swarthy elderly officer in gold-rimmed glasses, with a white skull on the sleeve of his uniform. The officers looked pale; they were tired after the long advance they had completed during the night.

The major drank a glass of dark brown baked milk and said with a yawn, "I really like this milk. It could almost be chocolate."

Kotenko pushed the dishes closer to his guests and said, "Please! Help yourselves! Why aren't you eating?"

But the tired officers did not want to eat. They were yawning, toying listlessly with the little rounds of sausage, turning them over with their forks.

"We should chuck this old man out, along with his wife," said the officer with the gold-rimmed glasses. "The stench of mothballs is literally suffocating me. We could do with our gas masks."

The major laughed. "Try the honey," he suggested. "My wife keeps telling me to eat all the Ukrainian honey I can. She says it's exceptionally rich in vitamins."

"Have they tracked down the boy yet?" asked the officer in glasses.

"No, not yet."

The major took a small piece of bread, buttered it, used a teaspoon to dig out a lump of the crystalized honey and placed this on top of the bread. He quickly swallowed all this and washed it down with several glugs of milk.

"Not bad at all," he said. "Upon my word!"

Kotenko very much wanted to ask whom he should inform about his claim to the various buildings and the collective-farm stables, apiary and orchard. But something held him back; he felt strangely timid. He had imagined that once the Germans arrived in the village, he would feel free and at ease, that they would all sit together and he would speak his mind. But the officers had not asked him to sit down with them, and all he could see in their mocking, yawning faces was indifference and boredom. They frowned impatiently when they spoke to him, and in their incomprehensible speech he sensed a note of contempt and derision directed towards both him and his wife.

The officers got up from the table, muttered the same indistinct word – probably some casual goodbye – and went outside. They made their way to the school, where the orderlies had brought their bedding.

It was dawn. The night's fires were still smoking and smouldering.

"Motrya, will you lie down now?" Kotenko asked his wife.

"No," she replied. "I won't be able to sleep."

Kotenko felt still more alarmed and frightened. He looked again at the table and the untouched food. He had dreamed for so long of this day – of a merry, triumphant banquet, of the heartfelt words he would pronounce at the beginning of a new, wealthy life.

He lay down but did not fall asleep. He couldn't stop thinking about his sons who had died while serving in the Red Army, and about old Maria Timofeyevna. He had not witnessed her last minutes. When she raised her hand against the officer, he had run outside and stood by the fence. He had heard a shot from within, and his teeth had begun to chatter nervously. But the officer who then came over to him seemed so composed, and the soldiers had sounded so good-natured and matter of fact as they carried stuff out of the hut, that he had calmed down. "The old bag must have lost her head," he said to himself. "Imagine – trying to slap an officer in the face!" He groaned, then rolled onto his side. He felt tormented by the smell of mothballs. It made his temples throb, and his head feel like lead. He quietly got up, walked over to the trunk where they kept their winter clothes, and took out the photographs of his two sons that his wife had hidden there. Sabres at their side, they were wearing the khaki helmets of the Civil War. After a quick glance at the two high-cheeked, round-eyed boys looking up at him with such alert curiosity, he began to rip up the photographs and throw the pieces under the stove. Then he lay down again. He felt sad now, but more at peace. "Now everything will go smoothly," he thought, and fell asleep.

He woke up some time before nine and went outside. There was dust everywhere. There were more and more huge trucks carrying infantry. Mobs of soldiers were roaming about. There was a hostile look on their gaunt, sunburnt faces.

"Now this is what I call power," Kotenko said to himself. Hearing screams from the direction of the village well, he looked around. Young Ganna Cherevichenko was rushing back from the well with buckets of water. A tall German in thick-soled yellow boots was chasing after her. "Our hut's on fire," Ganna was screaming. "It's on fire and they won't let us put out the flames, God damn them!"

The tall soldier caught up with her and made her put down the buckets. He said a few quick words, seized her hand and looked into her tear-filled eyes. Two more soldiers joined them. They talked and laughed, spreading their arms wide so that Ganna couldn't get past them. Meanwhile the thatched roof went on blazing. The flames were like the early-morning summer sun – bright yellow, lively, carefree and cheerful. Dust lay thick on the street and settled on people's faces. The air was full of the smell of burning. Wisps of white smoke rose like incense over the fires that had already burned out. Tall slim chimneys stood like sad memorials on the sites of perished homes. Women and children, eyes red from tears and smoke, were digging about in the ashes, trying to rescue blackened pots and pans. Kotenko saw two Germans preparing to milk a cow. One was holding out a plate of salted, finely chopped potatoes. The cow was mistrustfully nibbling at this delicacy with a moist lip and looking askance at the second German, who was placing an enamel bucket beneath her udder. From the pond came excited German voices and the frightened cries of geese. Several soldiers were jumping about like frogs, spreading their arms out to catch geese being driven towards them by two identical-looking young redheads standing waist-deep in the water. These two redheads then emerged from the water, stark naked, and went over to Anna Petrovna, the old school-teacher, who was walking across the central collective farmyard. They pulled faces and began to skip and dance. The other soldiers howled with laughter. The two redheads were drunk. Anna Petrovna looked down at the ground. Her face had gone white; her fingers trembling, she was trying to straighten her old blouse.

Kotenko walked over to the school. He came to where the children used to play during breaks from lessons and saw a man hanging from the crossbar of the swing. It was Grishchenko, the collective-farm chairman. His bare feet – living feet, with calluses and crooked toes – looked as if they were about to step down onto the earth. His face had gone purple and he was looking Kotenko straight in the eye. Kotenko let out a cry of shock. Grishchenko was laughing at him. His head lolling down, his tongue sticking out, he was staring wildly at Kotenko and asking, "So, Kotenko, lived to meet the Germans, have you?"

Kotenko was unable to think clearly. He wanted to cry out, but he couldn't. With a little shrug, he turned on his heels and set off again.

"My stables," he said aloud, examining their blackened remains – the broken posts and jutting-out beams and rafters. He went on towards the apiary, but even from a distance he could make out the wrecked, overturned hives and hear the tense, angry buzz of the bees; it was as if they were keeping guard over the body of the young beekeeper lying under the ash tree. "My hives," he said, "my hives." And there he stood for a while, looking at the dark mass hovering over the dead body. Next, he went to look at the collective-farm orchard. Not a single apple, not a single pear was left on the branches. The soldiers were sawing away at the trees and hacking at them with axes, cursing the stubborn, fibrous trunks. "Pear and cherry are hard to chop," he thought. "Nothing harder. They have a twisted grain."

Field kitchens in the collective-farm orchard were smoking and steaming. Cooks were plucking geese, shaving the bristles off newly slaughtered young boars, and peeling potatoes, carrots and beetroots from the vegetable garden. Hundreds of soldiers were lying or sitting under the trees, chewing and chomping away, smacking their lips, swallowing down the juice of Antonovka apples and tender, sugary pears. And to Kotenko this chomping seemed to drown out every other sound: the hoots of the ever-growing number of vehicles, the hum of engines, the gobbling of geese, the long-drawn-out mooing of cows and the desperate cries from the mill – from the beautiful young daughters of the miller who had died only the previous week.[64] Even sudden bolts of thunder, it seemed, would be drowned out by this mighty chewing and chomping of hundreds of cheery soldiers.

Kotenko now felt more confused than ever. He wandered about the village, not knowing where he was going or why. At the sight of him, young women shied away to one side, children ran into yards and hid in the tall grass by the fences, men looked at him with blind, unseeing eyes and walked by without replying to his questions, and old women, unafraid of death, cursed him with their foulest curses. He kept on walking, constantly looking around him. His black jacket was layered with dust, his sweating face was covered in grime, and his head was aching more painfully than ever. And it seemed to him that the pain in his temples was from the mothballs – from their overwhelming smell, now some-how stuck in his nostrils – and that his ears were still ringing from the chorus of cheery chomping.

And the black vehicles kept on coming, coated in yellow and grey dust. More and more lanky Germans kept jumping over the trucks' high black sides and down onto the ground, not waiting for the tailgate to be lowered. More and more of them scattered around the white huts and found their way into orchards and vegetable gardens, into barns and chicken coops.

Kotenko eventually got back home but stopped short on the threshold. The splendid table he had prepared the previous even-ing was covered in filth, vomit and overturned bottles. Drunken Germans were staggering from room to room. One was probing the black womb of the stove with a poker. Another, standing on a stool, was taking down the new, embroidered towels specially draped around the icon; he winked at Kotenko and rattled out some long German sentence. And from the kitchen came the sound of more loud, quick chomping. The men were eating salt pork, apples and bread. Kotenko went out into the entrance room. Standing in a dark corner, near the water barrel, was his wife. A terrible pain gripped his heart. There she was, his meek, quiet, obedient wife, who had never in her life contradicted him, never once said a loud or harsh word to him.

"Motrya, my poor dear Motrya," he said gently, but he suddenly faltered. His wife's eyes were strangely bright and young.

"I wanted to take the pictures of my sons," she said, in a voice he had never heard before, "but you tore them up in the night and threw them under the stove." And she left the now desecrated hut.

Kotenko stood there in the entrance room. In the half-dark he glimpsed an Estonian kulak. He was wearing a red, fur-trimmed cloak and smacking his lips loudly, juicily and merrily. As if in a bright circle of moonlight, he caught sight of Maria Timofeyevna Cherednichenko, her grey hair slipping out from under her shawl. Once again, he felt seared by envy. Now, though, what he envied was not her life but her pure death.

For a moment he was able to see the ghastly abyss into which his soul had fallen. He groped about, trying to find the bucket with a rope tied to its handle. The bucket fell over, clattering in its familiar way, but there was no rope. The Germans must have taken it.

"You liar!" he muttered. He took the thin, strong belt from his trousers, and there and then, in the dark entrance room, made a noose and fastened it to the large hook up above the water barrel.[65]

IO

WHO IS RIGHT?

That night, at the regimental command post, Major Mertsalov and Commissar Bogariov were eating preserved meat out of small tins. Kudakov, the chief of staff, was still asleep. As he brought a chunk of meat coated with congealed white fat to his mouth, Mertsalov said, "Some people warm this up, but I prefer it cold."

Next, they had some bread and cheese, and then tea. With the back end of the bayonet he had used to open the tins, Mertsalov began to chip at a large loaf of sugar. Splinters of sugar flew in all directions. A few hit Kudakov, who let out a little cry of alarm.

"Oh, I clean forgot," said Mertsalov. "We've got some raspberry jam. How do you feel about that, Comrade Commissar?"

"Extremely positive. It happens to be my favourite jam."

"Splendid. Though I myself prefer cherry. That's the best jam of all!"

Mertsalov picked up a large tin kettle.

"Careful! It's black, covered in soot. Must have been put on an open fire."

"It was boiled in the field kitchen, but Proskurov heated it up again on a campfire," Mertsalov replied with a smile.

"You certainly have a good seventy times more experience of camp life than I do, Comrade Mertsalov. What should I do with the jam? Straight into the mug? That'll be simplest, won't it?"

The two men simultaneously took a noisy sip of tea and simultaneously looked up, glanced at each other and smiled.

The last few days had brought them close together. In general, life at the front brings people together with precipitate speed. Live alongside someone for twenty-four hours and you feel you know everything about him: what he likes to eat, which side he prefers to sleep on, whether, God forbid, he grinds his teeth in the night, and where his wife's been evacuated to. You learn whether or not he's selfish, whether or not he's brave, and whether or not he's honest. Sometimes you learn more about him than you learn about your closest friend in ten years of peace. Friendships formed in the sweat and blood of battle are strong friendships.

Continuing to sip his tea, Bogariov turned the conversation to a more important subject. "What do you think, Comrade Mertsalov? Would you call our night attack a success?"

"What a strange question!" Mertsalov replied. "We attacked at night. The enemy took to his heels. We captured an inhabited point. We deserve a few medals for what we did. But why do you ask, Comrade Commissar? Wouldn't you call the operation a success?"

"Certainly not," said Bogariov. "I'd call it an utter failure."

Mertsalov leaned towards him. "Why?"

"First, Kochetkov was late – and so their tanks got away. That's no small matter! With better coordination, we could have destroyed every one of them. None of our battalion commanders had any idea what their neighbour was doing – they just acted off their own bat. And so, our thrust at the German centre, where their tanks were concentrated, didn't work out. Second, when the Germans withdrew, we should have brought artillery fire to bear on their path of retreat. Again, we could have destroyed a great many tanks. But our artillery did damn all. It seems we lost communication with them and they weren't given any new orders after their preliminary barrage. And they didn't dare show any initiative themselves. We could have truly smashed the Germans, but we let them all slip away.

"And there were other omissions," Bogariov continued, counting them off on his fingers. "For instance, we should have moved some machine guns behind enemy lines. That grove over there would have made an ideal emplacement. Then we could have shot up the Germans as they retreated. Instead, we put everything into a frontal attack. We did everything head-on – we barely even touched their flanks."

"You're right," said Mertsalov. "They put up a screen of sub-machine gunfire, and that held your unit back."

"So why the medals?" asked Bogariov. He laughed, then went on, "Because the regimental commander, a certain Comrade Mertsalov, at the most complex moment of the operation, instead of controlling the fire and deployment of rifles, machine guns, sub-machine guns, heavy and light artillery, and company and regimental mortars, preferred to seize a rifle and dash forward to lead a company into the attack! The situation was unusually complicated. The commander should not have been running about with a rifle. He should have been taking swift, clear decisions. He should have been thinking so hard as to bring beads of sweat to his forehead."

Mertsalov pushed his mug to one side and asked in a hurt tone, "Any other thoughts, Comrade Commissar?"

"Quite a few," Bogariov replied with a smile. "It seems that something all too similar happened near Mogiliov. Each battalion did as it pleased and the regimental commander went into the attack with a reconnaissance company."

"Anything else?" Mertsalov asked slowly.

"Well, the conclusion is clear enough. There is no proper coordination. The individual units, for the main part, fail to keep to their schedules. On the whole, the regiment moves slowly and clumsily. Communications during combat are atrocious, simply atrocious. An advancing battalion has no idea who is on its right flank: friend or foe. Superb weapons are deployed ineffectually. Mortars, for example, are hardly used at all. You drag them around everywhere, but most of them hardly ever fire a single shell. The regiment makes no use of flanking movements. It never seeks to strike at the enemy's rear. Every attack is head-on."

"Well," said Mertsalov, "this is all very interesting. So what's your conclusion?"

"What's my conclusion?" Bogariov repeated crossly. "That the regiment fights badly, a great deal worse than it should."

"I see. And your overall conclusion?" Mertsalov persisted. He seemed to be expecting the commissar to relent.

But Bogariov calmly continued, "You're a brave man and you're not afraid for your own life – but you command the regiment badly. This is entirely down to lack of experience. You don't yet understand the complexity of a commander's tasks. War truly is a complicated matter. You have to think about aircraft, tanks and artillery pieces of every kind, all moving swiftly and interacting with one another. New problems infinitely more complex than any problem in chess are constantly arising. They have to be solved, but this is a responsibility from which you shy away."

"So, Mertsalov's not up to it?"

"I've no doubt at all that he's up to it. But I don't want him to think that everything's as it should be and that he's got nothing more to learn. If our Mertsalovs slip into thinking like that, they'll never defeat the Germans. In this battle of nations, it's not enough to know war's simple arithmetic. To smash the Germans, we have to understand war's higher mathematics."

Mertsalov did not reply. Bogariov said genially, "You should drink up your tea!"

Mertsalov pushed his mug away.

"I don't feel like it," he said sullenly.

Bogariov laughed. "Well," he said, "we became friends on the very first day. That made me happy. And just now we drank tea with wonderful raspberry jam. Then I came out with a string of criticisms. I broke up our tea party. Do you think I enjoy making you angry with me? Knowing that you're probably deeply offended and calling down the foulest of curses on me? I most certainly don't. And yet I'm glad, glad from the bottom of my heart that this has happened. We need to win battles, not just to be friends. Be as angry as you like, Mertsalov, that's up to you – but remember. I've been talking about serious matters and I've been speaking the truth."

And with that, he stood up and left the dugout.

Mertsalov watched him leave, then leaped to his feet and shouted at Kudakov, who had just woken up, "Comrade Major, did you hear the dressing down he just gave me? What does he take me for! Would you believe it? Me who fought against the White

Finns! Me who was made a Hero of the Soviet Union! And who's been wounded four times in the chest!"

Kudakov yawned and said, "He's a hard man, I knew it straightaway. But he's got a head on his shoulders."

Not quite taking this in, Mertsalov went on, "Would you believe it? Sits there over his tea and raspberry jam and calmly pronounces, 'What's my conclusion? Very simple. You command the regiment badly.' I could hardly believe it!"

COMMANDERS

That night, Colonel Petrov, the divisional commander, spoke to Mertsalov on the telephone. They found it hard to talk; it was an unusually bad line and it kept going dead. In the end, they were cut off completely, no doubt with help from the Germans. Nevertheless, Mertsalov managed to grasp that the situation on their sector of the front had worsened considerably during the last few hours. He ordered Myshansky, who had been asleep, to drive the twelve kilometres to divisional HQ. Myshansky returned an hour later with written orders.

A German tank column, together with a large force of motorized infantry, had penetrated to the division's rear, taking advantage of the fact that a bog to the east of a large deciduous forest had dried up in the August heat. The Germans had reached the main highway, bypassing the road defended by Mertsalov's regiment. And so the division as a whole had been ordered to take up a defensive line to the south of its present position. And Mertsalov's regiment, along with the howitzer unit attached to it, was to withdraw, while still covering the road.

Myshansky also informed Mertsalov that, while he was at HQ, telephone cables were being reeled in, radio masts being taken down, and stores being loaded onto trucks. The field hospital had left at six o'clock and by ten o'clock the two infantry regiments, the divisional artillery and the howitzer regiment had all formed up in marching order.

"So, you didn't get to see Anechka?" asked Lieutenant Kozlov.

"You must be joking!" said Myshansky. "While I was there, a couple of signals officers arrived. One was from Army HQ, the other was Major Beliaev, from the regiment on our right flank. I've met him before, in Lvov. He said there's been terrible fighting on their sector day and night. Our artillery's given the enemy quite a battering, but they still keep advancing."

"Yes," Kudakov said. "Things certainly aren't easy."

Myshansky leaned over towards Kudakov and said quietly, "One word says it all – encirclement."

"Cut it out!" Mertsalov said angrily. "Our duty is to follow orders – not to speculate about encirclement." Turning to his orderly, he said, "Call the battalion commanders and the commander of the howitzer unit. Where's our commissar?"

"With the sappers," Kudakov replied.

"Call him too."

The night was dark, still and full of alarm. There was alarm in the flickering light of the stars. Quiet rustles of alarm came from beneath the boots of the sentries. Alarm lurked in the form of dark shadows amid the motionless night trees. Alarm made dry branches creak; it was there beside the scouts even after they had long passed the regiment's outposts and were approaching the command post. Alarm splashed and rippled in the dark mill pond. Alarm was everywhere – in the sky, on the earth, in the water. Above all, it filled human hearts. Fearing bad news, men looked intently at anyone entering the command post. A mere flicker of distant sheet lightning was enough to put someone on guard. At the least rustle, sentries would take aim into the darkness and shout, "Halt – or I fire!" And throughout this night of alarm Bogariov observed Mertsalov with silent admiration. He alone spoke loudly, confidently and cheerfully. He laughed and joked. The responsibility for guns, land and the lives of thousands of men lay on his shoulders, but he did not allow this to overwhelm him.

All this set Bogariov thinking: How a man could change! What precious traits could mature in him during just one such night! And over the length and breadth of the whole enormous front, thousands of lieutenants, majors, colonels, generals and commissars were living through days, nights, weeks and months of equally grave responsibility. This was steeling them and honing their wits. There could be no teachers wiser and more severe than these fateful night-time battles for the life and freedom of a people faced with death and slavery.

Mertsalov spent some time briefing the other commanders. He seemed to be establishing countless unshakeable links between himself and the men lying in the forest, standing on guard at outposts or beside artillery pieces, or gazing into the night from forward observation posts. He was calm, cheerful and straight-forward – this thirty-five-year-old major with reddish hair, a bronzed, high-cheekboned face and eyes that seemed sometimes grey, sometimes light blue.

"Shall we order the men to stand to?" asked Kudakov.

"Let them sleep another hour. They won't need long to get to their feet," Mertsalov replied. "It's not as if they'll have taken their boots off." Turning to Bogariov, he went on, "Read the orders from the divisional commander."

Bogariov read out the orders, which stipulated the regiment's mission and line of march. One battalion was to delay the Germans, to prevent them from advancing along the road before evening. The main part of the regiment was to hold the ford across the River Uzh.

"And then there's one other thing," said Mertsalov, as if recalling some minor detail. He wiped his forehead with his handkerchief. "Damn hot, isn't it! Shall we go out for a breath of fresh air?"

For a few moments, the two men stood silently in the dark. Then Mertsalov said in a low voice, "There's a bit more to say. About fifteen minutes after Myshansky drove down it, the Germans cut the road. I have no contact with divisional HQ or with the regiments on either flank. In short, we're encircled. Here's what I've decided. The main part of the regiment to proceed to the river crossing, carry out its mission there, then join the rest of our forces. Babadjanian's battalion to remain in the wooded sector of the road, to slow the enemy's advance."

There was another silence.

"Those devils and their tracer bullets," said Mertsalov. "There's no let-up."

"You've taken the right decisions," Bogariov replied.

"And now, a green flare," said Mertsalov, looking up at the sky. "You can give me another dressing-down, Comrade Commissar, but I'm staying here, along with Babadjanian. Yet another flare . . . One thing I can do, Comrade Commissar, is die a straightforward death, the death of a true Russian."

"Certainly not!" Bogariov retorted with feeling. "It's *my* role to stay with Babadjanian – and I can explain why. *Your* role is to command the regiment."

Bogariov said a little more and the two men parted in the dark. Bogariov was unable to see Mertsalov's face, but he could sense that he was still hurt, that their difficult earlier conversation still rankled with him.

An hour later, the ordnance and ammunition carts set off. The horses let out quiet snorts, treading almost noiselessly, as if understanding the need for silence during this night retreat. Red Army soldiers appeared silently out of the dark and disappeared again into the dark. Those staying behind watched out of the dark, also in silence. This silent parting of battalions was imbued with great sadness and solemnity.

The howitzer unit set off for its firing position shortly before dawn. Rumiantsev and Nevtulov, the unit's commander and commissar, organized the placing of ammunition dumps. They worked out from what points enemy tanks were most likely to approach. Trying to allow for every contingency, they decided on the best locations for gun emplacements, slit trenches and communication trenches. The gunners dug their trenches, constructed bunkers and found branches to camouflage their guns. They were already well supplied with Molotov cocktails and heavy anti-tank grenades, the weight of flatirons.

Bogariov outlined the battalion's mission. "This won't be easy," Rumiantsev replied, "but we've known worse." He went on to say a little about German Panzer tactics, about the strong and weak points of their fighters and dive bombers, about some characteristic features of their artillery, and about their employment of motorcycle troops armed with machine guns. After saying he was well supplied with mines, he suggested they mine the road.

"There's an ideal spot about a kilometre from the kolkhoz,"

said Nevtulov. Coughing a little, he added, "A gully on one side and a thick copse on the other."

"Good idea!" Bogariov said. Turning to Rumiantsev, he suddenly asked, "How old are you?"

"Twenty-four," Rumiantsev replied. With quiet dignity, he added, "But I've been fighting since the first day of the war."

"Put away a fair number of Germans, have you?" asked Bogariov.

"If you have a moment to spare, Comrade Commissar," said Nevtulov, "I can tell you precisely how many."

"Yes, Seriozha, read us a page or two," said Rumiantsev. He then said to Bogariov, "You see, he's been keeping a diary since the very first day."

Nevtulov took an exercise book from his map case. By the light of the electric lantern, Bogariov could see that its cover had been embellished with letters elaborately cut out from coloured paper.

Nevtulov began to read, "On 22 June, the regiment received orders to come to the defence of the Motherland, and at 1500 Captain Rumiantsev's unit fired powerful salvos at the enemy. Each minute, twelve 152 mm howitzers dropped one and a half tons of metal on the heads of the Fascists."

"Seriozha writes well," Rumiantsev said with conviction.

"Keep going," said Bogariov.

"On 23 June, our regiment wiped out two artillery batteries, three mortar batteries and more than a regiment of infantry. The Fascists retreated eighteen kilometres. Today, the regiment expended 1,380 shells.

"On 25 June, Captain Rumiantsev's unit kept the Kamenny Brod bridge under fire for some time. The bridge was destroyed, and one motorcycle company and two companies of infantry were eliminated."

"And so it continues," said Rumiantsev. "Doesn't he write well, Comrade Commissar?"

"You fight well," Bogariov agreed. "No doubt about it."

"Seriozha has real literary talent," said Rumiantsev. "Before the war, he even had a whole story published in *Smena*."[66]

"Well," thought Bogariov, "there's not much to worry about here! I'll go back and join Babadjanian."

As he walked away, still dazzled by the lantern and picking his steps carefully, he heard Rumiantsev's calm voice, "One thing I can say for sure is that we won't get our game of chess tomorrow."

"Where did you leave the road tractors, Rumiantsev?" Bogariov called out, pausing for a moment on his way.

"All the trucks, tractors and their fuel are in the forest, Comrade Commissar. I can bring them up to the gun positions along a track protected from enemy fire," Rumiantsev replied into the darkness.

Back at the command post, Bogariov asked Babadjanian to outline his preparations. As he listened, Bogariov looked several times at the battalion commander's glittering black eyes and hollow, swarthy cheeks. "Yes," he thought. "If I'm fated to die, I can't ask for better and nobler comrades to stand by me during my last day." Then he remembered cheerful, handsome Ignatiev. "He must be here too," he said to himself. And then, with a twinge of regret, "I haven't talked enough with these men. I shouldn't have spent the last ten years behind books. I'd like to have a good talk with Ignatiev, a true heart to heart." But Bogariov understood that everything was in order; there was nothing more he needed to ask Babadjanian.

"There'll be just one shared command post," he said. "Me, you and the gunners. Like that, we can make instant decisions."

"Lightning decisions," Babadjanian replied, without his usual smile.

"You look sad today," said Bogariov. "Why's that?"

Babadjanian shrugged, then said, "I haven't once heard from my wife and children, Comrade Commissar, not since the first day of the war. I left them in Kolomeya, six kilometres from the Romanian border." He went on, now with a wistful smile, "And then I somehow took it into my head that, since it's my wife's birthday tomorrow, I'm sure to get a letter from her. Or at least news of one kind or another. I've been waiting and waiting. I waited a whole month. And now – now the regiment is encircled . . . Our regimental post was bad enough anyway – even when communications were generally good. Now there's not a hope in hell. It'll be a long time now before we get any letters."

"No, you won't be hearing from her tomorrow," Bogariov replied thoughtfully.

"You know, there's something I keep noticing," he suddenly went on. "Real family men, men who really love their wives and children and mothers, always turn out to be outstanding fighters."

"You're right," said Babadjanian. "And there are a number of such men in this battalion. Rodimtsev, for example – and there are many like him."

"And at least one who's not at all like him!" said Bogariov.

This nonplussed Babadjanian. He hesitated for a moment, then said, "Anyway, it's simple enough. This is a war for the fatherland. Our families make us fight all the better. We're defending our children."

12

THE FRONT LINE

The Germans got going at dawn. The tankmen had opened their hatches and were munching apples as they watched the sunrise. Some of them were wearing shorts and shirts with short sleeves. The lead tank, a heavy Panzer, kept some distance ahead of the rest of the column. The Panzer's commander, a fleshy German with a little string of red coral on his plump white arm, turned his large round freckled face towards the sun and yawned. A lock of blond hair peeped out from beneath his beret. Sitting up there on his tank, he seemed the image of supreme military self-confidence, a god of unjust war. By then, his tank had moved at least six kilometres from Marchikhina Buda, but the column's rumbling iron tail had yet to uncurl and was only slowly moving off from the village square.

Suddenly, like a school of pike darting between lumbering carp, a detachment of motorcyclists tore by, doing at least seventy kilometres per hour. They did not slow as they passed the tanks, bouncing about over the uneven surface. As if trying to break free from the motorcycles, the dark-green sidecars shook, rattled and swayed, and the light machine guns mounted on these sidecars swung their thin black muzzles this way and that. As they passed the lead tank, each of the thin dark crouching figures, bronzed by the fierce sun, looked round and raised a hand in greeting before quickly bringing it back to the handlebar. In return, the tank commander gave a lazy wave of his podgy hand. The motorcyclists sped on, leaving white tails of dust in the air behind them. The rising sun painted this dust pink; the dust hovered above the road, and the lead tank rumbled its way into what was now a light cloud.

A group of Messerschmitt-109s flew by overhead. Their slender dragonfly bodies veered first to the right and then to the left, climbed, then went into swift dives. Sometimes, they overtook the tank column, then turned back, banking steeply. Not even the mighty rumble of the tanks could drown out their shrill, piercing whine. They flew close to the ground, over every grove and ravine, sweeping low over the fields of uncut wheat.

Bumping along after the tanks were the black three-axle trucks carrying the motorized infantry. The soldiers sat in rows on folding benches, all holding black sub-machine guns and wearing forage caps cocked to one side. By now the dust clouds had become so dense that not even the fierce summer sun could find a way through them. A long, broad carpet of dust stretched over fields and groves; trees were drowning in a turbid fog; it was as if the earth were burning up in foul dry smoke.

All this was a classic deployment of German mobile forces, tried and tested. The fat man in the beret had sat in the same pose on top of his Panzer at five o'clock in the morning of 10 May 1940 as he led a tank column along a hilly road winding between the stone walls of green French vineyards. Then too, their covering aircraft had prowled through the French skies and motorcyclists had sped by at the scheduled moment. And before this, early in the clear morning of 1 September 1939, his Panzer had crossed the

Polish border, among tall beeches, with thousands of tiny spots and patches of sunlight dancing swiftly and silently over its black armour. The Panzers had driven with the same crushing weight along the highway to Belgrade; Serbia's swarthy body had been crunched and battered beneath their tracks. This tank commander had also been first to emerge from a chilly, half-dark gorge and glimpse the vivid blue and rocky shores of the Gulf of Thessaloniki. And so, this god of unjust war, photographs of whom had appeared in all the illustrated newspapers and magazines of Berlin, Leipzig and Munich, was only too used to such affairs – and he gave another little yawn.

★

When the sun rose, the commanders climbed to the top of the hill. Babadjanian borrowed Rumiantsev's binoculars and carefully scanned the road. Bogariov, for his part, simply drank in the joy of the world around him as it woke to cool dew and a light mist. Grasshoppers were chirping tentatively, like musicians tuning their violins and cellos before an important concert.[67] A black beetle walked by, sullen and businesslike, sometimes getting stuck in the sand. Ants were setting off to work. A few birds fluttered down from a tree; after trying to bathe in the cold dust, which the sun's first rays had still barely touched, they called out and flew off to the stream.

The impressions made during a war are often so vivid as to eclipse images from the eternal world of nature. To the commanders standing on the hill, the light clouds in the sky seemed to be traces of shell bursts from anti-aircraft fire; the distant poplars seemed like tall, black columns of earth and smoke, flung up into the air by heavy bombs; the wedges of flying cranes were squadrons of fighters in strict formation; the mist in the valley was the smoke of burning villages, and the bushes by the side of the road were a column of well-camouflaged trucks, waiting for the signal to move. More than once, during air raids in the twilight, Bogariov had heard someone call out, "Another flare!" And in reply, accompanied by laughter, "What's got into you? It's the evening star." More than once, on sultry evenings, distant lightning had been mistaken for gunfire. And now, when a flock of black jackdaws appeared from the east, skimming swiftly over the treetops, they could have been planes that had just broken formation. "Damn them!" said Nevtulov. "There should be a law forbidding jackdaws from taking to the air before a German attack."[68]

But only a few seconds later, peeling away from the treetops just like the birds, aircraft really did appear. Staying low, the dark, swift planes filled the air with their tense drone.

And all along the slopes where Babadjanian's battalion had dug trenches and constructed bunkers, men flung their forage caps in the air or waved hands in greeting. They had seen the red stars on the planes' wings.

"Ours!" exclaimed Babadjanian. "Our ground-attack aircraft!"

"Yes!" said Rumiantsev. "Look – the lead plane's dipping its wings. It's saying, 'I can see the bastards. I'm about to attack.'"

This glimpse of nine Soviet planes cheered everyone up.

Planes and guns can seem strong and beautiful. To an infantry-man, the thunder of supporting artillery sounds sweet and full of joy. The drone of planes with red stars on their wings, the howl of shells, the whistle of mortar bombs hurtling overhead towards the enemy – all this not only provides physical support as you creep forward. It also provides moral support; it is a proof of friendship.

But on this day, apart from those nine planes with their morning greeting, the battalion had no support. It was alone on the battlefield.

★

Foxholes have been dug in the tall grass about ten metres from the road. Men in khaki tunics and forage caps with red stars are standing in these small pits, which are chest deep.[69] Fragile glass bottles are lined up along the floor of the foxholes, and rifles have been propped against the walls. In the soldiers' trouser pockets are red tobacco pouches, matchboxes they have almost crushed in their sleep, and sugar lumps and dried rusks of bread; jumbled in their tunic pockets are grenade fuses, pencil stubs wrapped in scraps of army newspaper, and crumpled pages of letters from wives in faraway villages. Hanging by the sides of these half-hidden men are canvas bags of grenades.

The exact placing of these foxholes is far from random. Two foxholes side by side were dug by two friends determined not to be separated. A little further along are five foxholes dug so close that they almost merge; they shelter five lads from the same village. The sergeant may have admonished these men, "Not so close, lads – it's against the rules!" – but at the moment of a German tank attack it's a joy to glimpse a friend's sweating face and be able to call out, "Don't chuck that fag-end – give us a puff!" Along with the hot smoke, you then sense the warmth and moisture of a lip-crumpled, nibbled-at roll-up.

There the men stand, up to their chests in the earth. In front of them lies only empty country and an empty road. Twenty minutes will pass and fast-moving, fully armed tanks, each weighing around thirty tons, will roar up in swirls of dust. "Eyes peeled, lads!" the sergeant will shout. "They're coming!"

Just behind them, a little further up the slope, are machine-gunners in dugouts. Still further up, the infantry wait in their trenches. Behind the infantry are the gun emplacements, and behind these – the command post and medical battalion. Further and further back, but still providing support, lie HQs, airfields, reserves, roads, fortified points, forests, and cities and railway stations that are blacked out every night. Then comes Moscow, and still further east, but still a source of support, the Volga, factories lit all night by brilliant electricity, windows not criss-crossed by strips of paper,[70] and fully illuminated white steamers on the Kama river. Behind these soldiers lies a whole great country. But in front of them, to the west, there is no-one. They smoke coarse tobacco rolled in pieces of an army newspaper; they put their hands in tunic pockets and feel for crumpled pages of letters they've read and reread so many times that they can no longer read the words on the folds. Above them are clouds. A bird flies past, then disappears. There they stand, up to their chests in the earth, looking around them and waiting. It is for them to repel the German tanks. They no longer see friends – they have eyes only for the enemy.

When the day of peace and victory dawns, may those now standing behind them remember these tank-busters. May they remember these men in khaki tunics with fragile bottles of flammable liquid, carrying canvas bags of hand grenades at their side. May they give up their seat to them in a train. May they share their water with them during the journey.

To their left, a broad anti-tank ditch, walled with thick logs, stretches from a marshy river up to the road. To the right of the road is a forest.

Rodimtsev, Ignatiev and Sedov – the young Komsomol member from Moscow – stand deep in the ground, looking out at the road. Their foxholes are very close to one another. To their right, the other side of the road, are Zhaveliov, Sergeant Major Moriov and Junior Politinstructor Yeretik – the leader of this group of volunteer tank-busters. Behind them are two machine-gun crews – Glagolev's and Kordakhin's; if you look closely, you can see their machine guns peeping out from a dark timber-and-earth cave. To the right and still further back are artillery observers, rustling about among the already wilting oak branches that serve as their camouflage.

"Hey there, you lot, let's go fishing!" shouts one of the observers. "The little critters bite well first thing in the morning."

But the tank-busters ignore this. It's all very well for the observer – he's got an anti-tank ditch in front of him, and to his left, between him and the road, are the broad backs of these men in sweat-discoloured tunics. It's the sight of these backs, and the tanned napes of their necks, that makes the observer want to keep joking.

"How about a smoke?" says Sedov.

"Good idea," says Ignatiev.

"Try this – it's got a real kick!" says Rodimtsev. And he tosses Ignatiev a flat eau de cologne bottle, half-full of makhorka.[71]

"But what about you?" asks Ignatiev.

"I've overdone it. My mouth feels like leather. I'd rather chew on a rusk. Give me one of yours – they're whiter."

Ignatiev throws him a rusk. Rodimtsev carefully blows away the tobacco dust and fine grains of sand and begins to chew.

"If only they'd get a move on!" says Sedov, and puffs on his cigarette. "There's nothing worse than waiting."

"Getting bored?" asks Ignatiev. "I'm sorry – I forgot my guitar."

"Cut it out!" Rodimtsev says crossly.

"But you can't say it's not frightening," says Sedov. "The road looks so pale and lifeless. Everything dead still. I'll remember this till my last days."

Ignatiev says nothing. He is standing on tiptoe and staring into the distance. His palms are resting on the edge of his foxhole and he is slightly craning his neck.

"This time last year, I was away on holiday," says Sedov. Irritated by his comrades' silence, he spits crossly. He can see that Rodimtsev – just like Ignatiev – is staring into the distance.

"Sergeant Major, the Germans!" Rodimtsev shouts.

"Here at last," Sedov says quietly – and relieves himself with a few swear words.

"Some dust cloud," mutters Rodimtsev. "Could be a thousand bulls."

"And we're going to fight them with bottles!" Sedov yells. He laughs, spits and goes on swearing.[72] His nerves are at breaking point, his heart pounding wildly, his palms drenched in warm sweat. He wipes them against the coarse sand on the edge of his foxhole.

Ignatiev says nothing. The blood drains from his face. Narrowing his eyes, biting his lower lip, he watches the dust rise from the road.

★

The telephone rang at the command post. Rumiantsev answered. It was one of his artillery observers: the advance detachment of German motorcyclists had entered the mined section of the road. Several motorcycles had blown up on the verges, trying to avoid the mines, but the detachment was now moving forward again.

"Very well," said Babadjanian. "Time to send them our greetings!" He called Lieutenant Kosiuk, the commander of the machine-gun company, to the telephone and ordered him to wait until the motorcyclists were within close range and then open fire.

"How many metres?" asked Kosiuk.

"Forget about metres!" Babadjanian replied sharply. "When they reach the dead tree on the right-hand side of the road."

"Understood," said Kosiuk.

Three minutes later, the machine guns opened fire. The first burst fell short – swift little clouds shot up from the road, as if a flock of sparrows were enjoying a hurried dust-bath. Without stopping, the motorcyclists opened fire in reply. They were shooting at random, unable to see their target, but their fire was extremely concentrated. The air resounded, filled with invisible death-dealing streams. Puffs of dust and smoke, merging into a single cloud, spread up the slope. The soldiers in the trenches and dugouts crouched down, casting wary looks at the pale blue air singing above them.

Then the heavy machine guns sent a burst of fire right into the middle of the speeding motorcyclists. A moment ago, it had seemed that no power on earth could stop or slow this powerfully armed column, but now it was dissolving before the soldiers' eyes. Motorcycles fell on their sides, wheels still spinning and raising clouds of dust. The surviving motorcyclists took to their heels, dashing away from the road.

"Well?" Babadjanian said to Rumiantsev.[73] "What do you say to that? Seems our machine-gunners know what they're doing!"

The motorcyclists were then pursued by quick, repeated rifle fire. A young man with a wounded or injured leg extricated himself from beneath his overturned motorcycle and held his hands up over his head. The rifle fire stopped. For a moment the soldier stood there in his torn uniform, a look of anguish and horror on his grimy face, trying to sniff back the blood and snot from his smashed nose[74] and stretching his arms high into the air, as if picking apples from the top branch of a tree. Then he shouted something and, slightly waving his outstretched arms, staggered towards our trenches. He kept on shouting as he moved closer, and gradually peals of laughter spread from trench to trench, from dugout to dugout. He was clearly visible from the command post, but the commanders could not understand what was making everyone laugh so much. Then the telephone rang. It was Lieutenant Kosiuk, from the forward observation post.

"Comrade Battalion Commander," he shouted down the line, almost choking with laughter, "the man's hobbling along, hands in the air and shouting like a man possessed, 'Russky, to me surrender! Russky, to me surrender!' He's so scared it comes out all garbled."

Bogariov began to laugh too, saying to himself, "I like it! Hearty laughter as the tanks approach. Our morale must be pretty good!" Then he turned to Rumiantsev and asked, "Fully prepared, Comrade Captain?"

"Fully prepared, Comrade Commissar. Firing data has been

calculated and the guns have been loaded. The entire sector along which their tanks will pass will be subjected to concentrated fire."

"Air attack!" several voices called out in chorus. And at the same moment, two telephones began to ring.

"They're coming! The lead tank is now two thousand metres distant," Rumiantsev said slowly. His eyes were now stern and serious, but his mouth was still smiling.

13

NO MATTER WHAT THE COST,
STAND FIRM!

The planes and tanks appeared at almost the same moment. There were six Messerschmitt-109s, skimming the ground. Above them were two flights of bombers. Still higher, at around fifteen hundred metres, was another flight of Messerschmitts.

"Their classic deployment," muttered Nevtulov. "The Messers below cover the bombers as they come out of their dive, and the Messers above cover them as they enter it. We'll have to keep on our toes!"

"So much for our camouflage," said Rumiantsev. "We'll be giving our position away. But we'll make them pay for it." And he ordered his battery commanders to open fire.

A few moments after this, every sound was extinguished. There was nothing but deafening hammer blows from the guns. And then a long, penetrating sigh as the shells flew through the air. It was as if whole groves of tall poplars, aspens and birches were bending and swaying, rustling millions of young leaves in a sudden and mighty wind; it was as if their slender branches were tearing at the wind's strong, elastic tissue; it was as if the wind engendered by this flying steel would carry away both people and the earth itself. Then came the sound of distant explosions. One, two, several at once, then another.

Bogariov heard a voice down the line, calling out corrections. All the passion of the battle was encapsulated in the tone of these voices that spoke only figures. This was a triumph of numbers, a jubilant triumph of numbers and long decimals. Numbers had come to life, and gone on the rampage, tenacious and furious. Suddenly came another voice, "Lozenko, did you sneak off with my *makhorka*? A pack I'd already opened?" And then a reply, "So bloody what! Have you never nicked any of mine?" And then, once again, the commander calling out firing data, and a second voice, repeating these data.

Meanwhile, the bombers were circling overhead, looking for targets. Nevtulov dashed across to the gun positions.

"Keep on firing, no matter what!" he shouted to the commander of the first battery.

"Keep on firing," the lieutenant repeated.

Two of the Junkers went into a dive. The four-barrelled anti-aircraft machine guns fired burst after burst at them.

"Quite a dive," said Nevtulov. "Bold pilots!"

"Fire!" commanded the lieutenant.

The three-gun battery fired another salvo. The roar of the guns merged with the roar of exploding bombs. Earth and sand showered down on the gunners.

Wiping the sweat and grime off their faces, they quickly reloaded.

"Still in one piece, Morozov?" called the lieutenant.

"Still in one piece, Comrade Lieutenant," Morozov replied. "Let's liven things up for them, Comrade Lieutenant!"

"Fire!" the lieutenant commanded again.

The other German planes were still circling over the front

line. There was no let-up in either the machine-gun fire or the explosions of bombs.

The gunners worked with dogged fury, with swift passion. Their well-coordinated movements, united by a brotherhood of purpose, exemplified the power of shared labour. It was not a matter of hard-working individuals: a short, broad-shouldered Tatar ammunition bearer; a dark-eyed Jewish-Ukrainian charge handler; a gaunt Georgian rammer; Morozov, their famed gun-layer. It was, rather, as if a single person were working there. This single person cast a quick glance at the Junkers as they came out of their dive, banking sharply and preparing for another attack. He wiped the sweat from his face, smiled for a moment, let out an accompanying yell as the guns fired, and returned to his skilled, intricate task. He was quick and determined. It was as if he had a hundred hands, as if every last trace of fear had been washed from his face by the sweat of his labour. This same man was also serving the second and third guns of the battery and all the guns of the second battery. He did not stop; he did not drop to the ground or run to the dugout when the bombs howled down. The iron crashes of explosions did not interrupt his work. Nor did he stop to look up in glee when soldiers from the third company, which was being held in reserve, called out, "They've downed him! Our ack-acks have downed him! He's going down in flames!" He wasted no time; he worked. For these men, who had been welded into one, there existed only one word: "Fire!" And this word, wedded to their noble labour, gave birth to fire.[75]

Morozov the gun-layer, with his freckles and shaggy hair, repeated, "Time to liven things up!" And the observers, aware how much the gunners were achieving, went on with their calculations, pouring more and more of their numbers and decimals into the flames.

★

Unexpectedly for the Germans, shells had begun to burst in the midst of the tanks. The first round smashed the turret of a heavy tank. The observers watched through their field glasses as the tankmen quickly stopped poking their heads out of the hatches and retreated below.

"Like ground squirrels slipping into their holes, Comrade Lieutenant," said one of the scouts at the artillery observation post.

"Very true!" said the lieutenant. He then nodded to the telephonist and said, "Ogurechenko, get me no. 4."

Only the stout man sitting on the lead tank did not hide away down below. As if wanting to cheer on the tanks behind him, he gave a wave of his hand; he still had a little string of red coral round his wrist. Then he took an apple from his pocket and bit into it. The column moved on, not breaking formation. Only where the road was blocked by wrecked or burning tanks did the drivers make detours. Some of these drivers, however, then chose to continue across the fields, not turning back onto the road.

Some two kilometres from the fortified line, the tanks finally abandoned formation completely. Hemmed in by trees to their right and a river to their left, they advanced in a compact block, several tanks deep. By then, about twenty tanks had been left burning on the road.

Now blanketed by artillery fire, the Panzers began to reply. Their first shells flew over the tank-busters and exploded amid the infantry trenches behind them. Then the Panzers directed their fire higher up the slope, trying to silence the Russian guns. Most of them came to a halt. A Henschel Hs 126 – the small reconnaissance plane known to the Red Army men as "the humpback" – appeared in the sky up above and established radio contact with them. The radio operator at the Soviet command post lamented, "All I can make out, comrades, is 'Gut, *gut, gut*.' It's as if the man's rapping away with a hammer."

"Don't worry," said Bogariov. "Things aren't going so very *gut* for them."

Babadjanian turned to Bogariov and said, "Any moment now, Comrade Commissar, their tanks will advance. I know their tactics – I've seen all this twice before." After ordering the mortars to open fire, he said, "Well, so much for the field post and my wife's birthday!"

"If they break through," said a gunner lieutenant, "we should withdraw our artillery."

Rumiantsev retorted crossly, "Once we start withdrawing guns, the Germans will break through and wipe out the lot of us. Comrade Commissar, please allow me to move two batteries forward so we can open direct fire."

"Yes – and don't waste a moment," Bogariov replied quickly. He was agitated, understanding that the decisive moment had come.

The Germans clearly took the cessation of fire to mean that the guns were being withdrawn. A few minutes after this, they launched an all-out attack. The tanks tore forward at top speed, cannons and machine guns blazing away.

Several soldiers, crouching down, dashed out from one of the dugouts higher up the slope. One was felled by a stray bullet;

the others, crouching still lower, were running past the command post.

"What the hell!" yelled Babadjanian, pulling out his revolver and rushing towards them.

"Tanks, Comrade Captain!" gasped one of the men.

"What's up with you lot? Why are you all doubled over? All got bellyache or what?" Babadjanian yelled furiously. "Stand tall! Your task is to greet the tanks, not to run like rabbits!"[76]

At that moment Rumiantsev's howitzers opened fire. Now, for the first time, the gunners could see the enemy. The blows struck by the heavy shells were shattering. Direct hits made the tanks slide apart and the metal curl up; flames burst from the hatches, then climbed high above the tanks. And even the splinters and fragments of these mighty shells pierced the tanks' armour and crippled their tracks. Engines still roared away, but these tanks no longer moved forward.

"Well, Comrade Babadjanian?" Rumiantsev shouted in the commander's ear. "Seems like our gunners know what they're doing!"

The tanks in the fields had all been halted. Those that had kept to the road, however, were still moving forward. The heavy lead tank, cannon firing and all its machine guns chattering away, broke through into the sector where the tank-busters were waiting in their foxholes. There were four more tanks just behind him, all going at top speed.

The Russian artillery fire had weakened. Two guns had been damaged and put out of action; a third had been wrecked by a direct hit. Some gunners, severely wounded, had been carried away by orderlies. The bodies of the dead were still in position by their guns; they had kept on fighting, labouring to their last breath.

"Now or never!" shouted Rodimtsev. "No matter what the cost!"

The three men grabbed hold of their Molotov cocktails.

Sedov got to his feet first. The lead tank was going straight for him. A machine-gun round got him straight in the head and chest. A bloody mass, he fell to the floor of the foxhole.

Ignatiev saw his friend die. Then a machine-gun burst howled over his head and slashed into the earth. The lead tank passed so close that he involuntarily flinched. He had a momentary recollection of how, as a boy, he had stood at a station where his father had just taken someone in his cart and a locomotive pulling an express train had thundered past; he still recalled the locomotive's warmth and the smell of hot oil. Ignatiev rose to his full height and flung his bottle, thinking with something close to despair, "Not much you can do to a locomotive with a one-litre bottle!" The bottle landed on the tank's turret. Quick flames flared up. Fanned by the wind, they began to roar. Then Rodimtsev threw some grenades under the tracks of the second tank. Ignatiev threw a second bottle. "This tank's not so big," he said to himself drunkenly. "Half a litre will do for it. But that first one only needed a quarter."

The huge lead tank was crippled. The driver had clearly tried to turn it around, but without success. The upper hatch opened. Germans with sub-machine guns clambered out, shielding their faces from the flames, and leaped to the ground.

Some voice inside Ignatiev said, "That's the one who killed Sedov."

"Halt!" he shouted. Seizing his rifle, he jumped out of his foxhole.

The huge, broad-shouldered German with the string of red

coral round his wrist stood there on his own. The other members of his crew, bent almost double, were running away, keeping to the overgrown roadside ditch. This man alone stood tall. Seeing Ignatiev dashing towards him with a rifle, he held his sub-machine gun beside his belly and let rip. Most of the round missed, but the very last bullets hit Ignatiev's rifle and splintered the butt. Ignatiev stopped for half a second, then rushed at the German. The German tried to reload his gun but realized he wouldn't be able to do it quickly enough. He showed no sign of fear – he was clearly no coward. Instead, with a gait somehow both light and heavy, he moved towards Ignatiev.

Ignatiev saw red. This was the man who had killed Sedov, who had burned down a large city in a single night, who had killed the beautiful Ukrainian girl, who had trampled down the fields, who had destroyed the white huts and brought shame and death to so many.

"Ignatiev!" from somewhere in the distance came the voice of the sergeant major.

The German believed in his own strength and courage. He had undergone many years of training. He knew all the quickest and most vicious tricks of hand-to-hand fighting.

"Komm, komm, Ivan!" he called out.

It was as if this man were intoxicated with the magnificence of his own image. Standing tall on conquered land, alone among burning tanks, to the thunder of bursting shells, he could have been a statue or monument – he who had marched through Belgium and France, who had trampled the earth of Yugoslavia and Greece, whose chest Hitler himself had adorned with an Iron Cross.

The long-ago days of single combat seemed to have returned. Many eyes were watching this meeting of two men on battle-scarred soil. Ignatiev, from the province of Tula, swung his arm. The blow he struck was dreadful and simple.

"Bastard," he shouted hoarsely. "Fighting young girls!"

Then came the quick, dry crack of a rifle – Rodimtsev's.

The German assault was beaten off. Their tanks and motorized infantry attacked four times. The battle was savage and unequal. Four times Babadjanian led his battalion forward; his men were armed only with grenades and bottles of flammable liquid.

The battery commanders went on shouting their hoarse commands, but the guns thundered less and less often.

Men die simple deaths on the field of battle.

"You and I have played our last game of chess, Vasya," said Nevtulov. A large-calibre bullet had got him in the chest and blood was flowing from his mouth with every breath. Rumiantsev kissed him and wept.

"Fire!" shouted a commander – and Nevtulov's last whispers were drowned by the thunder of guns.

Babadjanian was mortally wounded in the stomach during the last of the German attacks. His men laid him on a tarpaulin and wanted to carry him from the field.

"No!" he said. "I still have a voice. I can give commands."

And until the last of the German attacks was repelled, the soldiers did indeed continue to hear his voice. Babadjanian died in Bogariov's arms.

"Don't forget me, Commissar," he said. "In only a few days you've become a true friend."

And looking at the thin face of the dying commander, Bogariov understood that there were no people closer to him than those who had fought beside him in defence of the people's freedom.

Men died. Who will tell of their brave deeds? Only the swift clouds saw how Riabokon went on fighting until he had no cartridges left; how, with a hand grenade he was too weak to throw, Politinstructor Yeretik blew up both himself and a group of advancing Germans; how, knowing he was surrounded, Glushkov went on firing until his last breath; how machine-gunners Glagolev and Kordakhin, faint from loss of blood, went on fighting as long as their weakening fingers could pull the trigger, as long as their dimming eyes could distinguish a target in the sultry haze.

In vain do poets make out in song that the names of the dead will live for ever. In vain do they write poems assuring dead heroes that they continue to live, that their memory and names are eternal. In vain do thoughtless writers make such claims in their books, promising what no soldier would ever ask them to promise. Human memory simply cannot hold thousands of names. He who is dead is dead. Those who go to their death understand this. A nation of millions is now going out to die for its freedom, just as it used to go out to work in field and factory.[77]

Great is the people whose sons die such stern, simple and sacred deaths on these vast fields of battle. The sky and the stars know about them; the earth has heard their last sighs; the unreaped rye and the roadside trees have witnessed their deeds. They sleep in the earth, with the sky, the sun and the clouds above them. They sleep soundly, they sleep an eternal sleep, as do their fathers and grandfathers, men who worked all their lives as carpenters, navvies, miners, weavers and peasant-farmers of a great land. They gave their toil and sweat to this land, sometimes labouring beyond their strength. The hour of war came – and they gave this land their blood and their lives. May this land, then, be famed for labour, reason, honour and freedom. May there be no words more sacred and majestic than "the people"! This nation, like no other nation in the world, knows how to die sternly and simply.

At night, after the dead had been buried, Bogariov went to his dugout.

"Comrade Commissar," said the sentry. "There's a messenger waiting for you."

"What do you mean?" Bogariov asked in astonishment. "Where from?"

A soldier appeared, a short man carrying a haversack and a rifle.

"Where have you just come from, comrade?"

"Divisional HQ. I've brought you your post."

"How the hell? The road's been cut."

"I found ways, Comrade Commissar. I crept four kilometres on my belly. I crossed the river at night and I shot a German sentry. Look – here's his shoulder strap."

"Weren't you scared?" asked Bogariov.

"Scared?" the soldier replied, with a little smile. "Why? My soul's not so precious. I'd price it at five kopeks. No more than a balalaika. Why should I be afraid for it?"[78]

"Really?" Bogariov asked thoughtfully. "Is that how it feels to you?"

The soldier just went on smiling.

The first letter was for Babadjanian. Bogariov glanced at the return address – it was from Yerevan, from Babadjanian's wife.

Company commanders Ovchinnikov and Shuleikin and Polit-instructor Makhotkin went quickly through the letters, quietly saying, "Present . . . dead . . . dead . . . dead . . . present . . . dead . . ." They placed the letters for the dead in a separate pile.

Bogariov took Babadjanian's letter and went to his grave. He laid the letter on the mound, covered it with earth and pressed it down with a shell splinter.

For a long time, he stood there in silence.

"When will I get a letter from you, Lisa?" he then asked aloud.

At three in the morning, the radio operator received a brief coded message. The army commander thanked everyone for their courage. They had executed their mission brilliantly, inflicting huge losses on the German tanks and so holding up the advance of a powerful column. What remained of the battalion and artillery was to withdraw.

Bogariov knew that there was nowhere to withdraw to. Scouts had reported that the Germans had been moving during the night along tracks intersecting the main road.

His company commanders kept coming up to him, saying that they were encircled and questioning him anxiously.

Now that Babadjanian was no more, Bogariov had to come to decisions alone. For the first time, addressing the commanders and politinstructors gathered in the dugout, he solemnly came out with the words so often uttered by men on the front line: "I sized up the situation and came to a decision." Men like saying these words, even if it's merely a matter of where to eat a meal or to stop for the night.

A little surprised by himself, he thought, "If only Lisa could see me now." This, though, was something he'd already thought many times. He wanted Lisa to see how the man she knew as a scholar and philosopher, studying day and night in the Marx–Engels

Institute, had now become one of the cooks tending to the fiery cauldron of the war.[79]

"Comrade commanders, here is what I have decided," he said. "We shall withdraw into the forest. We shall rest and regroup there, then fight our way to the river in order to cross to the east bank. I appoint Captain Rumiantsev as my deputy. We shall move one hour from now."

He looked around him. Everyone looked exhausted. Rumiantsev's stern face already looked older. In a very different voice, a voice that reminded him of his life in Moscow before the war, he went on, "My friends, with blood and fire, we are forging our victory. Remember this day. Remember that if we can fight like this as we retreat, we shall be advancing tomorrow. Let us stand, in honour of our true friends – the Red Army soldiers, politinstructors and commanders who have died in battle."

14

AT FRONT HQ

Front HQ was located in a forest. The commander's bunker lay between tall oaks, and the bunkers of the members of the military soviet were nearby. The rest of the staff – members of the operations and intelligence departments, the political administration and the Front quartermaster service – lived in huts and dugouts camouflaged by green branches. Office desks stood beneath hazel bushes and, to refill the inkwells, orderlies had to walk down fairy-tale paths strewn with acorns. Early each morning, the song of birds would be drowned out by the clatter of typewriters beneath dew-covered leaves. Typists would get cross with junior quartermaster staff bringing them statements and registers to type out. Through dense thickets you might glimpse tinted lips and heads of blonde hair; you might hear women's laughter and the sullen voices of clerks. One tall and gloomy hut was full of huge desks covered in maps. Guards constantly paced around this hut, and the sentry stationed by the door stuck visitors' passes on a nail hammered into a hollow old aspen. At night, rotten tree stumps gave off a faint, bluish light. HQ lived a life of its own and this life never changed; it made no difference whether HQ was in the ancient halls of a Polish nobleman, in the huts of a large village, or deep in a forest. And the forest, too, went on with its own life.

Squirrels laid in their winter supplies, mischievously dropping acorns on the heads of typists; woodpeckers hammered away at tree trunks and extracted grubs; kites skimmed over the tops of oaks, aspens and lindens; fledglings tried out the strength of their wings; and a whole vast world – millions of red and black ants, unicorn beetles and ground beetles – hurried about its work.

Sometimes Messerschmitts appeared in the clear sky, circling over the forest, searching for troops and HQs.

"A-a-a-i-r-cr-a-a-ft!" sentries would call out. Typists cleared papers from their desks and threw dark kerchiefs over their heads; commanders removed their caps to hide the shine of their visors; the staff barber hurriedly rolled up his white sheet and wiped the lather from his client's still unshaven cheeks; waitresses laid green branches over plates they'd just set out for dinner. The only sounds were the drone of the planes and – from artillery command, located among pine trees on a sandy hillock – the hearty voice of a rosy-cheeked general reprimanding his subordinates.

And as preparations were made for the military soviet to meet in a shelter made from the branches of leafy trees – just as they had previously met in the vaulted, half-dark hall of a palace and in the bright room of the pre-war Military District HQ, with its sparkling clean, mirror-like windows – a plate of green apples would be brought in for the Front commander, along with packets of Northern Palmyra cigarettes for the other commissars and commanders.

Day and night, the dynamo that powered the Front radio hummed away in the hazel copses; hundreds of cables stretched along poles through the forest and out into the fields beyond; telegraph operators clattered their keys while their machines went on tapping away. Telephone, telegraph and radio waves connected this leafy shelter with the HQs of armies, divisions, tank brigades, cavalry corps and air force units. On a low tree stump dotted with mushrooms stood an ordinary Moscow telephone. Its ring was like that of any other telephone. Nevertheless, the sound made everyone in the hut fall silent. The sentries almost stood to attention, and the Front commander, who seldom made hasty movements, rushed to pick up the receiver. This was the high frequency telephone that connected Front HQ with the Stavka.[80]

"Yeromin speaking," he said agitatedly.

Front HQ was located forty kilometres from the forward positions. In the evenings, when the wind in the treetops quietened, they could hear the sound of artillery. The chief of staff believed that they should withdraw at least seventy to eighty kilometres further east, but Yeromin was reluctant; he liked being close to the front line. He could make frequent visits to the divisions and regiments, he could observe the course of the fighting in person – yet be back by his huge operations map within forty minutes.

HQ had been in a state of alarm since early that morning. German tank columns had advanced as far as the river. It was rumoured that motorcyclists had been seen on this side of the river, that they had crossed in large flat-bottomed boats and reached the edge of the forest where HQ was located.

The staff commissar reported all this to Yeromin, who was standing by a hazel bush and picking the ripe nuts. The various heads of sections who'd come with Cherednichenko watched their commander's face apprehensively, but the news seemed to make no impression on him. He nodded in acknowledgement, but then just said to his adjutant, "Lazarev, can you pull down this branch for me? Look, it's got dozens of nuts on it!"

The men watched attentively as Yeromin went on diligently picking nuts. He evidently had good eyesight – he did not miss a single nut, not even the ones hiding most cunningly in green husks between the rough leaves. This lesson in sangfroid lasted for some time.

Yeromin then walked briskly over to the waiting heads of sections and said, "I know very well why you've come. But HQ remains where it is. We're not moving anywhere. Kindly report to me only when I summon you."

The embarrassed section heads left. A few minutes later the adjutant reported that Samarin, the commander of an army group, was on the line.

Yeromin went into the shelter.

He heard Samarin out, repeating every now and then, "Yes . . . Yes . . ." And then, in the same tone, he said, "That you've suffered casualties, Samarin, goes without saying. But I've assigned you a particular task and – even if you're the only man left alive – you are to carry that out. Understood?"

A moment later, he said, "I'm glad that's understood," and hung up.

Divisional Commissar Cherednichenko had heard all this. He said, "Samarin's a tough man. He must be in real trouble."

"Yes," Yeromin replied. "He's a man of iron."

"I'm sure he is. All the same, tomorrow I'll go and see this iron man."

"What weather! What wonderful weather!" said Yeromin. "Like a few nuts? I picked them myself."

"I noticed," Cherednichenko said with a smile. He took a handful of nuts.

"Did you?" Yeromin replied animatedly. "Did you too hear about the motorcyclists and assume I'd give orders to move our HQ?"

"It's all right," Cherednichenko said. "You don't need to worry. By now I've seen at least two hundred new men here at HQ. They all look the same – brand new tunics, pale hands and faces, an anxious look in their eyes. It's only too clear that they've spent the last few years in military academies or such like. And then, day by day, they change. Their noses peel, their skin tans, their tunics hang differently. Their faces weather. Even their eyebrows bleach. And it's not only the man's skin that changes – it's the same deep inside him. The war tempers the whole of him – it tempers his nerves and his heart. He gains some experience, he gets to understand the enemy better. And so, with every day, with every battle, with every skirmish, our people is tempered. Our people is rock strong. Strong enough to smash anything, even tanks."

"Yes," said Yeromin. "I don't disagree. But I have to say that I don't see anything so very praiseworthy about these men getting tempered and learning to fight properly. What's so special about that? Damn it, they're military, they're soldiers!"

Turning to his adjutant, he asked, "Will dinner be ready soon?"

"They're laying the table now," the orderly on duty quickly put in.

"Good," said Yeromin. "Now, don't stuff down too many nuts before dinner – you'll spoil your appetite!" He laughed. "To be honest with you, I love war. It's not something I have to get used to. Once the war began, I started to feel righter – as my grandfather used to say. My appetite, my nerves – everything about me improved. I felt calmer. I felt twenty years younger. Before the war, I was constantly seeing top doctors, important professors. They came to see me and I went to see them. Either it was my liver, or I couldn't sleep, or it was my metabolism as a whole. And now I've got a hearty appetite – the appetite of a soldier – and I bathe in the river, and the sun shines down on me. Sinner that I am, I love to fight. I wake in the morning and think, 'Ah, we're at war!' And I've forgotten what nerves are. I'm calm, I'm confident. I feel as if I've been cast from metal.[81] So, for me it's not enough for a commander to gain experience and become tempered, to acquire a little wisdom. A commander should live a full life in wartime. He should sleep well, eat well, read a few books, feel calm and cheerful and have the right style of haircut. And he should be able to bring down enemy aircraft, and destroy tanks that try to outflank him, and motorcycles, and machine-gunners, and you name it . . . And all this should just make him feel calmer. It should make him live better in the world. That's what I call a true soldier. Remember that regimental HQ where you and I ate dumplings with sour cream?"

Cherednichenko chuckled. "You mean, when the cook kept complaining, 'All this damn dive-bombing. Again and again! How can I shape my dumplings properly?'"

"That's right. *All this damn dive-bombing. And how can I shape my dumplings?* But they were damn good dumplings, weren't they!" He thought for a moment, then added, "Yes, the important thing is to love one's work – and our work is war."

Cherednichenko moved closer to Yeromin and said hoarsely, "We'll smash them. We'll see them on the run yet. Yes, we will. And they'll end up cursing that day – 22 June 1941. And that hour – four in the morning. And their sons, and grandsons, and great-grandsons – all of them will curse that day and that hour."

During the afternoon, aerial reconnaissance confirmed

information provided by a wounded lieutenant who had escaped from encirclement: German tank columns, advancing along various roads, were now concentrating not far from Gorelovets, about twenty-two kilometres from the river. The lieutenant had pointed on the map to a low-lying area sparsely planted with firs. Scouts had also spoken to herdsmen who had recently forded the river. Apparently, after the women had gone to milk the cows in the early afternoon, these tanks had been joined by two powerful columns of motorized infantry. Knowing how few aircraft the Soviet commanders had at their disposal on this sector of the front, the Germans were not observing the usual precautions. Armoured vehicles and trucks were massed close together. Come twilight – to make it easier for the cooks to peel the following day's vegetables – some drivers were even switching on their headlamps.

Yeromin summoned the general in command of the artillery.

"Is that within range?" he asked, pointing to an oval pencilled in on the large-scale map.

"Yes, Comrade Lieutenant General," said the artillery commander.

Yeromin had at his disposal the guns of the High Command artillery reserve – the steel monsters that Bogariov had encountered on the day he arrived at HQ. Many of the staff had worried that it might prove impossible to transport these huge guns safely across the river; the bridge would have to be exceptionally strong and the Germans were already close to the river. The battle at the state farm, however, had allowed the sappers the time they needed to reinforce the bridge – though not even Bogariov knew this.

"At twenty-two hundred hours, unleash all your fire power on that target!" Yeromin ordered.

The artillery commander, a rosy-cheeked general who was almost always smiling, loved his wife, his old mother, his daughters and his son. There were many other things he loved: hunting, lively conversation, Georgian wine and a good book. Most of all, though, he loved his long-range guns. He was their servant and admirer, and he experienced the destruction of any piece of heavy artillery as a personal loss. It distressed him that today's highly mobile warfare offered few occasions for long-range artillery to show its full power. The concentration of so much heavy artillery around Front HQ had left him deeply agitated. Not knowing whether he would ever have the opportunity to employ it, he had felt both happy and sad. And hearing Yeromin say, "Unleash all your fire power!" had probably been the most joyful and triumphant moment in his whole life.

That evening, the Central Committee of the Belorussian Communist Party met in a forest glade. A bright evening sky gleamed through the foliage above them. Dry grey oak leaves, as if laid out by a woman's careful hand, covered a smart carpet of springy dark green moss.

Who can convey the austere simplicity of this meeting on the last free patch of Belorussian forest? The wind from the west sounded sad and solemn – as if a million human voices were whispering in the leaves. People's commissars and Central Committee members, all in military tunics and with tired, weather-beaten faces, gave brief speeches. And it was as if thousands of wires fanned out from this glade, linking it to Gomel and Mogiliov, to Minsk, Bobruisk, Rogachov and Smolevichi, to villages and shtetls, to orchards, apiaries, fields and bogs. Partisans, old peasant women, collective-farm herdsmen, village children – people of every age and profession made their way to this glade by secret paths, bringing grim news from the rest of their now subjugated country. And the evening wind in the dark leaves was the calm, twilight voice of a people that knew it must either die in slavery or fight for its freedom.

Darkness fell. The artillery opened fire. Long flashes of lightning lit the dark west. The trunks of oaks emerged from the shadows, as if the entire forest had stepped forward and then stood motionless in the trembling white light. The guns did not seem to be firing isolated salvoes; the sound was not like cannon fire at all. It seemed, rather, to be how the air had howled over the earth in prehistoric days, as the mountain ranges of today's Europe and Asia rose from the ocean floor.

Two war correspondents and a photographer were sitting on a fallen trunk, not far from the leafy shelter of the military soviet. They watched and listened in silence.[82]

Then came the voice of Yeromin, "And by the way, comrades, do you remember Pushkin's *Journey to Arzrum* and his splendid description—"[83]

They were unable to make out the rest of the sentence. A few moments later they heard another calm, slow voice, which they recognized as Cherednichenko's: "You know, I like Garshin. There's a man who wrote truthfully about the life of a soldier."[84]

At twenty-two fifty, Yeromin and the artillery general flew over the valley where the Germans had concentrated their Panzer columns. What they saw filled the artillery general's heart with lasting pride.

15

THE GENERAL

One of the tasks of Major General Samarin, the commander of an army group, was to hold the river crossings. His HQ, his rear support services, the office of the army newspaper, his forward and reserve echelons – almost all his forces were positioned on the east bank. Only his forward command post remained on the west bank, in a small village on the edge of a large, unharvested field. Working alongside Samarin were Major Garan from the HQ operations section and grey-haired Colonel Nabashidze, his artillery commander. Samarin had little by way of equipment: a field radio, a telegraph and ordinary field telephones connecting him to his unit commanders. He worked, dined and received the other commanders in a light, spacious hut. He slept outside under an awning, since he could not do without fresh air.

There were camp beds in the main part of the hut for three other men: Liadov, Samarin's adjutant, who had a snub nose, very red cheeks and round, very dark eyes; a melancholic cook who liked to sing "My Little Blue Shawl"[85] before going to bed; and Kliukhin, Samarin's driver. For some time now, Kliukhin had been carrying around with him a copy of *David Copperfield*. By the first day of the war, he had read only fourteen pages and – since Samarin seldom allowed his men any leisure – he had made no further progress. One day the cook had asked Kliukhin what he thought of this stout volume. "Worth reading," Kliukhin replied. "Stories of Jewish life."[86]

At dawn Samarin would emerge from his barn. His breakfast would already be waiting for him on the table. First, though, the roguish, cowardly and impudent[87] Liadov would greet him with a towel and a large jug. He would pour cold well water on Samarin's neck, which was covered by fine reddish down, and say, "Did you sleep well, Comrade Major General? The Germans were sending up tracers all night long."

Samarin was short in stature, taciturn, stern and decisive. He was entirely fearless and he paid regular visits to the most danger-ous sectors of the front, much to Liadov's despair. He crossed battlefields with unhurried, proprietorial self-confidence, show-ing up at regimental and battalion command posts at the most critical moments. He always wore all his orders and medals and walked about among exploding shells and mortar bombs with the Gold Star of a Hero of the Soviet Union on his chest.[88] If he appeared when a regiment was in action, he could always grasp the essence of the situation straightaway – in the smoke of burning huts and barns, amid shell-bursts and rifle fire, amid the complex manoeuvres of Soviet and enemy tanks and the confusion of infantry dashing this way and that. Divisional, regimental and battalion commanders all immediately recognized his curt manner of speech, his large nose and the often sullen, sometimes unkind look on his face. He seldom smiled. The moment he appeared, blazing vehicles or buildings and the thunder of guns became somehow less important; for a minute he seemed to absorb into his own being all the tension of the battle. He did not stay at the command post for long, but his brief visit would affect the entire course of subsequent events; it was as if the commanders could still sense his cool, calm gaze even after he had left. If he saw an operation being conducted badly, he did not hesitate to remove the commanders responsible. On one occasion he ordered a major, a regimental commander, to join in an attack as an ordinary soldier – to atone for his fear of exposing himself to danger and reluctance to take responsibility. He was stern and merciless in his treatment of cowards. Anyone who showed cowardice on the battlefield – whether he was a commander or an ordinary soldier – would be executed.

The hatred and disgust he felt for the enemy were unshakeable. If he walked through a village the Germans had set on fire, his face would become frightening to look at; he could have been some ancient god of revenge. The men were all aware not only of his fierce hatred but also of his courage. They liked to tell how once, in the thick of the fighting, he had seen a wounded soldier, got out of his armoured jeep to help him and placed the man on his own seat. He himself had then walked behind the jeep beneath a hurricane of enemy fire.

They also liked to tell how he had once picked up a rifle that a soldier had thrown onto the ground during a battle. It was covered in stinking mud. In front of the assembled company Samarin had carefully and lovingly wiped it clean and silently handed it over to the soldier, who by then had nearly died of shame. And so, the men whom Samarin led into battle had faith in him. They forgave him his severity and his moments of cruelty.

Liadov knew his general well. More than once, as they neared the front line, Liadov had got out to ask for directions from other commanders and then reported, "Comrade Major General, we can't get through. No-one's going this way any longer. The road's under mortar fire, and apparently there are sub-machine-gunners encamped in the woods. We'll have to find some other route."

In response, Samarin might just carry on rolling a cigarette. Then he would light it and say, "Sub-machine-gunners? Huh!" And he'd tell the driver to keep going.

And Liadov would crouch down behind his general's back, almost sick with fear. Like many men who are far from brave, he carried on him a formidable armoury: an automatic, a Mauser, a Nagan and a Browning. Also, in his pockets, he had a second Mauser and a trophy Parabellum. Once Samarin had sent him on a mission to the east, far away from the front line. With his stories and menacing appearance, he had duly impressed the women he met in the trains and even railway station commandants. Probably, however, he had never once fired a shot from any of his pistols and revolvers.

★

Samarin had spent the whole day on the front line. Every sector was under increasing pressure. Day and night there was no let-up. The men were often so exhausted by the sultry heat that they were unable to eat the hot food brought to them in the trenches.

On returning to his command post, he had spoken to Yeromin on the telephone, asking to be allowed to withdraw to the east bank. Yeromin had categorically refused, determined to keep control of the crossings in order to bring back the remaining ordnance and the last of the rifle corps. This had upset and angered

Samarin. When Major Garan brought him the latest field report, he did not even glance at it. Instead, he snapped, "Forget it. I know the situation already." Then he turned to his cook and asked crossly, "Will I ever be getting my dinner?"

"Your dinner is ready, Comrade Major General," the cook replied. He clicked his heels and spun round, his white apron flapping. The elderly mistress of the hut, a collective-farm worker by the name of Olga Dmitrievna, smirked disapprovingly. She resented the way the cook sneered at her village food.

"Well, Dmitrievna, tell me how you would go about preparing a *côtelette de volaille*. Or perhaps spuds *dauphinoise*," he would say.

"Oh, get along with you!" she would reply. "Don't teach your grandmother to suck eggs."

"I don't mean fried spuds village style. I mean like I cooked them in a restaurant in Penza before the war. What'll you say if the major general asks you for a dish like that, eh?"

Olga Dmitrievna's daughter-in-law, Frosya, and her sick grandson listened attentively. This bickering had been going on for several days. The old woman was upset that she didn't know how to cook dishes with stupid names and that this skinny beanpole of a cook was more adept than her in kitchen matters.

"Timka, Timka – your name really suits you!" she said, knowing how he hated being spoken to in such a familiar way and how he beamed with pleasure when he was addressed more formally, as Timofey Markovich. That was how Liadov addressed him when he was hungry and wanted a bite to eat before the general sat down to dinner.

Samarin had no complaints about his cook and seldom got angry with him. Now, though, as he sat down at the table, he said,

"How many times must I tell you about the samovar? I want it brought over from HQ straightaway."

"The quartermaster's bringing it this evening, Comrade Major General."

"Don't say you've done me roast mutton yet again!" Samarin went on. "Twice now I've said I'd like some fish. It's not far to the river and I don't think you're short of time."

Olga Dmitrievna snickered. With a glance at the discomfited cook, she said, "What does he care if a general asks for some fish? All he ever wants is to make fun of some poor old woman."

"Is that so?" asked Samarin.

"It certainly is! 'Can you fry me a cutlet de volley?' he asks. And off he goes with his strange words. That's our Timka for you!"

Samarin smiled. "Never mind," he said. "He doesn't know everything either . . . Cook, how do you make the dough for a sponge cake?"

"I don't know, Comrade Major General."

"Well, well. And what about a wheaten dough? What do you think works best with that? Yeast or baking soda? I'd like to know."

"I've never worked in the pastry section, Comrade Major General."

Everyone laughed.

After dinner, Samarin invited Olga Dmitrievna to sit down and have some tea with him. She slowly wiped her hands on her apron, whisked some dust off the stool and sat down at the table. She drank her tea from the saucer, wiping the beads of sweat from her wrinkled forehead.

"Help yourself to sugar," said Samarin. "But tell me – how's your grandson? Did he have another bad night?"

"His foot's still festering. He's in a bad way. He's worn himself out and now he's wearing all of us out."

"Cook, take the boy some jam."

"Yes, Comrade Major General."

"How's it going in Riakhovichi?" Olga Dmitrievna asked. "Are we still fighting?"

"You can say that again!" Samarin replied.

"No end to people's suffering," said Olga Dmitrievna, crossing herself.

"There's no-one left there," said the general. "The huts are all empty. And everyone's taken all their belongings with them. But tell me one thing, Olga Dmitrievna. Every hut I've been into, people have taken everything they own – but they've left their icons behind. They take junk you wouldn't touch with a bargepole. They leave their huts empty as empty can be. They even take down the newspapers they've stuck on the walls, but they don't take their icons. It's the same everywhere. I can see that you're someone who prays. Please, tell me what's going on. Are they leaving their God behind?"[89]

The old woman laughed. Quietly, so no-one else could hear, she said, "Who knows? Maybe he's up there, maybe he isn't. But we oldies, we go on praying. Bow ten times – maybe he'll hear."[90]

"Oh, Dmitrievna, Dmitrievna," Samarin replied with a chuckle. He then shook his finger admonishingly at a kitten as it jumped down from the stove.

Just then an orderly brought in a radio message from Bogariov – a detailed report of the destruction of the German tank column.

Liadov knew his general well. He knew that the prospect of visiting a particularly dangerous sector of the front always put him in a good mood; the tenser the situation, the cooler and calmer he would be. He also knew that this severe man had an unexpected soft spot. Knowing that cats are always faithful to their homes and that any abandoned hut was sure to harbour a cat or two, the general always kept some small pieces of bread in his pocket. He would enter a hut, call out to a hungry tom or to a mother of many kittens, squat down and start to feed them. Once he said to Liadov in a thoughtful tone, "Know why village cats won't play with a piece of white paper? They're simply not used to it. They'll always jump at dark paper – they think it's a mouse."

Liadov understood that, after the radio message and his conversation with Olga Dmitrievna, Samarin was once again in a good mood.

"Comrade Major General," he said, "allow me to report. Major Mertsalov has arrived."

Samarin frowned and, once again, wagged his finger at the kitten.

"What's that you're saying?"

"I'm reporting, Comrade Major General, that the commander of the 111th Infantry Regiment has now arrived."

"All right," Samarin replied. "Tell him to come in." Olga Dmitrievna began to get to her feet. "What are you doing?" said Samarin. "Please stay where you are and drink your tea. Make yourself comfortable!"

That morning, Mertsalov had set off along a back road. He had, in the end, joined up with his division, but the day had not gone well for him. Part of his artillery had got bogged down in the forest just as his tractors ran out of fuel. The transport column had lost its way, after its commander had been given the wrong route.

Later, they had had to fight off an attack by German sub-machine-gunners. Myshansky's company, bringing up the rear, should have fought its way through to the rest of the regiment. Instead, it had wavered. Along with its commander, who was afraid of exposing himself in open country, it had slipped off into the forest.

Samarin had asked Mertsalov one question: how much ammunition had he left Bogariov? He had then told Mertsalov to report again at seventeen hundred hours.

Mertsalov had expected this second conversation to be extremely brief and probably unpleasant. He was surprised and delighted when Samarin said, "I'm disappointed in you, but I shall give you the opportunity to make good your mistakes. You are to establish contact with Bogariov and agree on a joint plan of action to enable him to break through. You are to recover the abandoned guns and other ordnance. You may leave."

Mertsalov understood that he had been assigned an extremely difficult task. But he was not afraid of danger or difficulty. He was more afraid of the wrath of his intimidating superior. [91]

16

MASTER OF THIS LAND

Bogariov and what remained of his battalion spent the next two days in the forest. Their guns, camouflaged by branches, were trained on the road. Lieutenant Klenovkin, a tall young man with a habit of constantly glancing at his watch for no particular reason, was put in command of the reconnaissance detachment. He and most of his men were from the artillery; there were also three infantrymen: Ignatiev, Zhaveliov and Rodimtsev.

Bogariov sent for Klenovkin and said, "You're not only a scout. I'm also putting you in charge of food supplies. We'll soon be running out of bread." He added thoughtfully, "We've still got medicines, but what can we give the wounded to eat? They need a special diet. They need fruit kissel.[92] They need cranberry juice."

Wanting to test the men who were new to him, Klenovkin chose Rodimtsev and his infantry comrades for the first reconnaissance mission. He outlined their task, ending with the words, "And we also have to get some bread for the men, and provide the wounded with fruit kissel. The cook's already got the potato starch, but he needs some juice."

"Fruit kissel!" Zhaveliov exclaimed. "Comrade Lieutenant, we're in the middle of a forest and there are German tanks on the roads!"

Klenovkin smiled. He too had been surprised by Bogariov's instructions.

"Come on!" said Ignatiev. "Don't worry – we'll find something all right."

Ignatiev was eager to explore the forest. As always, he felt the call of the earth, of his eternal love for leaves, grasses and streams. He and his two comrades made their way past soldiers lying under the trees. One of them, who had a bandaged arm, looked up and said crossly to Ignatiev, "What do you think you're doing? Blundering about like a bear! Careful – or you'll give us away!"

And someone else asked in a whisper, "All sneaking off, are you? Going back home?"

The three men went on, deep into the forest. Rodimtsev kept repeating in bewilderment, "What's happened? I can't believe it! They stood up to two hundred German tanks. They weren't scared then – but now, after two days lying about in the forest . . . What's got into them all?"

"Simple enough," said Zhaveliov. "It's what happens to people when they've got nothing to do."

"No, I just don't understand. I just can't believe it."

After a while, they came to a track cut through the forest. For more than two hours they lay in a ditch beside it, observing the Germans. Dispatch riders passed by on motorcycles; one stopped very close to them, filled his pipe, lit it and rode on. Eighteen heavy tanks went by – and a great many trucks carrying infantry and equipment. The soldiers were mostly chatting away, their shirts unbuttoned at the neck as if they were hoping to get a suntan; in one truck they were singing. There were branches hanging low over the road and, from almost every truck, hands reached out to pick a few leaves.

Then the three men split up. Rodimtsev and Zhaveliov went through the forest to where the back road crossed the main highway, and Ignatiev crossed the back road and made his way along a ravine to the village where the Germans were encamped.

For a long time, he just stood in the tall hemp and watched. There were both tankmen and infantry, evidently resting after their recent advance. Some were bathing in the village pond or lying naked in the sun. Officers were dining in an orchard, sitting beneath a tree; they were drinking from metal tumblers that sparkled in the sunlight. After they had finished eating, one of them kept putting on the phonograph. Another played with a dog, while a third, sitting a little way off, was writing something or other. Some of the soldiers, sitting on the earth banks around the huts, were darning their clothes. Others had hung towels around their necks and were shaving, with safety razors. Still others were shaking apple trees or using long poles to knock down ripe pears from branches that were out of reach. And some were just lying on the grass, reading newspapers.

Everything he saw reminded Ignatiev of his own village. The forest was like the forest where he had so loved to wander, and the river was like the river where, as a boy, he had caught gudgeon and thin little roach. And as for the orchard where the officers were dining and listening to their phonograph, it could hardly have looked more like Marusya Pesochina's orchard. Yes, what glorious hours he and Marusya had spent in that orchard during warm summer nights! He remembered the apples' pale little faces gleaming against the dark leaves, and Marusya quietly sighing and laughing beside him. She had seemed like a little bird. These memories tugged at his heart strings.

A skinny young woman appeared on the threshold of a hut, barefoot and wearing a white kerchief. A German gestured to her and shouted a few words. The young woman went back inside, then came out with a mug of water.

Ignatiev's heart clenched tight, in pain, sorrow and rage. Never – neither during that night in the burning city, nor when he passed through devastated villages, nor in the midst of battle – had he experienced what he felt on this bright, cloudless day. The sight of these Germans quietly enjoying themselves in a Soviet village was more ghastly than any battle. He knew these oaks, aspens, birches and maples like he knew his own home – yet now he was creeping like a thief through the forest he loved, crouching low, speaking in a whisper, looking warily about him. In the past, he had walked through just such a forest and sung, at the top of his voice, the songs he had learned from sullen old Granny Bogachikha; he had lain on dry, rustling leaves and gazed at the sky; he had observed birds going about their busy little routines; he had examined moss-covered tree trunks; he had known the most likely spots for berries and mushrooms; he had known where foxes had their earths and which hollows in tree trunks were homes to squirrels; he had known the glades where hares liked to play in the twilight amid the tall grass. And now a German was lighting his pipe in the heart of this forest – and Ignatiev was watching him from his hiding place in an overgrown ditch. A black cable, laid by a German signaller, now passed between his beloved trees; in childish ignorance rowans and birches allowed their slender branches to support this cable – and German words sped down it through the Russian forest. Where there were no trees, the Germans brought along the bodies of young birches, stuck them in holes in the ground and nailed little signboards to them. And there the dead birches stood, their leaves small and yellow like copper coins, supporting that same vile cable.

It was then that Ignatiev truly understood, in his heart and soul, what was happening in his country: that his nation was fighting for its life, fighting to be able to breathe freely.

These contented German soldiers were a chilling sight. For a moment Ignatiev imagined that the war was over. And just as today, the Germans were swimming, listening to nightingales, wandering through forest glades, picking raspberries and blackberries, gathering baskets of mushrooms, playing music under apple trees and drinking tea in village huts, with young women at their beck and call. At that moment Ignatiev, who had survived long battles, who had more than once crouched in a foxhole while German tanks passed over his head, who had tramped thousands of kilometres in the stifling dust of roads close to the front, who had looked death in the face day after day and stepped forward to meet it – at that moment Ignatiev understood with every fibre of his being the need to keep fighting until every last German had been driven from Soviet soil. Blazing towns and villages, the thunder of exploding bombs, battles high in the sky – all these seemed almost sweet in comparison with the sight of these Fascists quietly enjoying themselves in an occupied Ukrainian village. Their complacent quiet was terrifying. Ignatiev involuntarily patted the butt of his sub-machine gun and touched his hand grenade to remind himself of his strength and his readiness to fight. He, a Red Army soldier, was committed heart and soul to this war.[93]

This present war was a far cry from the 1914 war that his elder brother had told him about, a war that the rank-and-file soldiers had cursed and that had not mattered in any way to the Russian people.

Watching the Germans at rest in the deceptive midday silence of this sunny day, Ignatiev understood all this very well.

"Yes, the commissar was right when he told me I must never forget that night," he thought, remembering Bogariov's words in the blazing city.

Ignatiev made his way back to the agreed meeting place. His two comrades were already there.

"How are things on the highway?" he asked.

"One transport after another," Zhaveliov said wearily. "Carts, carts and more carts, all full of cackling chickens and geese. And they're making off with our cattle too."

Zhaveliov was looking upset, without his usual mischievous, sometimes mocking grin. It seemed that he too felt anguished and enraged.

"Well," said Rodimtsev, "should we be getting back now?"

Rodimtsev was calm as ever – just as when they were waiting for the German tanks to attack, just as when he had slowly and carefully divided up the bread rations before dinner.

"We need to capture a tongue,"[94] Zhaveliov said.

"Yes," said Ignatiev, brightening up. "And I think I know how we can do it." And he went on to outline a simple plan.

What Ignatiev wanted, above all, was to work. He felt he should be fighting day and night, that he could not afford to waste a single minute. No-one in his home village, after all, had been a better hand with a scythe, and he had been admired by the Tula gunsmiths not only for his skill but also for his indomitable working energy.

The three men reported to Klenovkin. Klenovkin told Ignatiev to report to Bogariov, whom he found sitting beneath a tree.

"So, Comrade Ignatiev," he said with a smile. "How's your guitar? Still in one piece?"

"It certainly is, Comrade Commissar!" he replied. "I played and sang to the others only yesterday – but the men are in a bad way, you know. They hardly dare talk now, they only whisper." Looking Bogariov in the eye, he went on, "Comrade Commissar, allow me to do some real work, something to make the sparks fly. I can't bear to see Germans winding up their gramophones in our villages and driving through our forests."

"There's plenty that needs doing," said Bogariov. "More than enough. First, we need bread. Second, the right food for the wounded. And we need to capture a tongue. Yes, there's more than enough to be getting on with."

"Comrade Commissar," said Ignatiev, "give me five men. With five men, I could do all of that before nightfall."

"Truly?" asked Bogariov. "You're not just bragging?"

"You'll see soon enough."

"You'll be in hot water if you fail."

"Understood, Comrade Commissar."

Bogariov ordered Klenovkin to provide five volunteers. Fifteen minutes later they all set off into the forest, towards the road.

Their first task was quickly completed. Ignatiev had already noticed several glades that were red with berries.

"Come on, my girls," he shouted. "Fill your pinnies with berries! Squat down and get picking!"

And then he told one funny story after another, until the men were all splitting their sides.

"Some berries," said Rodimtsev. "There for the asking!"

"Blueberries, blackberries and raspberries all separate, with leaves in between them," Ignatiev ordered.

Within forty minutes their mess tins and helmets were filled to the brim.

"So, all very simple," Ignatiev explained enthusiastically. "We boil the blueberries for men with stomach pains, and the raspberries for those with a fever. As for the blackberries, they give a slightly sour juice, a bit like kvas.[95] The wounded are always wanting something to drink."

And he set to work, quickly and deftly squeezing the juice from the berries. To keep the juice clear, he strained it through two layers of gauze from his first-aid kit. Soon there were several cans of clear, thick liquid. This even attracted an ordinary housefly. Ignatiev took the cans to the hut where the wounded were lying; he could hear them moaning. The old doctor looked at Ignatiev's contribution, sobbed, wiped away a tear and said, "The men could go to the grandest hospital – and they'd be lucky to get anything as good as this. You've saved more than one life, comrade soldier – but I don't know your name."

Not knowing what to say, Ignatiev shrugged, grinned sheepishly and went back to his comrades. Things seemed to be going his way.

A soldier sent to watch the forest track reported that a German truck had stalled there. Most likely, there was a serious problem with the engine. The Germans had talked for a long time. Then another truck had come by and all of them, including the driver, had left.

"What's inside this truck?" asked Ignatiev.

"No idea. Everything's covered up by their smart tarpaulins."

"You didn't look underneath?"

"What do you mean? There were trucks zipping by every minute!"

"You and your zipping!" said Ignatiev. "A brave little bird you are!"

"All right, Mister Eagle!" the soldier replied crossly.

Ignatiev went over to the truck and called out, "Come on, lads, this way!"

The men gathered around him, all eyes on his cheerful face. Ignatiev was the master of this forest – he and he alone. No-one could have challenged him. His voice was loud and confident, as if he were in his own home, and there was laughter in his bright eyes.

"Quick!" he shouted. "Hold the tarpaulin by the corners and don't let go. The Germans have brought us some bread. They must have been in a hurry, doing their best to get it to us fresh and warm. They even wrecked their poor truck!"

He began throwing loaf after loaf into the spread tarpaulin, keeping up a running commentary, "Fritz burned that one, he's not used to a field oven, we'll have to fine him. But this one's good – Hans really did his darndest. This one's a little overdone – Herman may have dozed off for a moment. But this one's splendid, best of the lot. Must have been baked by Adolf himself."

Ignatiev's tanned forehead was beaded with sweat, and the sun, flickering through the trees, cast mottled shadows on his face, on the loaves flying through the air, on the black sides of the German truck and on the green grass of the track. Ignatiev unbent, spat, stretched to his full height, wiped his forehead and looked around at the trees, the sky and the road.

"Like pitching hay," he said, "and I'm the foreman." And then, "Now, boys, take all this bread a few hundred metres away from the road, hide it in the bushes and come back here again!"

"You out of your mind?" one of them shouted. "They'll be back any moment. You should hide in the bushes yourself!"

"Hide?" he replied. "This forest's my home, I'm the master. And masters don't hide."

And there he remained, standing tall in the truck. Thrushes and jays called out in the trees above him, praising his daring, his good cheer and his kindness. He crumbled up a piece of the bread and threw it to them. He hummed to himself a little. All the time, though, he kept a keen watch on the road. It was a straight road, and he could see a good kilometre in each direction. After a while, he went quiet. He was now listening intently, knitting his brow, wondering whether he could hear the sound of an engine. Then he saw a cloud of dust in the distance: a motorcycle.

"Run and hide?" he said to himself. "No, you're the master."

Someone would be coming soon to tow away or repair the truck – but not on a motorcycle. Ignatiev checked his grenade, gripped it firmly and lay down in the hollow left by the loaves he had removed. The motorcyclist sped past without even slowing down.

It took the six of them an hour to fully unload the truck. Then Ignatiev glanced into the driver's cab and took a bottle of cognac from the door pocket. Most of it had already been drunk, but he slipped it into his trouser pocket anyway. And as the men were carrying away the last load of bread, they heard another engine.

Ignatiev lay down in the bushes, eager to see what would happen next. A jeep approached, slowed down, turned around and stopped by the empty truck.

Clenching his teeth to keep from laughing, Ignatiev watched the ensuing performance. He could not understand a word of the Germans' angry yells, but their movements and facial expressions said it all. First, they looked in the ditch and under the truck. Then the sergeant shouted at the corporal while the latter stood stiffly to attention, heels pressed tightly together and fingers pointing down the seams of his trousers. To Ignatiev it could hardly have been clearer: the sergeant was shouting, "You son of a bitch, why didn't you leave anyone on guard? What's there to be scared of?" Gesturing at the dense forest, the corporal was replying, "My men are an obstinate lot. How could I make them stand guard in a place like this?" To which the sergeant snapped out, "You should have stood guard yourself, you blockhead. For this, I'll dock your rations and lock every one of you in the guardroom." "Understood, Sergeant Major," said the corporal. Next it was the corporal's turn to lay into the driver. His bluster was equally easy to interpret: "Finished off that bottle, did you? No wonder we broke down in the middle of the forest!" And after the sergeant had disappeared to answer a call of nature, the driver answered back, "Heavens, why make such a song and dance about it! So what if I helped myself to a few swigs!"

Even the thrushes were hopping about on the branches and laughing. Then one of the soldiers found a cigarette end close to the truck and showed it to the sergeant. Ignatiev guessed that the sergeant was looking at the Russian letters on the remaining scrap of charred newspaper. "Russian soldiers!" he must have yelled. This seemed to panic the Germans. They drew their pistols – some even unslung sub-machine guns – and fired randomly into the trees; leaves and twigs showered onto the road. Ignatiev crawled off into the bushes where the others were hiding. He laughed as he told them his story, then took the cognac out of his pocket and said, "Only a thimbleful left. Not enough for all six of us. Seems I'll have to drink it myself!"

With his usual calm, Rodimtsev unscrewed the top of his water flask and said, "All right – and this can be your glass. You won't catch *me* touching anything German."

And before evening, Ignatiev brought Bogariov a tongue. He had captured this German in the simplest of ways: he severed a German telephone cable, dragged one end some distance along the track and lay in ambush with his comrades. An hour later, two German signallers came to look for the break in the cable. Ignatiev and his men leaped out from the trees. One of the Germans tried to escape, so they had to shoot him. But the other froze in shock, and they took him prisoner.

"It's easy enough to deal with them here in the forest, Comrade Commissar," Ignatiev said with brisk cheerfulness. "A wire across the road will bring down a motorcyclist. As for infantry, all you need do is tether a few chickens to a tree. When they start clucking, every German within earshot will come running."

"Good thinking!" Bogariov replied with a smile. "Yes," he then said to himself, "in a partisan war, here in these forests, our men are formidable."

Soon after this, Rumiantsev lined up his men and read out a brief commendation, thanking Ignatiev for his work. Ignatiev stepped forward out of the twilight to reply, "I serve the Soviet Union, Comrade Captain!"[96]

★

Mertsalov found it painful to recall his ill-starred retreat. The short march had felt like a panicked flight rather than an orderly withdrawal. Mertsalov had been overwhelmed by a humiliating sense of impotence. The sight of Myshansky's company had been especially dispiriting. Heads bowed, the men had shuffled wearily along. They had looked crushed; some had not even been carrying weapons. Every loud sound had alarmed them and they kept glancing up at the sky, scattering when anyone glimpsed a plane, no matter how far away. Myshansky had forbidden his men to open fire on German planes and ordered them not to walk on the road itself but to keep whenever possible under cover of trees or bushes. All in all, his company had been nothing more than a disorderly mob.

There was nothing Mertsalov hadn't got wrong. He should have given his commanders precise, detailed instructions; he shouldn't have left anything to their discretion. Sensing their commanders' uncertainty, the men had forgotten all discipline.[97] Some of the peasants from around Chernigov had simply abandoned their weapons during the night and slipped off to their home villages. Mertsalov ordered them to be arrested, but no-one had been able to catch them.[98]

In the afternoon, Mertsalov's advance units had reached open country. Five or six kilometres away they could see another patch of forest – and beyond it lay the river. This had cheered the men. Once they had crossed, they would join up with our main forces; their dangerous march behind German lines was nearly over. Sensing that they were not far from water, the horses whinnied; the drivers no longer needed to keep urging them forward. But as the regiment moved on – as the countless boots, worn-out tyres, squeaking cartwheels and broad road-tractor caterpillars raised long clouds of dust – a German reconnaissance aircraft appeared above them. It circled once over the dust cloud, then flew off. Realizing that they would soon be under attack, and expecting this to come from the air, Mertsalov had moved the trucks with turret machineguns to the head and tail of the column and given strict orders for the carts and trucks to keep at least twenty metres apart.

Certain that enemy bombers were about to appear, he had said sourly to Kudakov, "Just look at Myshansky's company – all standing tall now, heads high as they gaze up at the sky! Even Myshansky looks proud as an eagle. A far cry from how he was back in the forest. Then he looked like a seventy-year-old, shuffling along with his head bowed."

Reaching the crest of a hill, Mertsalov surveyed the expanse of sky and earth spread out before him. Now and then, the unharvested wheat rustled, swayed and bent in the wind. The golden ears would bow to the ground, revealing the stalks' pale bodies, and the whole field would change colour, from gold to pale green. It was as if a deathly pallor had spread over the wheat, as if the life blood were draining from its face, as if the field were in shock, appalled by the Soviet retreat. The field rustled, pleaded, turned pale, bowed to the ground – and then rose up again, in all its bronzed beauty. Mertsalov gazed at the field, at the women's shawls he glimpsed here and there, at some distant windmills, and at the white huts of a distant village.

He looked at the sky – the washed-out, milky-blue, hot summer sky he had known since childhood. Pale clouds were drifting across it, so thin and transparent that the sky shone through them. This vast field and still vaster, sultry sky were crying out in anguish, begging for help from the troops stirring up the dust on the road. And the clouds continued their journey from west to east, as if someone invisible were driving a huge flock of white sheep across this Russian sky now under the sway of the Germans.

The clouds were moving the same way as the Russian troops and their shroud of dust, hurrying towards a place where they would not be slashed by the sharp iron wing of a German plane. And the wheat went on rustling, bowing down at the soldiers' feet, pleading without knowing what it should plead for.

"Enough to make you weep!" said Mertsalov. "Enough to make you weep salt blood!"

A barefoot old woman with a half-empty knapsack on her bent back and a round-eyed boy walking beside her watched the retreating army in silence. There was unspeakable reproach in their sad, frozen eyes. The old woman had a look of childish helplessness, while the little boy looked old and weary. So they stood, alone in the vast space.

It was a cruel day, a day Mertsalov would never forget. He had been expecting to be attacked from the air – and the German sub-machine-gunners had caught him off guard. In a short battle, he had lost not only his transport column but also the whole of Myshansky's company.

The regiment reached the river just before evening. Their difficult march was over. But this brought little joy to Mertsalov.

The chief of staff handed him a report from the political instructor of the second company. A Red Army soldier had deserted, slipping off into the forest and telling his comrades that he intended to wait out these hard times with a young widow who lived in a hamlet they'd passed through. Mertsalov ordered the sergeant major to go back immediately in a small truck to pick up this deserter. He was brought to the regimental command post at night, in peasant clothes and bast sandals – he had drowned his uniform, tying a stone to it and throwing it into a pond. Mertsalov overheard some of the other men speaking to him.

"Drowned your side cap and its red star, did you?" asked the number one of a machine-gun crew.

"Uh-huh," the deserter grunted morosely.

"And your rifle into the bargain?" asked the number two of the same gun crew.

"Wouldn't be much use to me in that hamlet."

"What he drowned in that pond was his soul," said Glushkov, a tall, sullen man whose brother had been killed during the initial German tank attack. "He tied a brick to his soul and sent it to the bottom."

"Why'd I want to do that?" the deserter asked in a hurt voice. And he began scratching his leg.

The sergeant major said with a smirk, "Him and his young widow were already in bed. All neat and proper, good bedding, two empty vodka bottles on the table, two glasses. They'd been eating roast pork."

"Damned hussy. Should have arrested her too. Could have shot them together."

"Or trampled them to death!" said a thin soldier with a haggard face and sick, feverish eyes.

Mertsalov walked over to the deserter. He remembered the whole bitter day – the wheat fields, the sky, the old woman and the little boy with the reproachful eyes – and for the first time in his life he pronounced the grim, weighty words, "Execution before the regiment."

That night Mertsalov did not sleep. "No, I won't yield or waver," he was thinking. "I've got the strength for this war. I've got what it takes."

17

THE COMMISSAR

In the morning Myshansky appeared at Bogariov's forest command post.

"Good morning, Comrade Commissar," he said cheerily. "Seems we meet again!"

Myshansky's men were unshaven, their tunics were in tatters, and some were not carrying weapons.[99] Myshansky looked little better; he had torn off the hook and top buttons of his tunic and unstitched the badges of rank from his collar. He was carrying neither map case nor dispatch case; evidently, he had discarded them so as not to look like a commander. He had even removed his revolver from its holster and stuffed it into a trouser pocket.

Sitting down beside Bogariov, he said quietly, "No doubt about it, Comrade Commissar, we've blundered into a classic encirclement. The only correct course of action, in my view, is to disperse and allow every man to find his own way across the front line."

At these words, Bogariov felt the blood drain from his face; it was as if his cheeks had turned cold, white with rage.

"What's got into your men?" he asked with apparent calm. "Why are they so badly turned out?"

"Why do you think?" Myshansky replied with a shrug. "We're not a company of heroes. We stopped for the night in a forest glade. When the Germans sent up their flares, the men all dropped to the ground as if they were under a hurricane of fire."

Bogariov stood up, shifting his weight heavily from one foot to the other. Myshansky remained as he was, sitting on the grass. Unaware that Bogariov's face was contorted with rage, he went on, "You haven't got a smoke, have you, Comrade Commissar? And yes, I think it has to be every man for himself. There's no other way. We'll never break through en masse."

"Stand!" ordered Bogariov.

"What?" asked Myshansky.

"Stand!" Bogariov repeated, in a loud, authoritative voice.

Myshansky looked at Bogariov's face and jumped to his feet.

"Stand to attention!" Bogariov bellowed. Looking at Myshansky with real hatred, he went on, "What do you think you look like? Is this how you report to a senior commander? Get yourself and your men into presentable shape straightaway. Not one unshaven soldier. Not a single torn shirt. Badges of rank on your collar tabs. In twenty minutes, form up your company and report to me, commander of a regular unit of the Red Army operating behind enemy lines, to whom you are now subordinate."[100]

"Understood, Comrade Battalion Commissar!" Myshansky replied. Still failing to grasp that this was no joking matter, he continued, with a smile, "Only where can I find badges? We're surrounded, in a forest. Do you want me to sew acorns to my collar tabs?"

Bogariov glanced at his watch and said slowly, "Within twenty minutes, if my orders have not been carried out, you will be shot before your company, beneath this tree."

Only then did Myshansky sense the commissar's unbending

strength. Meanwhile, Bogariov's scouts and gunners were questioning Myshansky's men.

"You with the whiskers!" Morozov the famed gun-layer called out to one of them. "How old are you?"

"I was born in 1912," the man replied in a whisper. Raising a finger to his lips, he said pleadingly, "You over there, don't laugh so loud."

"What's the matter, old man?" asked Ignatiev, speaking especially loudly.

"Quiet!" the man replied in a pained voice. "Can't you hear?"

"Hear what?" asked the gunners and scouts, genuinely curious.

"There are Germans all around. Can't you hear them talking?"

Bogariov's men looked at one another in surprise. Ignatiev laughed loudly. Several of Myshansky's men hissed at him to keep quiet.

"What's got into you all!" Ignatiev replied. "It's not Germans – it's crows! Caw, caw, caw – it's the way crows talk!" A burst of laughter spread through the forest. The gunners laughed, the foot soldiers laughed, and the scouts laughed. The wounded laughed, even though they were groaning in pain. Even the newcomers laughed, shaking their heads in embarrassment and spitting on the ground. Just then, they were joined by Myshansky.

"Look lively now!" he shouted. "You have fifteen minutes to shave and get yourselves in order. Comrade platoon commanders and sergeants, replace your badges of rank and draw up your men."

He grabbed his knapsack and ran quickly towards the stream.

Bogariov paced about under the trees, mulling over Myshansky's words. "'We're not a company of heroes,' he says. Maybe he's right, but what of it? If we've got no heroes, we'll have to create them."[101]

The company formed up. Captain Rumiantsev walked slowly through the ranks, scrutinizing rifles and uniforms and seizing on even the most trifling of faults.

"Tighten that belt!" he snapped. Or, in a more preoccupied tone, "Call that a proper shave? No, you need to think when you're shaving – not just do it any old how! And you – what the hell have you done with your rifle? You haven't cleaned it at all. I don't believe it. How can a Red Army soldier take so little care of his rifle?"

Anyone would have thought that this meticulous inspection was taking place in a military academy, in rehearsal for some important parade – not in a forest behind German lines. Rumiantsev, however, was simply carrying out Bogariov's instructions. As for Bogariov, he was watching from a distance. And just as Rumiantsev reached Myshansky and was criticizing him for failing to line up his men in the correct order, according to height, Bogariov stepped forward. "Stand to attention!" Myshansky shouted. He then reported to Bogariov in a loud, clear voice.

Bogariov passed along the ranks, addressing the men directly. He spoke simply and truthfully, without raising his voice, and the men took in every word. He spoke about the hardships of the war, about the bitterness of the retreat and the suddenness of the German invasion. Keeping nothing back, he spoke of the dangers and complexities of their present position behind German lines. He spoke about the German Panzers and the roads that had been cut. He gave them his assessment of the German forces in the area. He talked about the life and death battle the Russian people was now fighting.

"What else can we do, comrades?" he ended. "You are all adult sons of your people. You have been through the stern school of labour and this People's War. Our position is difficult, but we have no choice. We are a regular unit of the Red Army. In two or three days' time we shall engage with superior enemy forces. We will strike hard, break through their lines and rejoin our division. You must win, comrades, and you will win. Within you beats the heart of Lenin."[102]

And the men listened, standing tall and calm, looking at their commissar with the wise eyes of men who know what's what and don't need to be taught anything.

In those difficult days, people wanted only the truth, however difficult and cheerless it might be. And Bogariov told them this truth. A cold wind, harbinger of autumn, sounded high in the trees. And after the sultry heat, after the black thunderstorms of summer nights, after stifling afternoons and evenings filled with the buzz of mosquitoes – after all this, there was something infinitely pleasing about this wind from the north, with its reminder of snows and blizzards to come. The wind said that the suffocating summer was coming to an end and that a new time was approaching. Everyone could feel this change; it was linked both to the commissar's words and to the November-like gusts in the oak trees.

That night Bogariov did not feel like sleeping. He walked to a sandy hillock, lay down among the tall pines, covering himself with his greatcoat, and looked up above him. The moon was moving slowly across the indigo of the sky, between the black tree trunks. There in the forest, the moon's smooth, even movement was unusually easy to observe. The moon was nearly full, and broader than even the thickest pines; as its yellow rim disappeared from one side of a tree, so it lengthened and filled out on the other side. Bogariov was smoking and in the moonlight the transparent smoke of his cigarette was like glass. The sky seemed spacious and empty – the bright moon had extinguished the stars. Spreading over the deciduous trees lower down the slope was a grey-blue mist, thin as the smoke he was puffing out. And beneath the pines, as if thousands of ants were labouring through the night, there was a continual rustle – dewdrops falling to the ground from the slippery pine needles. Dew was constantly flowing down the grooves in the needles and collecting on their tips, forming what seemed like small, gleaming, swiftly ripening berries.

The night was so beautiful that it filled Bogariov with sadness. The sound of the falling dew, the moon sailing across the sky, the pines' ethereal shadows moving silently over the earth – all testified to the wise beauty of a world deep in thought.

"Might this war be the last war of all?" Bogariov wondered. He passionately wanted to do all he could for the world, so that all its nights and days would be as beautiful as this present night.[103]

But the world was quaking from the blows struck by the war. The war crept beneath the ploughed land; it slid underwater, and it climbed ten thousand metres into the sky. It raged in field and forest, over rivers and cities, and over quiet ponds carpeted with duckweed; it knew neither day nor night. And Bogariov had the thought that, were Hitler to win this war, the sun and stars would cease to exist for the world. Never again would there be such a night.

Just then Bogariov caught sight of someone sitting in a moonlit clearing. He called out to the man. It was Ignatiev.

"What are you doing here, Comrade Ignatiev?" he asked.

"I can't sleep, Comrade Commissar. Some night!"

Bogariov liked this strong, cheerful young man. And he was aware of Ignatiev's influence over the other soldiers. He had heard them repeating his jokes to one another and talking about his shrewd, merry courage. Ignatiev was seldom alone. Wherever he chose to sit, others would soon gather around him.

"What are you thinking, Comrade Ignatiev?" he asked.

"I was thinking about Sedov. He was my friend. I feel sorry for him. There were nights like this at the very beginning of the war. Once he said to me, 'What a night, Ignatiev – but how much longer I have in this world, there's no knowing.' And now he's gone."

"And Babadjanian's gone," said Bogariov. He sighed.

Bogariov went on talking, from the heart. And Ignatiev, who thought he had nothing to learn from anyone else and did not like being lectured or instructed, listened with interest.

Usually, Ignatiev was not the listener but the speaker – and he had a way of holding people's attention. He knew a great many stories of all kinds – true stories, odd memories, comic anecdotes – that he had first heard from veteran soldiers or old men and women in the villages. He had a kind of passion for collecting these seemingly simple-minded tales and he found it easy to remember them. He also had a vivid imagination; he would reshape what he'd heard and tell his comrades funny, sly, sometimes frightening stories about a Red Army soldier whom Hitler had taken it into his head to do battle with.

This night in the forest, however, was different. It was Bogariov who spoke and Ignatiev who listened. And Bogariov's words would stay in his memory.

"It's true, Comrade Commissar," he said, when Bogariov had finished. "I feel I've become a different man in this war. It's the same wherever we go. Each little stream, each bit of woodland – they make me so sad it breaks my heart. Our people never had an easy life, but their burdens were at least their own burdens. The land was our own land and the factories our own factories. It wasn't an easy life, but it was our own. How can we just give that land away? These weeks have set me thinking. When I was first called up, the war didn't seem that important to me. I didn't believe it really mattered. But now everything around me makes my blood boil. Just now it was a tree that upset me. Rustling, shaking, trembling. It was like something was tearing at my insides. 'No,' I thought. 'Surely we can't just hand you over to the Germans?' 'No,' I keep saying, 'we can't let that happen.' My mate Rodimtsev puts it well, 'Whatever the cost, we must stand firm. It's our own land that we're fighting for.' And he's right. We've been through a great deal. There are times we've gone without food. But this is our life. And it's the only life I have."

The moonlight faded; a dark veil covered the sky. Soon it started to rain – and this rain was like cold dust.

Bogariov turned up the collar of his greatcoat, coughed and said in his usual calm, rather quiet voice, "Comrade Ignatiev, we've been ordered to destroy a German transport. A new detachment is being formed for this mission. We're detailing all the least reliable of Myshansky's men. They need to be trained up a little and we must boost their morale. You are to join this detachment. Your role is to help them to grasp that the Germans are not invincible."

"Understood, Comrade Commissar," Ignatiev replied.

"And so our moonlit night comes to an end," Bogariov was

thinking. And, as he walked away, Ignatiev was thinking exactly the same.

Shortly after this, Bogariov woke Myshansky and said, "You're to set off in an hour's time. Your detachment's mission is to destroy a German transport column."

"Who should I report to for my operations directive?" Myshansky replied.

"The directive was issued to Lieutenant Klenovkin, the detachment's commander. You will be taking part as a foot soldier, with a rifle. From today, you are no longer in command of the company."

"Comrade Commissar," said Myshansky, "please allow me to explain—"

"Now, a word of warning," Bogariov interrupted. "Don't be afraid of the Germans – be afraid of showing weakness or lack of resolve. That's it. Remember – there will be no more explaining."

18

LIONYA

It was more than five days since Lionya Cherednichenko and Vasily Karpovich the cowherd had left Marchikhina Buda; all this time, they had been walking through occupied territory. The boy was very tired and his feet were bleeding. "Why's all this blood coming from my foot?" he once asked. "We've been walking on soft ground all the way." They had been eating quite well; the women in the villages they passed through had been giving them plenty of milk, bread and salt pork. Nevertheless, there was no getting away from the Germans. They had stopped the previous night in a hut belonging to a woman who had two daughters. The girls were in their last year at school; they had studied algebra and geometry, and they knew a little French. Their mother had dressed them in old rags; she had smeared dirt on their hands and faces and was making sure that their hair remained unkempt and matted. All this, of course, was because the girls were good-looking and the mother was afraid that the Germans would molest them. As for the two girls, they just kept looking in the mirror and laughing. They still believed that in a day or two this crazy, terrible life would come to an end, that they would no longer be sent out to work and that the village elder would return the geometry, physics and French-language textbooks that the

German commandant had ordered to be confiscated from them.

They had, admittedly, heard all kinds of rumours – that many young women were being marched away to distant work camps, that the most beautiful of them somehow disappeared without trace, that men and women were being kept apart in the camps and that weddings had been banned in all Ukrainian villages. Deep down, however, the two girls did not believe any of this. It was impossible; it was simply too crazy. They were, after all, preparing to go to Glukhov in the autumn, to study at the teacher-training college. They did a lot of reading; they could solve quadratic equations with two unknowns; they knew that the sun was a star which was already cooling, and that its surface temperature is about 6,000 degrees centigrade. They had studied *Anna Karenina* and written essays on such subjects as "Lermontov's Lyric Poems" and "A Character Study of Tatiana Larina".[104] Their older brother was on the staff of the Pasteur Institute in Leningrad; he supervised the work of graduate students.[105] Their late father had been a collective-farm foreman and a crop breeder; he had been the head of a field laboratory-hut and had corresponded with Academician Lysenko in Moscow.[106] And so the two girls had looked at their rags, laughed, and tried to console their mother: "Don't cry, Mama, this can't go on much longer. It'll be the same with Hitler as it was with Napoleon."

On learning that Lionya was in his third year at a school in Kiev, they set him a little test – a few long division and multiplication problems. All this was discussed in whispers and the girls kept looking out of the windows – with Germans in the village, it appeared that children were not supposed to study arithmetic. And one of the two girls, brown-eyed Pasha, took the piece of paper on which Lionya had noted down the problems, tore it into shreds and threw the shreds into the stove.

The girls spread out some bedding for Lionya and he lay down on the floor. For all his exhaustion, however, he could not get to sleep. Talking about his school had disturbed him. It had brought back memories of Kiev and the room where he kept his toys. He remembered how his father had taught him chess. Sometimes they'd played a game or two in the evening. Lionya used to imitate his father, frowning, wrinkling his nose and stroking his chin. And his father would laugh and say, "Checkmate!" And there were other memories too: a burning village, a murdered girl they'd seen in a field, a gallows in the main square of a shtetl, the drone of aeroplanes. These different memories clashed and interfered with one another. One moment it seemed that there had never been any school, or schoolfriends, or matinées at the main Kiev cinema; the next moment his father was about to come over to his bed and stroke his hair – and a sense of peace and happiness would suffuse the whole of his tired little body.

Lionya understood that his father was a great man; with a child's unerring instinct he sensed his moral strength. He was aware of the respect in which his father was held by his army comrades; he had noticed how, when they were sitting around a table together, the sound of his father's slow, calm voice was enough to make everyone fall silent and turn their heads towards him. And this helpless eleven-year-old, plodding through burning villages packed with advancing German troops, did not succumb to doubt for even a moment; to Lionya, his father remained as strong and wise as during the days of peace. And whether he was walking through open country or falling asleep in the forest or in a hayloft, he knew that his father was searching for him and would come to meet him.

Slowly Lionya dozed off, still half hearing the quiet voice of Vasily Karpovich. "We've passed through forty villages," the cowherd was saying to the mistress of the hut. "And I can tell you I've seen more than enough of this *new order*. To think that there were people who imagined the Germans would bring true order and good to our land. In one village, they made a list of all the families with cows and sent soldiers round twice a day to collect the milk. As if the cows belonged to the Germans – not to the collective farm. And in another village, the men were all ordered to hand over their boots. Everyone, it seemed, was to go barefoot. *Elders* have been appointed in every village. And these *elders* torment and oppress the people, but they don't get much sleep at night – they're as scared of the Germans as anyone else. No-one knows which way to turn. Whatever you do – the Germans say it's wrong. And then you do the opposite – and that's wrong too. And as for our land being returned to us . . . 'No,' say the Germans. 'You must be joking.' I haven't heard a single cock crow – not in any of the villages I've passed through. The Germans have wrung the necks of every last one of them.

"One old man was shot – he kept going up onto the roof, looking east to see if our soldiers were coming. And so he was shot. Seems we're not meant to look east. The Germans have put up little signs – but no-one knows what's written on them. There are arrows pointing all over the place, but no-one knows why. And our women say they have to keep the stoves going day and night – baking and roasting, baking and roasting. And the Germans keep babbling away – babbling their strange babble.

Our women never know what they're being ordered to do and it drives them quite crazy. And the Germans don't know shame – they walk about the hut stark naked, in front of old women. Not even the cats can put up with it – there's no keeping them in the huts. No-one's ever seen such a thing. Usually, nothing in the world will drive a cat from its home – neither fire nor water. But now they slip out of their own accord. They hide in the kitchen gardens. No, it's not what I call order – it's death. Everyone's afraid; brothers are afraid to look at brothers.

"In one village they summoned all the men and explained in perfect Ukrainian, 'Whoever oppressed you – Russian or Jew – that man is an enemy of Ukraine.' The old men kept their mouths shut, but on their way back to their huts, they were saying, 'Yes, we've heard that one before. *The whole world's cheated and swindled you – and now we Germans have come to do you good. A likely story!'*

"And in one village they rounded up all the men to build a toilet for a general. They marched them forty *versts*[107] to fetch bricks, so everything would be just so. One old man said to me, 'They can strangle me if they like, but you won't catch me doing work like that again.' And everyone talks in whispers. They're scared to look one another in the eye. No-one dares speak their heart. The Germans treat us like cattle. They register everyone, then they re-register them. Then they grade them and herd them along goodness knows where. Soon they'll be branding them and hanging numbers round their necks."

Lionya woke with a start and said, "Uncle, we must go on our way."

There was no answer. Lionya looked quickly around the hut.

There was no sign of Vasily Karpovich, but his knapsack was still lying on the bench.

"Where's Uncle?" he asked.

The mistress of the hut was sitting by the window, watching her sleeping daughters. Tears were flowing down her cheeks.

"They took him away, the fiends, they took him away in the night," she replied. "First him – and next it will be my daughters. We're lost. Lost, lost, lost."

Lionya leaped to his feet.

"Who took him away?" He was sobbing. "And where have they taken him?"

"It was the Germans," the woman replied. "Who else? And may their eyes fall out of their sockets. May cholera choke every one of them. May their arms and legs wither. May they never live to see their children again." And then, more quietly, "Don't cry, my son. We won't drive you away. Stay here with us – you'll be one of the family."

"I don't want to stay," said Lionya.

"Where else will you go?"

"I'll go and join my papa."

"Wait a bit longer. The samovar will boil soon. Have a bite to eat with us. Then we can talk things over."

Lionya suddenly felt afraid that this woman would not let him go. He got to his feet and walked quietly towards the door.

"Where are you going?"

"I'll be back in a moment." Lionya went out into the yard, glanced round at the door and broke into a run.

He ran down the village street, past black seven-ton trucks, their sides as high as the thatched roofs of the huts; past a field kitchen where the cook was lighting a fire; past ashen-faced prisoners-of-war, sitting in filthy, bloodstained underwear, without any boots, behind the wattle fence of the collective-farm stables. He ran past signs bearing yellow arrows, along with numbers and black Gothic letters. His head was a whirl of confusion; he thought he was running away from the old woman and her daughters, who were helping him solve arithmetic problems. The woman was going to heat the samovar and make him drink tea from morning till night, locked up in a boring hut.

He ran as far as the windmill, then stopped. He had come to a fork in the road. There were two yellow arrows: one pointing back towards the village, the other down a broad road battered by truck wheels and tank tracks. Lionya, however, set off along a narrow track ignored by the Germans' arrows; it led through fields towards the distant blur of a forest. It must have been months since anyone had last used this track, but there were deep ruts in the hard, dry clay. Probably someone had driven along it during the spring.

An hour later Lionya reached the edge of the forest. He was hungry and thirsty, and dazed by the fierce sun. In the forest, he was gripped by fear; he imagined that the Germans were watching him from behind trees or creeping out from bushes. Then he thought he could see wolves and wild black boars from the zoo, with long fangs and raised upper lips. He wanted to shout, to call out for help, but he was afraid of giving himself away and so he walked on in silence. Sometimes he felt overwhelmed, his fear and despair so acute that he screamed and took to his heels. He would keep on running, not even trying to make out the path, until he was out of breath. Then he would sit down, have a short rest and walk on further. And there were moments when he was filled with joyful confidence, when he felt that his father was there in the forest, striding calmly along, looking intently around him and drawing closer and closer all the time.

He came to a glade with lots of berries and began to pick them. Then he remembered reading about bears who like to wander about picking raspberries – and he hurried back into the trees.

Suddenly he caught sight of someone not far away. He stopped, pressed himself against a thick tree trunk, and watched. The man had a rifle and he was looking towards where Lionya was hiding – he must have heard something. Lionya looked and looked, but the dense shade made it difficult to see anything clearly. Then this Red Army soldier heard a joyful, piercing cry. He raised his rifle, but the boy was running towards him, shouting, "Uncle . . . Comrade . . . Soldier . . . Don't shoot! It's me, me, me!"

He ran straight up to the soldier. Weeping, he seized hold of his tunic, holding it so tightly that his fingers went white.

The soldier stroked the boy's hair. Shaking his head, he said, "What have you done to your feet? They're all bruised and bleeding. But you don't need to cling on like that. I'm not going to chase you away." He sighed and added, "Maybe my own boy's wandering about the forest on his own too. Yes, the Germans can kill me and kill me again – but as long as they're lording it over us here, I won't lie still in the ground. I'll be back on my feet!"[108]

Soon Lionya was lying on a bed of leaves. He'd eaten and drunk his fill and he had clean feet. He was wearing a Red Army belt. Hanging from it was a real leather holster with his toy black revolver. A group of commanders was sitting around him, and he was telling them about the Germans.

Bogariov came over to join them. Everyone stood up.

"Well," said Bogariov, "how are things with our new graduate student? Soon you'll be seeing your papa. Maybe tomorrow . . . But comrades, you must allow our young traveller to get some rest."

"No, I absolutely do not want to rest," said Lionya. "I'm going to play chess with the captain."

"A new opponent for you, Comrade Rumiantsev!" Bogariov said with a smile.

"Yes," said Rumiantsev. "We're about to start."

They set out the pieces. And then, for several long minutes, Rumiantsev frowned at the chessboard.

"What is it?" asked Lionya. "Why don't you make your first move?"

Rumiantsev stood up abruptly, choked back a sob and walked quickly away into the trees.

"Don't be upset, my boy," said an artillery sergeant. "It's because of his friend, Nevtulov. The two of them always used to play together."

Rumiantsev didn't once look back. And he kept muttering, "Never again, Seriozha. Not one more game."

19

PREPARE TO ATTACK IN THE MORNING

There seemed to be little going on in the forest camp. Bogariov, however, had probably never in his life felt such exhaustion as during these days of preparation for breaking through the German lines. He hardly slept; his mind was in a state of unremitting, alert tension. And not only was his determination unshakeable but he was also able to transmit this determination to all his subordinates – soldiers and commanders alike. He talked regularly to the soldiers, his commanders carried out frequent drills, and reliable telephone communication was established between individual units and sub-units. Every morning the radio operator took down the latest SovInform Bureau bulletin. This would be typed out in a number of copies and a despatch rider on a captured motorcycle would distribute these copies to the units. In the morning, a few small detachments would go out on reconnaissance, gathering information about the movements of German troops and transport columns. Uniforms were mended. The slightest infringement of discipline was penalized; any failure to salute was punished severely and reports were received with rule-book formality. The soldiers with least experience of battle were gradually accustomized to danger; they were sent out to ambush despatch riders, to capture signallers and to destroy lone trucks. For the first operation, they were accompanied by experienced scouts. After that, they were sent out alone, to act on their own initiative and to the best of their abilities.

In the evenings, Bogariov talked to the other commanders about the course of the war. His confidence in victory – a confidence that sprang not from empty optimism but from a grim understanding of the difficulties and losses of the war's first months – was entirely convincing.

"What annoys me most," said Rumiantsev, "is the way the Germans keep using the word "blitzkrieg" – a flash-of-lightning-war. They come up with these ridiculous deadlines: thirty-five days to capture Moscow and seventy days to bring the war to an end. And in the mornings, like it or not, we find ourselves counting how many days the war has lasted so far: fifty-three, sixty-one, sixty-two, now seventy-one. While they're probably thinking, 'Seventy days, a hundred and seventy days – what's the difference?' Damn them and their deadlines – war's not just a matter of dates."

"No," said Bogariov. "This war is very much a matter of dates. History shows that Germany hardly ever wins a protracted war. You only need look at a map to see why the Germans like to talk about blitzkriegs. For them, a lightning war means victory, while a long war means defeat.[109] He laughed and added, "But mark my words, comrades, the day is not so distant when it'll be us Soviets saying that the war will soon be over – and the Fascists making out that it will drag on for years to come. And they'll say that not with confidence of eventual triumph, but in uncertain hope of postponing their ruin. So it's natural enough that we should be counting the days. Each page torn from the calendar brings us closer to victory, and the Germans closer to defeat."[110]

Bogariov looked round at the other commanders and added, "Comrades, we sent a scout across the front line to Army Group HQ. I'm expecting him back today. Probably we'll be attacking tomorrow."

He and Rumiantsev then lay down on the grass side by side and began to examine the map. Several days and nights of constant reconnaissance had yielded a great deal of information.

Rumiantsev accurately identified the weak point in the German front line. "This is where we should concentrate our forces," he said. "We can approach through forest and make our way under cover almost as far as the river. If we move at night, we should be able to reach the east bank without firing a shot. We can slip across unseen."

"Well, well, well!" said Bogariov. "Who'd have thought that Comrade Rumiantsev, a superb Soviet commander, an intelligent and well-educated gunner, could come up with such nonsense?"

"What do you mean?" Rumiantsev replied in surprise. "Why nonsense? I assure you we'll be able to slip across. The Germans are thin on the ground in that sector. I've been there. I've seen everything with my own eyes."

"Which is precisely what makes it such nonsense."

"I don't understand, Comrade Commissar."

"Nor me! Here we are, a regular unit operating behind enemy lines – and you want us to slip through at night without firing a shot. How can we let such an opportunity pass? No, we're not going to look for where they're thin on the ground. We'll go for where they've concentrated the most equipment. We'll strike from the rear, inflict severe losses on the enemy and cross the river victoriously. Yes, we will!"

Rumiantsev looked intently at Bogariov. "Forgive me," he said. "You're right. Why try to slip past if you can strike an unexpected blow!"

"It's all right," Bogariov replied thoughtfully. "In wartime the instinct for self-preservation often plays tricks on us. We need to keep reminding ourselves that we are here to fight to the death and for no other reason, that we dig trenches not to shelter in them but to shoot from them, and that if ever we do choose to hide in a slit trench, this is to preserve our lives in order to go into the attack an hour later. People somehow find it all too easy to imagine that a dugout is nothing more than a hiding place. But the truth couldn't be simpler. We're not here behind enemy lines because we like hiding in forests. We're here to mount a surprise attack. Agreed?"[III]

"How could I not agree?"

They were joined by Lieutenant Klenovkin.

"Excuse me, Comrade Commissar," he said, glancing out of habit at his watch. "We have a guest."

"Who is it?" asked Bogariov, looking at the soldier standing beside Klenovkin. And then he shouted out joyfully, "Why, it's Comrade Kozlov, our famous reconnaissance commander!"

"Senior Lieutenant Kozlov, just arrived, reporting by order of Major Mertsalov, commander of the IIIth Infantry Regiment," Kozlov said loudly, articulating each syllable with an exaggerated staccato emphasis. As at the meeting when Bogariov first encountered him, there was a smile in his intelligent brown eyes.

"Didn't so much *arrive* – more like crept here on my belly," he said to Rumiantsev in an undertone.

Kozlov sat down beside Bogariov and began to outline

Mertsalov's plan for a joint attack. It was a complex operation and Kozlov went through each aspect in turn: the signalling system that would enable them to coordinate their moves, the time at which they were to concentrate their forces, and the time they were to attack. He explained where our tanks would go into action, where our artillery and mortars would be positioned, how we would block the road along which the Germans would attempt to bring up their reserves, and how divisional artillery would keep the Germans' probable line of retreat under fire. Then he handed Bogariov a gold watch and said, "Comrade Mertsalov asked me to give you his watch. He has a nickel-plated one too, and the two watches have been synchronized to the second."

Bogariov took the watch, turned it over in his hand, then checked his own watch against it. His was four minutes slow.

"Very good," he said. "Seems my harsh words weren't wasted on Mertsalov." Then he laughed, saying to himself, "But who knows? Maybe they weren't needed at all!" "You will take over command of our rifle battalion," he said to Kozlov. "And you, Comrade Rumiantsev, will need to set off the moment it gets dark. Moving heavy guns through forest isn't so easy."

"We've already worked on the route. We've cleared trees. And we've prepared short lengths of log road through the patches of bog," Rumiantsev replied. He was not a man to leave things until the last moment.

"Very good. There's only one serious flaw in our plans. I've got nothing to smoke. Do you by any chance have a cigarette on you, Comrade Kozlov?"

"I don't smoke, Comrade Commissar," Kozlov answered guilt-ily. "And I'm afraid you'd have me shot if you'd heard Mertsalov trying to persuade me to bring you a couple of packets of cigarettes. I told him you had plenty of tobacco already."

"A man we can truly depend on," Rumiantsev said angrily. "So, here we are smoking clover."

"A friend and comrade indeed," said Bogariov. "And may I ask what kind of cigarettes you were offered?"

"A pale-blue box and a picture of white mountains with a man on horseback. 'Kazbek' or something."

"Yes, Kazbek. Well, Comrade Rumiantsev, what do you make of that?"

"Seems it's not our lucky day," Rumiantsev replied with a laugh. "He's probably the only reconnaissance commander in the army who doesn't smoke. And cruel fate has brought us together."

"Well, comrades, there's a lot to do," said Bogariov. "You'd better get going."

Kozlov walked a little way with Rumiantsev, then asked in a low voice, "What's all this about Myshansky?"

Rumiantsev told him what had happened.

"How very strange," Kozlov said thoughtfully. "I've known Myshansky since long before the war. He used to work in a factory. And he was always disliked for his relentless optimism. He would never come out with even a word of criticism, only endless shouts of 'Hurrah!' And he had no doubt we'd soon be wiping the floor with all our enemies. But once things got difficult, he changed his tune."

"Simple enough," Rumiantsev replied. "His was an artificial optimism. He was putting it on. And now, as our commissar might say, he's turned into his own antithesis."

"And what do you make of our commissar?" asked Kozlov.

"He's a strong man!" said Rumiantsev. "Quite something!" He sighed and went on, "But my Seryozha's gone. They killed my friend."

"I know," said Kozlov. "He was a good man. And we'll never see him again."

Shortly after this, the soldiers were informed about the impending night attack. They began to assemble. As during the preparations for any serious enterprise, their faces took on a preoccupied look. In the half-light of the setting sun and the shadows cast by the trees, they appeared darker and more drawn. The men seemed to have matured.

These men had made themselves at home in the forest. The tall trees beneath which they had held so many long conversations, the mossy hollows where they had slept so comfortably, the creak of dry branches and the rustle of leaves, the calls of the sentries behind the hazel bush, the raspberry brake and the spots most favoured by mushrooms, the calls of cuckoos and the tapping of woodpeckers – all this had become a part of their lives. But come morning, there would be no soldiers left here. And many would meet their death and the sunrise in open country.

"Here, take care of my tobacco pouch until tomorrow. And if I get killed, keep it for yourself. It's a damned good pouch, it would be a pity to lose it," one soldier was saying to a comrade from the same village. "It holds a packet and a half of tobacco and it's waterproof, all rubber."

"I might get killed too," his comrade replied in a hurt tone.

"But you're a stretcher-bearer, and I'll be one of the advance group. I'm more likely to cop it than you are."

"All right, give it to me. It'll be something to remember you by."

"But don't forget. If I come out of this in one piece, I want it back. I'm handing it to you in the presence of witnesses."

Everyone laughed. Several of the listeners said how much they'd give for a smoke.

Bogariov walked about, listened to conversations, walked a little further and listened again.

He was gripped by a calm, austere sense of the strength of a nation resolved to fight to the death. It was a strength he could both see and feel.

Filtering through the trees, the rays of the setting sun momentarily lit up the soldiers' tanned faces, their black rifle barrels, the white bandages of the wounded and the small brass bodies of the cartridges being handed out by the sergeant major. And then, as if born from this evening sun, came the sound of singing. Ignatiev's was the first voice. A second voice joined in, followed by a third and a fourth. The singers were all hidden behind the trees – it seemed to be the forest itself that was singing, sadly and majestically.

Then Rodimtsev appeared.

"Comrade Commissar," he said to Bogariov, "the men have asked me to give you this." And he held out a red cloth tobacco pouch embroidered with small green crosses.

"What do you mean?"

"The men decided among themselves that since we're all more or less out of tobacco, it would be best to pool our last scraps and allow at least one man a proper smoke."

"No," said Bogariov, his voice trembling. "Your last tobacco. How can I? I know how precious that is."

"Comrade Commissar," Rodimtsev replied quietly, "the men will feel very hurt. This is a gift – from all their hearts."

Bogariov looked at Rodimtsev's solemn face and silently took the small pouch.

"This was all we could collect. The Germans know how to hurt us – they landed an incendiary right on the truck with our tobacco supplies. But everyone's been saying the same thing, 'Our commissar isn't even getting any sleep. He spends all night studying the map. Let the man at least have a smoke.'"

Bogariov wanted to thank Rodimtsev, but he was too deeply moved. He couldn't get the words out.

Tears came to his eyes, for the first time since the war began.

The sad, slow song grew louder and louder, as if swelling in the glow of the red evening sun.

20

KNOW THYSELF

Mertsalov woke long before dawn. His aluminium mess tin was gleaming in the half-light. Lying beside it on the small table was an open map, held down by hand grenades on two of its corners. Mertsalov lit a candle and smiled. Yesterday Kudakov had brought in new maps from Army HQ and solemnly declared, "Comrade Mertsalov, on the old map we did nothing but record our retreats. Tomorrow, on these maps, we'll be marking where we've broken through the enemy front line."

They had burned the old map, which was covered in grime and no longer even legible on its many folds. Its now worn-out paper had borne witness to bloody battles as the Red Army retreated. The map had indeed been through a great deal. Mertsalov had studied it at dawn on 22 June, when the Fascist bombers had flown across the border and suddenly appeared above sleeping Soviet artillery and rifle regiments. Since then, the map had seen rain and thunderstorms and had been bleached by the sun of hot July noons. It had fluttered in the wind in broad Ukrainian fields. Old trees in Belorussian forests had towered above it, gazing down over the heads of commanders.

"Hmm," Mertsalov said to himself, looking crossly at the gleaming mess tin. "We need to paint these tins green. Otherwise, they'll give us away – what with the sun playing on them in daytime and the way they gleam like this in the dark."

Mertsalov took his little case from beneath the bunk and opened it. There was a mixture of smells: smoked sausage, eau de cologne and scented soap. His wife had packed this case for him on the first day of the war and he thought of her whenever he opened it. He took out some clean footcloths and underwear. He shaved, then went up outside.

It was still about an hour before dawn, and there was no more light in the east than in the west. The earth was shrouded in gloom, and a cold dank mist was spreading between the willows and reeds on the riverbank. The sky seemed unmoving, like a blind man's eye, and it was impossible to tell whether it was clear or cloudy.

Mertsalov undressed. Breathing deeply, almost panting, he walked across the cold, wet sand to the river. The feel of the water on his body made him gasp. He spent a long time washing his head, neck and ears, then scrubbed his chest with a loofah; the dark night water around him turned light blue from the soap. Next, he put on his clean underwear and went back to the dugout. Sitting on his bunk, he took out a starched strip of white cloth and sewed it to his tunic collar.[112] He poured the last drops of eau de cologne into his palm and moistened his cheeks, then patted on some talcum powder, shaking out the last little particles from the cracks in the small round box. After that, he wiped his cheeks with a damp towel and slowly began to dress, putting on his dark blue trousers, a gabardine tunic and a new belt. He slowly and carefully cleaned his boots, first wiping off the dust, then bringing them to a shine with a brush and cloth. He washed his hands again, combed his damp hair, drew himself up to his full height, checked his revolver and placed it in its holster, took his pistol from its little case and slipped it into his pocket, and tucked the photograph of his wife and daughter into his tunic pocket.

"So, here we are!" he said. He glanced at his watch and woke Kudakov.

It was beginning to get light. The cold wind whistled among the reeds, rippled across the water like a quivering net, moved briskly through open spaces, leaped carelessly across trenches and anti-tank ditches, sent fine sand whirling over the mounds of dugouts and hurled tumbleweed bushes against entanglements of barbed wire.

Like an elderly judge who has passed beyond excitement and passion, the sun rose calmly into the sky, preparing to assume its usual lofty position over field and forest. The night's clouds now seemed like cooling lumps of coal, glowing with a wan, brick-coloured flame. Everything about this morning seemed ominous, prophesying the grim labour of battle and many deaths. Nevertheless, it was an ordinary autumn morning. On a similar morning the year before, fishermen had passed sleepily by on their way to the nearest village – and to them, the sky, the sun and the wind had seemed the epitome of peace and rural beauty. Today, though, could hardly have been more different. Wells whose cool greenish-blue depths had been poisoned, moonlit haystacks, apple orchards, white walls now splattered with the blood of people who had been shot, the paths and tracks, the wind sighing through cables, the deserted nests of storks, the melon plantations, the russet buckwheat – all this wonderful world of Ukraine was now blood-soaked, salted by tears and heavy with the bodies of the dead.

★

The attack began at five o'clock in the morning. Black ground-attack aircraft passed over the infantry. These were new planes that had only recently arrived at the front. They were flying low and the soldiers could see the bombs tucked under their wings, ready to drop. Smoke rose over the German positions and a low rumble rolled across the broad horizon. The regimental artillery opened fire at the same time. The air, where a moment ago there had been only the morning wind, was filled with the whistle and roar of explosions; the wind was now crowded out.

Mertsalov had very much wanted to lead the first battalion into the attack, but he restrained himself. Now, for the first time, he truly felt the importance of his presence at HQ. "Damn it, the man was right after all," he thought angrily. He was still hurt by Bogariov's criticisms and he remembered them every day. Now, though, he had a clear sense of the complexity of the fighting, of the many different threads he held in his hands. Every commander had been given precise orders the evening before and had a clear understanding of his task. Detailed instructions had been issued to fighters, bombers and ground-attack aircraft. He and Major Seriogin, the commander of a heavy tank battalion, had pored over the map for more than an hour. The enemy, however, immediately adopted vigorous countermeasures, and Mertsalov's complex plan required swift adjustments.

Soviet planes had twice bombed the German advance positions, and columns of black smoke were rising from their trenches and dugouts. But when the Soviet infantry tried to move forward in the wake of Seriogin's heavy tanks, the Germans had opened fire with all their artillery, mortar batteries and anti-tank guns. Mertsalov's battalion commanders had reported to him by telephone, saying that their men were pinned to the ground. It was impossible, they made out, to advance under such heavy fire. Mertsalov had leaped to his feet and unbuttoned his holster. Whatever the cost, he felt, the infantry simply *had* to advance and break through. And to a man who knew no fear, it seemed easy enough to yell, "Come on, lads, follow me!" – and throw oneself into the thick of the fray. For a moment Mertsalov felt angry and bitter: had all his long, painstaking preparations been simply a waste of time? Was it all for nothing that he had elaborated his battle plan in a completely new way, with almost academic rigour?

"No, Comrade Chief of Staff," he said angrily, "war always has been and always will be the art of fearing neither the enemy nor death. We must get the infantry back on their feet."

But Mertsalov did not leave HQ. The telephone rang again. Another call followed straight afterwards.

"Our air attacks have had little effect," said Kochetkov. "The enemy remain in their trenches. And their guns and mortars are keeping up a constant fire."

"Our tanks are meeting heavy artillery fire," said Seriogin. "The infantry has ceased to advance. Two of our tanks have had their tracks smashed. The rest are still moving forward, but any further advance, in my view, would be inadvisable."

The telephone rang yet again. An air-force liaison officer asked about the effectiveness of the bombing and whether it might be advisable to make any changes. Our infantry, according to reports from pilots, was failing to advance and the enemy's artillery was still operating. And, at almost the same time, an artillery lieutenant colonel appeared at HQ, with important questions that required immediate answers.

Mertsalov lit a cigarette and sat down at his desk, knitting his brows.

"Shall we carry out more bombing raids on the infantry?" asked Kudakov.

"No," said Mertsalov.

"We should order the infantry to move forward again. The advance units are now only three hundred metres short of the enemy. They could advance another hundred metres in spurts," said Kudakov.

"No," said Mertsalov.

Mertsalov was so deep in thought that he did not even look up when Divisional Commissar Cherednichenko entered HQ. Kudakov also failed to notice him. Cherednichenko walked past the sentry, who sprang to attention. He then sat down in the dark corner near the bunks where the messengers usually sat. Puffing on his pipe, watching Mertsalov and Kudakov, he listened calmly and attentively to the various conversations and telephone calls.

Cherednichenko had gone straight to Mertsalov, without first visiting Samarin's command post. He had wanted to be present when the attack began. Knowing that Samarin made a point of being on the scene of any important operation, he was expecting to find him at Mertsalov's HQ.

Mertsalov continued to study the map. Racking his brains till they ached, he tried to imagine the battle as an integral whole, with nodes of tension repeatedly strengthening and fading away like an alternating magnetic field. In his mind's eye, he was able to make out the axis of the enemy's defence, the blade against which his attack was being cut to pieces. And he understood why his attack was proving ineffectual. Its separate elements were not fusing together; they merely existed side by side. The various waves of his attack were failing to combine with one another into a single more powerful wave – a wave of greater amplitude.

In his imagination Mertsalov created a dynamic representation of all the components of this complex battle. He balanced the stubbornness of straightforward manpower against the roar of planes and the rumble of heavy tanks. He sensed the pressure of light and heavy artillery and the potential energy of Bogariov's men waiting behind the enemy lines. And suddenly it was as if his heart and mind, everything inside him, were illuminated by a bright, joyful light. An extraordinarily simple and mathematically irrefutable solution flashed into his mind.

A mathematician or physicist is often overwhelmed in the first stages of his research by the complex and obstinate contradictions he has discovered in some apparently simple and ordinary phenomenon. He struggles to reconcile the various elements of this phenomenon, but they continue to contradict one another, to slip away from his grasp. And then, as a reward for this arduous work of analysis, a clear and simple thought unexpectedly dawns on him, dispelling all confusion and complexity and yielding the only correct, astonishingly simple and irrefutable solution. This moment is what we call creative thinking. And what Mertsalov went through, as he wrestled with the problem before him, was no different from this. Never, perhaps, had he known such excitement and joy.[113]

Mertsalov outlined his new plan to Kudakov. "But this goes against all..." Kudakov replied, listing the various rules and orders that Mertsalov was about to infringe.

"What of it?" Mertsalov replied. "Remember Babadjanian's words: *The only norm I know is victory.*"

Mertsalov deliberated for a minute. Sometimes, it takes a great deal of strength and courage to go through with an important decision worked out on a map at HQ – still more than for some brave feat on the battlefield. And Mertsalov was able to draw on this courage. He was aware that Russian commanders often sought to justify moves undertaken in difficult situations by stating that they had put their own lives at risk. When asked to account for himself, a commander might say, "I could see we were in trouble, so I went forward at the head of my men. What else could I do?" But Mertsalov now understood that there are moments when the sacrifice of his own life is only a small part of what is required of a commander.[114] Not even this supreme sacrifice can relieve him of responsibility for the outcome of a battle.

He understood the situation as follows. Air strikes had failed to crush the German infantry, which was well protected in its trenches. German artillery and mortars were hindering the movement of our tanks and breaking the link between them and the advancing infantry. And any infantry units that did move forward, already weakened and demoralized, soon came within range of German machine guns and sub-machine guns. Mertsalov had almost twice as much artillery at his disposal as the Germans, but it was dissipating its strength, directing its fire against the whole of the broad German front. Evenly distributed as it was, only a quarter or a fifth of his total fire power – guns, tanks, aircraft and infantry – was being focused on the German guns and mortars, and it was crucial that they should be silenced. Knocking out the German artillery was the key to success in this first phase of the attack.

Without raising his voice, Mertsalov gave new orders to the regimental artillery, to the divisional artillery under temporary attachment to his regiment, to the heavy-tank battalion, and to the bombers, fighters and ground-attack aircraft that had been bombing and strafing the Germans. He ordered the infantry to withdraw, to regroup under cover and prepare to attack the main concentrations of German guns and mortars. He knew that the Germans had left only minimal forces of infantry to cover these positions. And he knew that, by using all the fire power at his disposal, he could easily silence the German artillery. By choosing to attack the strongest sector of the German front, he knew he could quickly transform it into the weakest, vulnerable to a breakthrough.

Kudakov groaned inwardly as he listened to his commander's orders. Pitching infantry against artillery and mortar batteries! An unforced retreat from positions captured at such great cost!

"Must the infantry really withdraw?" he asked. "Comrade Mertsalov!"

"That has been my name for thirty-five years now."

"Comrade Mertsalov, we have advanced eight hundred metres. Surely we should dig in?"

"I have issued my orders. I do not intend to countermand them."

"Serious accusations will be levelled at you," Kudakov replied quietly. "I am sure you are aware of Samarin's severity with regard to any infringement of the great order not to retreat.[115] And now, at the very beginning of the attack, and after our recent unfortunate withdrawal, you are staking everything on one card."

"I'm staking everything on this map," Mertsalov said grimly, pointing to the desk. "And there is no need for you to say any more, Semion Germogenovich. I'm not a child and I know what I'm doing."

There was the sound of loud voices from the entrance to the dugout. Mertsalov and Kudakov sprang to their feet; General Samarin was coming towards them.

Samarin nodded at Kudakov, who was looking shaken, and asked, "So, have you broken through?"

"No, Comrade Major General," Mertsalov replied. "We have not yet broken through, but we will."

"Where are your battalions?" Samarin asked curtly. On his way to regimental HQ, he had encountered retreating tanks and infantry and asked on whose orders they were withdrawing. "By order of the regimental commander, Hero of the Soviet Union, Major Mertsalov," a lieutenant had replied.

This had enraged Samarin.

"Where are your battalions? And why are they withdrawing?" Samarin now asked with terrifying calm.

"They are withdrawing in accord with my orders, Comrade Major General," Mertsalov replied. Suddenly he saw that Samarin was now standing to attention himself, looking at someone walking towards him from a dark corner of the dugout.

Mertsalov looked more closely and then stood to attention too. Coming towards them was Divisional Commissar Cherednichenko, the member of the Front Military Soviet.

"Greetings, Samarin! Greetings, comrades!" said Cherednichenko. "The sentry let me through and I slipped into your dugout without a word. I've been sitting here on a bunk, watching you go about your work."

"Whatever the man says," Mertsalov thought stubbornly, "I'm right and I'll prove it."

Cherednichenko looked at Samarin, who was scowling, and at Kudakov, who was still visibly upset, and then said, "Comrade Mertsalov!"

"Yes, Comrade Divisional Commissar."

For a moment Cherednichenko looked Mertsalov straight in the eye, calmly and with a touch of sadness. And Mertsalov realized, with surprise and joy, that Cherednichenko understood what an important, life-changing hour this had been for him.

"Comrade Mertsalov," Cherednichenko said slowly. "I'm happy for you. You are proving an excellent commander and I have no doubt of your success today." With a quick glance at Samarin, he added, "On behalf of the Red Army, I thank you, Major Mertsalov."

"I serve the Soviet Union," Mertsalov replied.

"Well, Samarin, shall we go on our way?" said Cherednichenko, throwing an arm around the general's shoulders. "There's a lot to talk about. And we should let these men get on with their work. They've got more than enough responsibilities as it is – without having to stand to attention because their bosses have suddenly descended on them. Let's leave them to it!"

On his way out, he went over to Mertsalov and said quietly, "Well, Major, how are you getting on with your commissar?" And then, still more quietly, "Did you have a fight with him? Perhaps just once? Have I guessed right?"

To Mertsalov it seemed as if Cherednichenko had been present during that painful conversation between him and Bogariov, and that he was choosing to remind him of the hidden connection between that evening and the present day.

21

AT BRUCHMÜLLER'S HQ

On the morning of the unexpected Russian counter-attack, Colonel Bruchmüller, the commander of the German unit preparing to force the river, was talking to his guest, Colonel Grün, a representative of the General Staff who had arrived the previous evening. The two men were having breakfast together in the school building that served as Bruchmüller's HQ. They had known each other for many years and had talked late into the night about recent developments both on the front line and back in Germany. As he sipped his coffee, Bruchmüller looked up now and then at a brightly coloured illustrated wallchart which, not long ago, had helped village schoolchildren to understand that man was descended from monkeys, or rather, shared common ancestors with them.[116]

Grün held a far higher and more distinguished post than Bruchmüller, but he respected him none the less. Bruchmüller was widely admired for his skill in handling artillery. Thinking of his more famous namesake, who had directed massive artillery attacks on the western front in 1914, Colonel General Brauchitsch had once said of him, "It's not for nothing that he bears the name Bruchmüller." As for the gaunt Colonel Grün, he chose to ignore the complex military hierarchy that allowed a man to speak freely only to other members of his own circle; he had been entirely frank in what he said to the stout, bald colonel about the mood among senior staff officers and the situation in Germany as a whole. His account had upset Bruchmüller.

"To hell with them all!" Bruchmüller had responded, with a soldierly directness that took Grün aback. "While we do the real fighting, they backbite and squabble. One intrigue after another – industrialists versus National Socialists, Frondists against anti-Frondists on the General Staff.[117] It all brings no end of confusion. We should say it straight out, *Germany is the army, and the army is Germany*. We, and we alone, should be taking the decisions that count."

"No," Grün had replied. "Tomorrow I'll tell you about matters every bit as important as military victories. Life's getting more impossible for senior officers every day. Sometimes every aspect of our situation is – to put it mildly – paradoxical."

But the two colonels never had the chance to resume this conversation. The Russians launched their counter-attack and this gave them more pressing matters to think about.

Communications were excellent. Bruchmüller, in his HQ, had a complete and accurate picture of the course of the battle. He received new radio or telephone reports every five or six minutes.

"The Russians usually attack head-on. They go in for frontal assaults – what they call 'blows to the forehead'." said Grün, scrutinizing the map. "Usually, they apply an even pressure against the whole of our front line. They seem to have realized that this doesn't work very well and often say as much in orders and dispatches. But that doesn't change anything on the ground – an instinct for head-on attacks seem to be a part of their national character."

"Yes," said Bruchmüller. "Their national character is certainly strange. And when it comes to actual battles, I've not once been able to make out the character of my opposite number. There's something vague about it – it always eludes me. I can't grasp what he's most comfortable with, what weapons he favours. And this disturbs me. I don't like murk."

"You're not likely to see any change there," said Grün. "They're accustomed to more primitive modes of combat – and we've confronted them with all the complexities of our modern German ways of waging war. Aircraft, tanks, paratroopers, swift tank manoeuvres, combined air and ground strikes, dynamic three-dimensional warfare."

"Yes, though I should say that on this front they've brought up a fair number of heavy tanks and new aircraft. These black ground-attack aircraft are very effective – our men call them *Schwarzer Tod*.[118]

"Maybe – but they haven't had much effect yet," said Grün. "Look!" And he held out a report that the clerk had just printed.

Bruchmüller smiled. "To be honest with you," he began, "even you or I would throw up our hands in despair if we came up against defences like ours." Leaning right forward, his broad chest against the table, he launched into an enthusiastic account of his system of gun emplacements. "It reminds me of a puzzle that my son likes to play with. It's very simple – just three interlocking rings. The first goes into the second, the second into the third, and the third links back into the first. And you have to find a way to separate them! Breaking any of the rings is out of the question – they're made of steel. The trick is that they come apart just where they seem most strong and solid."

There were more and more positive telephone and radio bulletins – from battalions, companies and artillery batteries: the Russian attack was clearly fizzling out.

"It's hard to imagine how they could have advanced even eight hundred metres. I certainly can't deny their courage," said Grün. Lighting a cigarette, he asked, "When are you planning to force the river?"

"Three days from now," Bruchmüller replied. "I've already received my battle orders." Suddenly feeling buoyed up, he patted his belly and went on, "With an appetite like mine, God knows what would have become of me if I'd stayed in Germany. I might well have simply pegged out. Here, though, things couldn't be better for me. I've been fighting since 1 September 1939 and I swear I've learned enough by now to hold down a job as a restaurant consultant in the very finest luxury hotel. I've made it a rule to eat the national dishes of every country I fight in. As regards food, at least, I'm a true cosmopolitan." He gave Grün a quick sideways look. Could such a lean man, who drank only black coffee and who liked to dine on bouillon with croutons and the plainest of boiled chicken, be interested in such matters? Perhaps his weakness for good food, a weakness on which Bruchmüller prided himself, might simply disgust Grün?

But Grün had a smile on his face and was listening with interest; he was enjoying his fellow colonel's animated discourse on food. There was something innocent and soldierly about it, something truly German and *völkisch*. He looked forward to telling people about it back in Berlin.

And Bruchmüller, laughing, said, "In Poland, I ate *zrazy* and *flaki*.[119] That's a meat roulade and a kind of tripe stew – it looks vile, but it's damn tasty. I ate *kluski*, *knishes* and sweet *mazureks*.[120] And I drank starka.[121] In France I ate any number of different ragouts, légumes, artichokes and delicate roasts – and I also drank truly imperial wines. In Greece, I stank of garlic, like an old market woman, and I consumed so much pepper I was afraid it would burn my insides. And here they have suckling pigs, geese and turkeys. And some tasty little dumplings they call *va-re-ni-ki* – a dough made from white flour, filled with cherries or curd cheese and drenched in sour cream. That's something you really must try today!"

"Oh no!" said Grün with a laugh, raising his hand as if to ward off some danger. "I want to see Berlin again. I want to see my wife and my children."

Just then, the adjutant reported that the Russian tanks were retreating, covering their infantry as it too retreated, that Russian planes were no longer appearing over the German infantry positions, and that their artillery had entirely ceased firing.

"Your notorious murk!" said Grün.

"I don't think so," Bruchmüller replied with a slight frown. "I know Ivan's tenacity."

"So you really do believe in this murk of yours?"

Bruchmüller was upset by Grün's slightly mocking tone.

"I believe in our weaponry," he replied. "Maybe the Russians have quietened down, or maybe not. Most likely, not. But that's not important. What's important is this!" And he struck the map with the back of his hand.

Between the green of the forest and the blue of the rivers and lakes were clusters of red circles, drawn with a thick Faber pencil. These were the German artillery and mortar emplacements.

"Here is what I believe in," Bruchmüller reiterated.

He pronounced these words slowly and weightily. And it seemed to Grün that Bruchmüller was stating his beliefs not only with regard to fighting the Russians but also with regard to what they had discussed the previous evening.

Fifteen minutes later, they were informed by telephone that the Russians were back in action.

The first bomber attacks were directed against the German heavy artillery. Then came a report that Russian heavy tanks had bracketed the battalion mortars and opened fire from their 75 mm guns. And then, the unruffled voice of Major Schwalbe reporting that his 105 mm guns were being subjected to a barrage of Russian heavy artillery fire.

Bruchmüller realized that the Russian attack, instead of being evenly distributed along the front line, was now sharply focused. He could all but feel the disturbing jabs of something sharp and dangerous that was searching around for his guns. His connection to his men and guns was so strong, so much a part of him, that these jabs seemed physically real and he unthinkingly ran his hand over his chest, as if to brush them away. But this did not change anything.

The Russian bombers had barely flown away before their fighters appeared over the artillery positions. Battery commanders reported that they were unable to maintain fire; the gun crews were taking cover in their dugouts.

"Maintain fire at all costs, with maximum intensity!" Bruchmüller ordered.

He felt alert and resolute. Damn it, it was not for nothing that he bore the name Bruchmüller! It was not for nothing that he was known and respected throughout the army. He was an experienced and capable soldier. Even while he was still a student at the Academy, his teachers had said he was a true embodiment of the spirit of the German officer class.

The whole of the large, well-oiled and supremely efficient staff machine seemed to tremble beneath the force of his will. Telephones rang; Bruchmüller's adjutant, along with other subalterns, hurried between the field telegraph transmitters and his office; the radio transmitter chattered incessantly; despatch riders gulped down a Russian schnapps, pulled down their side caps, drove out of the schoolyard and sped off this way and that, raising clouds of dust.

Bruchmüller spoke by telephone to each of his battery commanders.

As soon as the Russian fighters made off, the dive bombers reappeared over his artillery positions. It was clear that the Russian commander had set himself a single objective: to destroy Bruchmüller's big guns. And gun after gun was indeed being put out of action. Two mortar batteries, along with their crews, had already been eliminated. The Russians were systematically going for one emplacement after another.

Bruchmüller called up an infantry battalion he had been holding in reserve, but after a few minutes he was informed that black ground-attack aircraft had flown low over the advancing trucks and shelled and strafed them. Bruchmüller ordered the infantry to leave the trucks and proceed on foot. This too proved impossible – the Russians opened concentrated fire on the road and the soldiers were unable to move.

For the first time in this war, Bruchmüller felt unable to act freely. Someone else's will was hindering him, interfering with his dispositions. The realization that his antagonist had the upper hand, even if only for a moment, was intolerable.

Unexpectedly, he remembered how a year ago, in France, he had chosen to attend an unusually complex operation being carried out by an eminent professor, a world-famous brain surgeon who was visiting the front. This professor had inserted a strange, flexible, gleaming instrument, something halfway between a knife and a needle, into one of the unconscious patient's nostrils and with his quick, dexterous fingers had pushed it deeper and deeper inside. It was explained to Bruchmüller that the injury was somewhere above the occipital bone and that the professor was guiding his instrument to a point between the cranium and the cerebrum. Bruchmüller had been greatly impressed by this operation. And now it seemed to him that his present antagonist had the same intent face and the same quick fingers as that surgeon; it was as if he too were able to guide a steel blade through the darkness between precious nerve ganglia and delicate, thread-like blood vessels.

Bruchmüller summoned his adjutant. "What are you doing here?" he asked crossly. "You are a gunner and an officer. You have, in person, reported the deaths of three battery commanders and the heroic deaths of Major Schwalbe, the very best of my aides. It is now your duty to ask of your own accord to be transferred to the line of fire. Or do you think that your military duties are limited to the execution of old women and young boys suspected of sympathizing with the partisans?"

"Herr Oberst," the adjutant began in a hurt tone. Seeing the look on Bruchmüller's face, he quickly changed his tone and went on, "Herr Oberst, I have the honour to ask to be transferred to the line of fire."

"I grant your request," said Bruchmüller.

"What's going on?" asked Colonel Grün.

"Our Russian is finally showing his character," Bruchmüller replied.

He leaned over the map again. His antagonist was calmly developing the game. Bruchmüller had caught a glimpse of his face.

"Russian infantry are now attacking our artillery positions," the field telegraph informed him. Next, an officer ran in and shouted, "Colonel, Russian heavy artillery is firing on us from behind our lines!"

"No, I'll outplay him yet," Bruchmüller declared with conviction. "He won't get the better of me."

A gust of wind slammed open windows, set doors creaking and rustled the wall chart illustrating the evolution of mankind. As the chart shifted about, it was as if mankind's hairy brown relative were making stubborn chewing movements with its powerful jaws.

22

DEATH WILL NOT CONQUER!

Rumiantsev's observers were positioned very close to the Germans. Lieutenant Klenovkin, lying in the bushes, saw two officers emerge from an underground shelter, smoking and drinking coffee. He could hear them speaking. He saw a telephonist reporting to them and one of the officers, evidently the senior, dictating a message. Klenovkin glanced at his watch. He felt deeply frustrated. It was a shame he had never studied German; as it was, he could hear every word but not understand a thing.

The Russian howitzers were on the very edge of the forest, a thousand metres from where Klenovkin was lying. The infantry had concentrated nearby. The wounded had been brought up too; they were lying on stretchers and in trucks, so that they could be moved forward without delay, the moment the infantry broke through.

Lying beside Klenovkin was Martynov, the telephonist. He was watching his German opposite number with particular interest, both amused and irritated by him.

"A sly bastard, though I can see he drinks too much," Martynov whispered. "And put him in front of our own apparatus – the damned German will be totally lost."

There was tension everywhere. It was the same for Klenovkin, close to the German dugouts, and for young Lionya and the wounded, who were waiting impatiently back in the half-dark forest. They all heard the artillery barrage, the sound of machine guns and sub-machine guns, and the exploding bombs. Aircraft with red stars on their wings repeatedly roared over their heads, towards the German positions. The men found it hard to restrain themselves – not to shout or wave excitedly as the planes dived towards the German trenches.

Bogariov was alarmed by the long delay, and he could see that everyone else was no less alarmed. Not only did Rumiantsev look tense and exhausted, but so did the fearless, always laughing Kozlov. Mertsalov had already completed the first stages of his attack. The scheduled time for a joint blow had already passed, but Mertsalov had still not given the signal. When the din of the battle grew louder, the commanders fell silent, listening and watching ever more intently. Yet there was still no signal.

To the men behind the German lines, everything about this battle sounded strange and back-to-front. The meaning of every sound was inverted. The shells bursting nearby were from Russian guns, and it was German guns that they could hear firing. If a stray bullet whistled overhead, it could only be a Russian bullet. As for the crackle of German machine guns and sub-machine guns, this sounded more sinister than ever. This unaccustomed inversion of meaning was disconcerting.

The men lay behind trees, among bushes, or in the tall, still unharvested hemp and listened alertly, gazing into the clear morning air. Only here and there was the air darkened by smoke and dust.

★

How good the earth seems at such moments! How gracious its heavy folds, its yellowed hillocks, its ravines full of dusty burdocks, its sudden dips. What a wonderful smell of leaf mould, of dust and forest dampness, of earth and mushrooms, of dry berries and brushwood that has half rotted and dried out again time after time. On the wind from the fields comes a warm, sad smell of faded flowers and withered grass. And in the half-dark below the trees a spider's web sprinkled with dew is suddenly caught by the sun. It lights up like a rainbow – a breathing miracle of calm and peace.

Rodimtsev is lying with his face pressed to the earth. Is he asleep? No, he is gazing intently at the ground, and at a nearby briar rose. He breathes deeply, inhaling the smell of the earth. He is aware of everything around him, watching eagerly and with respect. A column of ants is marching along a highway invisible to the human eye, dragging little twigs and bits of dry grass. "Maybe they're at war too," he thinks. "And these are columns of soldiers mobilized to dig ditches and construct fortifications. Or maybe someone's building himself a new house and these are carpenters and plasterers on their way to work."

The world that Rodimtsev's eyes see, that his ears hear and his nostrils smell is enormous. A briar rose no longer in bloom and a single *arshin*[122] of land at the edge of a forest. And yet – how rich the rose and how huge the *arshin*! The ground is dry, and a long crack, like a streak of lightning, runs along its surface. The ants have found a bridge and are crossing this crack in orderly fashion, one after another, while ants coming the other way wait patiently on the far side. A ladybird, a stout peasant woman in a bright red *sarafan*,[123] rushes about, looking for somewhere to cross. No fooling her! A field mouse stands up on its hind legs. Its eyes gleam and then it rustles away through the grass. It might, perhaps, never have been there at all. A gust of wind – and the grass sways and bows, each blade in its own way. Some prostrate themselves quickly and obediently; others quiver angrily and obstinately, sticking out a poor emaciated ear that might serve as food for a sparrow. Fired by the fierce sun like clay in an oven, red and yellow hips stir on the briar. The spider's web sways in the wind too. Its owner clearly abandoned it long ago; dry leaves and small pieces of bark are caught up in it and in one spot it sags under the weight of an acorn. It is like a net, washed up on the shore after a fisherman has drowned.

And there is a lot of such land and such forests! Countless *arshins* full of life! And how many still more beautiful dawns there had already been in Rodimtsev's life! How many swift summer showers, how many bird calls, cool breezes and night mists! How much work! And how many wonderful moments when he had come home from work and his wife had asked sternly yet lovingly, "So, are you going to have something to eat?" In the quiet closeness of the hut, he had eaten mashed potatoes with sunflower oil and looked at his children and at his wife's tanned arms. And now – how much life lay ahead for him now? Did he still have much life to live? Or might everything end then and there, within a few minutes? And Rodimtsev was not alone. Hundreds of other Red Army soldiers were lying on the ground and thinking similar thoughts – calling up memories, looking at the earth or at trees and bushes, and inhaling the morning freshness. There was, after all, no better earth in the world!

Meanwhile, Ignatiev is saying thoughtfully to a comrade, "The other day I overheard two ack-ack gunners talking. 'Here we are, fighting away,' said one of them. 'And all around us are gardens and orchards. And the birds are still singing – they don't give a damn about us and our wars.' And I keep remembering that conversation and thinking that those two lieutenants couldn't have been more wrong. There's nothing in the world that hasn't been turned upside down by this war. Think of the torment we inflict on our horses. And I remember when we were stationed in Rogachov – the dogs used to creep into the cellars at the first sound of an air alarm. I saw one bitch tucking her puppies away in a slit trench. The moment the raid was over, she took them back out for a walk. And what about our poultry – our geese, our chickens and turkeys – don't they suffer at the hands of the Germans? And here, all around us, I've noticed that the birds get scared too. As soon as a plane appears in the sky, they twitter and screech and take off in great flocks. And think of all the forest that's been destroyed! And the orchards! Only just now I was thinking about the ants and mosquitoes here in the forest. A thousand of us come and set up camp – and we wreck their whole world. And what if the Germans start to use gas and we do the same? That'll play hell with life in these woods and fields. Mice, hedgehogs, birds, insects – there's no way out for them. They'll suffocate."

Getting to his feet, he looked at his comrades and said with a kind of wistful joy, "But it's good to be alive, my friends! It's only on a day like today that you realize. You could lie here on the ground for a thousand years and never feel bored. You can breathe – what more can you ask for?"

As for Bogariov, he was listening to the sounds of the battle. Suddenly, the rumble of explosions began to die down and it seemed that red-starred planes were no longer flying over the

German positions. Had the Russian attack been repelled? Had Mertsalov failed? Had he been unable to damage the German defences enough to give the agreed signal? Bogariov's heart clenched in anguish. The thought of Mertsalov's possible failure was intolerable – a weight he felt unable to bear. He no longer saw the light of the sun. The blue sky seemed to have faded and turned black. He could no longer see the broad glade that lay open before him. Trees, fields – everything disappeared. All that remained was his hatred of the Germans.

Here, on the fringes of the forest, he clearly imagined the black force that had spread over the people's land. The people's land! Thomas More's dreams[124] and Robert Owen's visions,[125] the works of the brightest minds of the French Enlightenment, the writings of the Decembrists, the essays of Belinsky[126] and Herzen,[127] the correspondence between Zheliabov[128] and Mikhailov,[129] the words of Alexeyev the textile worker[130] – all these were an expression of humanity's eternal longing for a land that does not know slavery, for a life built on the laws of reason and justice,[131] for a land of equals, for a land where the inequality between workers and those who employ them has been eliminated. Thousands of Russian revolutionaries had died in the struggle. To Bogariov, these men were like elder brothers. He had read everything about them. He knew their last words and the letters they had written to their mothers and children. He knew their diaries and the secret conversations recorded by friends who had lived to see freedom. He knew the roads along which these men had been taken to exile and forced labour in Siberia. He knew the post stations where they had spent the night and the jails where they had been shackled. He loved and honoured these men. They were his nearest and dearest. Many were workers from Kiev, printers from Minsk, tailors from Vilna, weavers from Bielostok – cities now held by the Nazis.

With every fibre of his being, Bogariov loved this land that had been won in the unprecedented struggles of the Civil War, amid the torments of hunger. It was still poor, it still lived a life of stern labour, according to stern laws – yet it was the motherland of the world's peoples, of all its peoples, the motherland of its best minds and best peoples. Bogariov was ready to die for it.[132]

He slowly made his way between the men lying on the ground. Sometimes he stopped for a moment to say a few words, then walked on.

"If Mertsalov doesn't give the signal within the next hour," he resolved, "I'll lead the men forward and break through the German defences on my own. One hour from now."

"Mertsalov simply has to succeed," he said to Kozlov. "There's no two ways about it. Otherwise, nothing makes sense to me."

Seeing Ignatiev and Rodimtsev, he went over to them and sat down on the grass.

"What are you talking about here?" he asked.

"We're discussing mosquitoes," Ignatiev replied with a shame-faced grin.

"Heavens!" Bogariov said to himself. It had not occurred to him that, at a time like this, these men might be thinking thoughts entirely different from his own.

Then came the signal – red rockets shooting from the Russian lines towards the Germans. These rockets were seen by scores of Bogariov's men. Rumiantsev's howitzers thundered out on the instant. Hundreds of Germans froze. They had not known there were Russian troops in the forest.

Bogariov looked quickly and joyfully around him, squeezed the hand of Kozlov, who was in command of the right flank, and said to him, "My friend, I'm counting on you." Then he drew a deep breath and yelled, "Follow me, comrades! Forward!"

And not a man remained lying on the sweet, warm, summer earth.

Bogariov ran on ahead, his entire being gripped by a feeling he had not known before; he was drawing his men after him – and yet these men, bound to him in a single, eternal and indivisible whole, were at the same time impelling him forward. He could hear their breathing behind him; the swift, passionate beat of their hearts was being transmitted to him. The Russian people was fighting to win back its freedom. Bogariov could hear the stamping of boots – the sound of Russia now taking the offensive. The men were running faster and faster, and the yells of "U-u-r-a-a!" kept growing louder and stronger, rising higher into the air and covering more and more ground. Mertsalov's men could hear these yells, through the roar of the battle, as they went into a bayonet attack. Peasants in a distant, enemy-occupied village could hear them. Birds heard them, as they flew up into the sky.

The Germans fought desperately. They quickly and skilfully adopted a perimeter defence and opened fire from their machine guns. But the two waves of Russian infantry continued to advance towards each other. Russian foot soldiers smashed dugouts, leaped over ditches and trenches, broke up barbed wire and threw grenades into cars and armoured vehicles. Steel tanks that the Germans had dug into the ground were suddenly ablaze. Staff vehicles caught fire and carts packed with looted goods were smashed to smithereens. Could many of these Russian soldiers really be the same men who, not long ago in the forest, had been frightened of speaking too loudly? The men who had mistaken the cawing of crows for the sound of German speech?

The bloody hand-to-hand combat lasted forty minutes. Now, Mertsalov's men could not only hear the yells of "U-u-r-a-a!" coming from behind the German front line; they could even make out their comrades' grimy faces, covered with the sweat of battle; they could see who was carrying a rifle and who was throwing grenades; they could distinguish the black shoulder tabs of the gunners and the star on Lieutenant Kozlov's forage cap.

The Germans fought on. Their stubbornness may not have been simply a matter of courage. It is possible that their intoxicating belief in their own invincibility was reluctant to abandon them even at this hour of defeat. It is possible that, after seven hundred days of taking victory for granted, these soldiers could not and did not want to understand that this seven hundred and first day marked their defeat.

The German front line, in any case, was breached. The first two Red Army soldiers met and embraced. Through the din of battle a voice called out, "Give us a fag, brother – I haven't had a smoke for a week!"

The first of the encircled German machine-gunners raised their hands in the air. A sub-machine-gunner with freckles and a hooked nose shouted, "Rus, don't shoot!" and threw down his black weapon, which he had suddenly begun to hate. Lines of prisoners were already being marched away, hanging their heads and without their side caps. Their jackets, flung open in the heat of battle, were still unbuttoned, and their pockets had been turned inside out, to show that they were not carrying pistols or hand grenades.

Elsewhere, clerks, telegraph and radio operators were being escorted from the German HQ. Stern, begrimed soldiers were looking silently at the corpse of a German colonel who had shot himself. A young commander was briskly counting the German tanks, trucks, artillery pieces and automatic weapons left on the battlefield.

"Where is the commissar?" the soldiers asked one another.

"Where is the commissar?" asked Rumiantsev.

"Who's seen the commissar?" asked Kozlov, wiping the sweat from his forehead.

"The commissar was with us," said the men. "He was with us all the time."

"Where is the commissar?" asked Mertsalov, picking his way between the wrecked trucks. He was covered in dust and grime and his new tunic had been ripped by bullets.

And the men answered, "The commissar was with us. He was leading us forward."

The now silent battlefield was mercilessly lit by the sun. A small khaki armoured car drove across it, past pools of blood that had gone dry and black in the heat, past still smoking tanks and skeletons of trucks. The car came to a stop and Divisional Commissar Cherednichenko stepped out of it.

"Comrade Member of the Military Soviet," said Mertsalov, "your son will be here soon. He's in the transport coming this way. He was with Bogariov's detachment."

"My Lionya," said Cherednichenko. "My son. And my mother?"

He looked at Mertsalov. Mertsalov looked silently down at the ground. Cherednichenko was equally silent; he was watching the trucks as they emerged from the forest.

"My son," he repeated. "My son."

Turning to Mertsalov, he asked, "Where is the commissar?"

Once again Mertsalov remained silent.

The wind whistled over the fields. Two men appeared from where the fires were starting to die out. Everyone could see who they were. They were Commissar Bogariov and Red Army soldier Ignatiev. Blood was seeping through their clothes. They were taking slow, heavy steps, each supporting the other. Where it flowed down onto the ground, the blood of the two men mixed together. They were brothers; nothing in life or death could now separate them.

22 June 1942
Central Front
Gomel – Briansk

22 мая 1942 г. — Вас. Гроссман

The last page of Grossman's manuscript of Народ бессмертен
(*The People Immortal*).

Afterword

1. Literature and Reality

In February 1942, Grossman visited a division manned entirely by miners from the Donbas – the Donets Coal Basin in eastern Ukraine. They recognized him from a photograph in his recently published novel *Stepan Kolchugin*, which is set in the Donbas. Grossman was moved by the warmth of their welcome. He wrote to his father that he often saw copies of his book in dugouts and that the men even referred to him as if he were its hero, Stepan Kolchugin.[133] The miners saw Grossman as one of themselves and the events he describes as entirely real.

A similar blurring of the boundary between literature and reality runs through much of Grossman's life and work. The figure of Viktor Shtrum, the nuclear physicist hero of Grossman's two Stalingrad novels, is based on that of his former teacher, Lev Shtrum, a Jewish-Ukrainian nuclear physicist executed in 1936.[134] The fictional Viktor Shtrum in turn prefigures the historical Andrey Sakharov, a similarly free-thinking nuclear physicist; the parallels between Viktor Shtrum and Sakharov are so close that one might well imagine that *Life and Fate* was itself responsible for Sakharov's turn to dissidence. This, though, is impossible; Sakharov's first act of open dissidence was in May 1968, when he circulated an essay on intellectual freedom – and there is no record of his having read *Life and Fate* before 1973. Grossman's fictional creation is not only a way of commemorating an important teacher – it is also close to an act of prophecy.

Two of the main figures in *The People Immortal* – Commissar Bogariov and Captain Babadjanian – provide similar examples of this interplay between literature and reality. The novel's central plot is based on an account given to Grossman in September 1941 by Regimental Commissar Nikolay Shliapin of how, earlier that summer, he led an ad hoc unit of Red Army soldiers and commanders out of German encirclement. Antony Beevor describes Grossman's meeting with Shliapin at the Briansk Front HQ in *A Writer at War*[135] and Grossman gives another, slightly fictionalized account of it in *Stalingrad*. Grossman's transcript of Shliapin's account takes up about six pages of his wartime notebooks. A comparison of these pages with corresponding passages in the novel shows how closely the latter is based on reality; even episodes or conversations one might think fanciful or propagandist have their counterpart in the notebooks.

Soon after his meeting with Grossman, Shliapin was caught in encirclement a second time; this time he did not survive. Wanting to pay homage to him, Grossman changed his name to Bogariov and made him a central figure in *The People Immortal*, creating an image that readers evidently found inspiring. According to a commissar who wrote to the editor of *Red Star*, "Grossman has succeeded in creating the image of a true, strong-willed commissar. It is not for nothing that, when things get difficult, one asks oneself how Bogariov would have acted in this situation."[136] And according to a political department lecturer who also wrote to

Red Star, "*The People Immortal* is a lasting work of art, a textbook for our commissars that they can read with pleasure."[137]

In similar vein, the two generals who played the most important roles in the defence of Stalingrad both spoke about how much Tolstoy meant to them. General Rodimtsev said he read *War and Peace* three times, and General Chuikov said in a 1943 interview that Tolstoy's generals were the model by which he judged his own performance.[138] There is a two-way movement; literature draws its inspiration from reality – and real people are then inspired by literary creations. This may be especially true with regard to Russia, where literature has long played a socio-political role of exceptional importance.

In Babadjanian's case, the relationship between literature and reality is still more complex. In September 1941, Grossman wanted to write about the 395th Rifle Regiment, which was holding a small area of ground on the west bank of the River Kleven, in Ukraine. Grossman applied to visit this regiment and speak to its commander, Major Hamazasp Babadjanian, and his soldiers. Considering this too dangerous, the authorities refused him permission. Six months later, having been informed that Babadjanian had been killed in action, Grossman lent his name to the Captain Babadjanian of *The People Immortal*. In 1944, however, Grossman visited a tank brigade in Ukraine, had dinner with its commander and eventually realized that this was the same Babadjanian who, three years earlier, had fought on the River Kleven. Babadjanian said affably, "But you killed me." Grossman replied, "I killed you, but I can bring you back to life too." The two men remained on good terms and in 1945, in Berlin, Grossman interviewed Babadjanian, who was by then a full colonel. On the basis of this interview, Grossman published an article titled "A Soviet Officer", which we include as an appendix.

Grossman's thinking was consistent over the years. What mattered to him during the war remained important to him for the rest of his life. The real Babadjanian served Grossman as a model not only for the young infantry commander in The People Immortal but also for Colonel Novikov in Stalingrad and Life and Fate. Novikov's thoughts about swift tank manoeuvres and the importance of coordination between tanks, aircraft, infantry and artillery are taken straight from Grossman's article about Colonel Babadjanian. More importantly, both Babadjanian and Novikov show courage of an unusual kind; they act decisively and according to their own judgment even when this entails ignoring orders from their superiors. Babadjanian's victory at Yelnya, as described in the article, is a model for Novikov's successful tank corps manoeuvre at Stalingrad; just as Babadjanian contravenes direct orders from his divisional commander, so Novikov contravenes orders from Stalin himself.

★

Stalin's explanation for the disasters of the war's first months was that the Germans were, at the time, better equipped with tanks and aircraft.[139] Many contemporary historians doubt this, saying that it was not so much a matter of the Germans' technical superiority as of their superior organization – their ability to employ their tanks, aircraft and other equipment in an effective, coordinated manner. In The People Immortal, Grossman repeats Stalin's explanation and he may, at the time, have believed it. Nevertheless, he clearly understood that there was a more important factor: the incompetence of the Soviet military leadership.

In 1937, at the height of the Purges, Stalin had removed from their posts many of his most eminent commanders – three of the five marshals, thirteen of the fifteen army commanders, and a similar proportion of other senior generals; some were executed, others merely demoted. The two most brilliant and forward-thinking – Marshal Tukhachevsky and Army Commander Iona Yakir – were both executed, absurdly accused of treason. In foresight and tactical understanding, Tukhachevsky and Yakir were the equals of Heinz Guderian and Erwin Rommel; like them, they were advocates of highly mobile warfare, entailing close cooperation between tanks and aircraft. Had they been still alive in summer 1941, had their gifts and understandings been valued in the Soviet Union as Rommel and Guderian's were in Germany, the initial stages of Operation Barbarossa might have gone very differently. As it was, the Red Army relied to an excessive degree on a system of fixed defences, most of which proved as ineffectual as the Maginot Line in France.

The men who replaced the executed or demoted marshals and senior commanders were mostly young and easily intimidated. And in the late summer and autumn of 1941 they were terrified, above all, of being held to account under the draconian Stavka Order no. 270. This forbade any unauthorised retreat and required everyone to fight to the death, even when surrounded. Commanders were also expected to remain present on the battlefield, not to conduct a battle from a command post further back.

Lack of experience, along with fear of being scapegoated, made it almost impossible for a commander to respond freely and creatively to a military situation that was changing day by day. On the one hand, units were flung into battle without the least preparation; on the other hand, they were expected to hold out in defensive positions that were clearly untenable. Grossman witnessed all this many times. He was also well aware how, in June 1941, Stalin had left the armed forces totally unready for a German invasion that his intelligence agents had repeatedly told him was inevitable. In his notebooks, Grossman wrote, "When the war began, many of our senior commanders and generals were on holiday in Sochi. Many tank units were having their engines replaced. Many artillery units were without shells and many aircraft without fuel."[140]

Grossman's portraits of Bogariov and Babadjanian are idealized; he wanted to honour two men he admired. Being almost unblemished, however, neither of these figures can evolve. Major Mertsalov, however, changes a great deal in the course of the novel; with Bogariov's help, he learns an important lesson. The Mertsalov we meet in the first chapters, for all his attractive good cheer and fearlessness, embodies many of the main faults of Soviet commanders during the first year of the war. The Mertsalov of the final chapters embodies Grossman's hopes for change – hopes that in many respects were fulfilled.

Mertsalov's name is derived from the verb *mertsat'*, which means "to glimmer". During the Soviet–Finnish War of 1939–40 Mertsalov was awarded the Soviet Union's highest honour, that of Hero of the Soviet Union. He is, no doubt, accustomed to admiration. It is not surprising that he is dumbfounded when, in chapter ten, Bogariov subjects him to fierce criticism, accusing him, in effect, of being over-ready to play the hero – or rather, over-ready to slip into acting with a kind of blind, unthinking heroism.

Instead of charging forward at the head of his men, Bogariov suggests, Mertsalov should stay at his command post and apply himself to the more demanding and responsible task of coordinating the actions of his various units. Mertsalov is stung by these criticisms. In the end, though, he proves big-hearted enough to benefit from them.

Mertsalov engages with the Germans three times. His first battle is a partial victory, which he fails to capitalize on because of poor planning. His second engagement is a dispiriting failure. The final battle, however, is a brilliant success – and Grossman goes to some length to explain how and why he achieves this. First, Mertsalov had "elaborated his battle plan in a completely new way, with almost academic rigour". Second, he directs the battle from a command post in the rear, which allows him to communicate effectively with his subordinates. Third, he has the courage, flexibility and creativity to switch to a completely different plan when he realizes that his original tactics are failing; among other things, this change of plan entails withdrawing his infantry without authorization. Mertsalov thus contravenes Order no. 270 in at least two respects. Had his change of plan failed, he would probably have been shot – as his chief of staff has warned him.

Grossman describes Mertsalov's change of plan as a moment of true creativity, an insight arising from the depths of his being. In his two Stalingrad novels, Grossman writes in similar terms about Viktor Shtrum's moments of insight into the structure of the atomic nucleus. And in an article published in 1944, he writes with no less admiration about a young sapper who comes up with a novel method of saving a bridge that the retreating Germans have set on fire. The sapper rushes up to the bridge and tosses hand grenades into the river below; huge fountains of water then extinguish the flames.[141] The importance of independence, inspiration and alert open-mindedness in all fields of thought and action – from scientific research and artistic creativity to the conduct of a battle or the routine activities of everyday life – is a central theme of all Grossman's work.

In a letter written on 25 February 1942, about six weeks before he began work on The People Immortal, Grossman wrote to his father, "What wonderful people we have here – and so many of them! What modesty and simplicity. And what kindness, going strangely hand in hand with a soldierly severity." Grossman's portrayal of Semion Ignatiev and his fellow soldiers may seem idealized, yet he succeeds in showing us the world through the eyes of these men. His description of the new recruits marching at night through unharvested fields and recognizing the different cereal crops "by the swish of falling seeds, by the creak of straw underfoot and by the rustle of the stalks that clung to their tunics" has the ring of truth. His account of Ignatiev's feelings as he watches the Germans at rest – eating, drinking and relaxing in a village just like his own – is equally convincing. It is also worth noting that Ignatiev – no less than Bogariov, the bookish intellectual – is often a mouthpiece for Grossman's own ideas and feelings. Ignatiev's concern about the harm the war is doing to the world of birds, insects and animals is Grossman's own concern, expressed at greater length in Stalingrad.

Ignatiev is honourable and reliable, but he is also a trickster. And he enjoys telling "funny, sly, sometimes frightening stories about a Red Army soldier whom Hitler had taken it into his head to do battle with". Both Ignatiev and the hero of the stories he tells have much in common with the trickster hero of Alexander Tvardovsky's comic epic *Vasily Tiorkin*. Ignatiev tells stories and plays the guitar; Tiorkin sings and plays the concertina. Both men fight a one-to-one duel with a German soldier. Ignatiev's antagonist represents a "god of unjust war"; Tiorkin's represents death. Grossman and Tvardovsky knew each other well and Grossman was working on *The People Immortal* at the same time as Tvardovsky was composing his poem. *Red Star* published Grossman's novel in July–August 1942, and Tvardovsky's hugely popular poem in September 1942. Grossman's mention of Ignatiev's storytelling may be a friendly acknowledgement of the work of his fellow writer. Or it may simply be that both Grossman and Tvardovsky drew their inspiration from the same source, that Red Army soldiers really did tell humorous stories about the exploits of picaresque soldiers like Tiorkin. There are, after all, many Russian traditional folk tales whose heroes are similarly bold, lucky and cunning.[142]

As always, Grossman's sense of balance is unerring. The story's optimistic ending is almost certainly a sincere expression of faith on his part and he is, of course, aware of his duty to instil hope in his readers. Nevertheless, he does not for a moment look away from the pain and suffering undergone on the path to victory. Babadjanian and Nevtulov are dead. Cherednichenko's mother, Maria Timofeyevna, has been shot – an incident that, no doubt, reflects Grossman's anxiety about the fate of his own mother, whom he had failed to persuade to join him in Moscow. As for the final paragraph, with its affirmation of eternal brotherhood between the Red Army soldier and the commissar, this is a fine example of Grossman's unique ability to infuse new life into a Soviet cliché.

In one of the first chapters, Babadjanian says to a commander who is over-concerned about compliance with military regulations, "What's all this about norms? The only norm I know is Victory!" At a key moment towards the end of the novel, as he steels himself to go through with his new battle plan, Mertsalov remembers these words. Babadjanian's apparently simple remark is another example of Grossman's ability to reconcile conflicting demands. Few writers could come up with two such short, memorable sentences that are both morale-boosting and sharply critical of the military establishment. Babadjanian's words gain added power from their link to Mertsalov's earlier complaint about his chief of staff's obsession with "norms and forms". And it is hard to imagine anyone – rank-and-file soldier or senior commissar – objecting to these words. They might very well even have pleased Stalin himself.

2. Manuscript and typescript versions

Both the original manuscript and the typescript of The People Immortal can be studied in the main state literary archive in Moscow.[143] Both are dated 22 June 1941, the first anniversary of the German invasion, but this date is clearly symbolic; on 12 June, in a letter to his father, Grossman wrote, "Things seem to be going well with my novel. The editor read it yesterday and praised it excitedly. He summoned me at night and smothered me in kisses. He said any number of flattering things and promised to publish it in Red Star without any cuts."[144] There are also two more typescripts, with both authorial and editorial corrections, in the section of the state archive devoted to the journal Znamia,

The ruins of Gomel, 8 August 1941.

which republished the novel in August 1942, immediately after *Red Star*.

The manuscript is the longest of the several versions. It includes not only passages deleted by Grossman himself but also passages omitted at a later stage by editors and censors. Together with the typescript, where some passages appear in shortened versions and others have been entirely removed, it allows one a glimpse of Grossman's working methods. It also makes it possible to reinstate passages one can reasonably assume to have been omitted against Grossman's wishes.

Many of the most interesting omissions relate to Bogariov. In the manuscript, as well as being a vehicle for Nikolay Shliapin's experience of encirclement, he has much in common with Grossman himself. Like Grossman, he lacks military training and has been flung straight from his study into what he calls the "fiery cauldron of the war". Like Grossman, he is deeply shaken by the firebombing of Gomel. Like Grossman, he is a free-thinking intellectual with a wide range of interests and a sympathy with the first generation of Russian revolutionaries.

Several paragraphs of the manuscript are devoted to Bogariov's pre-war career, as a philosopher on the staff of the Karl Marx and Friedrich Engels Institute. Founded in 1921, this was an independent institution dedicated to serious archival research, its main task being to bring out scholarly editions of the works of Marx and Engels, and of other early Marxists: Georgy Plekhanov, Paul Lafargue, Karl Kautsky, Franz Mehring and Rosa Luxemburg. There were even plans to publish the work of one of Marx's main ideological opponents, the anarchist philosopher Mikhail Bakunin. All this testifies to a surprising degree of open-mindedness; it is no surprise that Victor Serge, a fierce critic of Stalin, praises the institute, saying of its founder and director, David Borisovich Riazanov, "Alone, he had never ceased to cry out against the death penalty, even during the Terror, and never ceased to demand the strict limitation of the rights of the Cheka and its successor, the OGPU.[145] Heretics of all kinds, Menshevik Socialists or Oppositionists of Right or Left, found peace and work in his institute, provided only that they had a love of knowledge."[146]

In 1927, however, as Stalin began to consolidate his power, the institute's research work was curtailed, and in 1931 Riazanov was arrested and exiled to Saratov. This marked the end of the institute as an independent organization. More than half of the 243 employees were dismissed and the institute was eventually taken under the auspices of the Communist Party's Central Committee. The next two decades saw purges directed against "Riazanovites". Riazanov himself was re-arrested in 1938 and then shot.

In the manuscript, Bogariov is himself portrayed as a "Riazanovite"; he studies archival documents, takes part in philosophical debates and is writing a long theoretical work; the institute's directors and even the Central Committee take an active interest in his research. Grossman must have realized that this was unacceptable; he deleted from the manuscript most of the passages about Bogariov's philosophical concerns and recasts him simply as "a professor at one of the main Moscow higher education institutes". Such acts of self-censorship, however, were not enough to placate Grossman's editors. Bogariov's long conversation with the old lawyer was deleted from the Red Star version, and yet more passages were deleted from subsequent published editions.

Grossman may well have known Riazanov personally, perhaps

through his cousin Nadya Almaz, whose close connections with Victor Serge led to her arrest in 1933 and subsequent exile. There is certainly no doubt that Grossman wanted to commemorate Riazanov, even if he could do this only through the subtlest of hints. There is one such hint in the first chapter – a mention of letters sent by Marx to Lafargue; Grossman and at least a few of his readers would have known that it was Riazanov who first published this correspondence. In the manuscript Bogariov says to his wife, "I read several amazing letters from Marx to Lafargue. They were in some old archive and they've only recently been discovered." The *Red Star* version of this passage is identical except that the unexpected word "amazing" (*izumitel'nykh*) has been omitted. In the text of the later published books, however, this sentence has been cut down to "I read a letter from Marx." Here, at least, Grossman seems to have been fighting a losing battle.

Grossman is often seen as a relatively plain and straightforward writer; he knew how to address a mass readership and he had little sympathy with the hermeticism of many more modernist writers. In his late memoir *An Armenian Sketchbook*, he wrote, "Sometimes I think that the poetry of the twentieth century, for all its brilliance, has less of the universal humanity and passion that imbues the great poetry of the nineteenth century. As if poetry had moved from a bakery to a jeweller's shop and great bakers had been replaced by great jewellers." It would be wrong, though, to imagine that all Grossman's work is entirely transparent. Like Isaak Babel and Andrey Platonov, he knew how to exploit hints and silences. Censorship often made it impossible for him even to hint at something important, as he tried to do with these letters from Marx to Lafargue. When it was clear that a subject was absolutely taboo, he adopted a different strategy. Rather than simply keeping silent, he went out of his way to draw attention to his silence, thus prompting readers to think for themselves about what it might be that he was leaving unsaid.

Thus, in the course of the novel, Bogariov takes part in three important long conversations. The first – about Lenin's policies in 1917 – is with the old lawyer in Gomel; this is present in the manuscript but was omitted from all the published editions. The second conversation is with Cherednichenko; Grossman emphasizes how important this conversation was to both men, but says not a word – even in the manuscript – about what they discussed: "In the company of Bogariov, Cherednichenko was a changed man, anything but taciturn; once he had sat in his office with Bogariov and talked almost the whole night through. Orlovsky had hardly been able to believe it; he had never heard Cherednichenko speak so loudly and animatedly, asking questions, listening and then speaking again. When he went in, they were both looking flushed; it seemed, though, that the two men were not arguing but simply talking about something that really mattered to them." Reading between the lines, we can be sure that Bogariov and Cherednichenko were discussing history and politics and that they were criticizing Stalin. This understanding is confirmed by two of the passages we have reinstated from the manuscript: the account of Bogariov's work at the Marx–Engels Institute and Bogariov's exhortation to his men in the forest. Instead of the customary invocation of Stalin, he concludes, "Within you beats the heart of Lenin!" This is surprising – and the total absence of any mention of Stalin in any version of the novel is truly astonishing.

Grossman tells us equally little about Bogariov's long

night-time conversation with Ignatiev, saying only that "It was Bogariov who spoke and Ignatiev who listened. And Bogariov's words would stay in his memory." Here again, though, a reader can infer that the two men have been speaking about the general hardships of peasant life and, above all, about collectivization and the subsequent famine. This is clear from Ignatiev's last words in the conversation, "We've been through a great deal. There are times we've gone without food. But this is our life. And it's the only life I have." Ignatiev has already said that when he was first called up, the war didn't seem that important to him. No doubt, he saw conscription simply as yet another imposition on the part of a brutal government. Now, though, after witnessing the fire-bombing of Gomel and the death of Vera, and after listening to Bogariov, Ignatiev senses anew how deeply he loves his homeland. He now has no doubt that his land is worth fighting for.

⋆

There are yet other respects in which a study of the original manuscript bears witness to Grossman's determination to write truthfully. Rather like Major Mertsalov, Grossman had to struggle to avoid easy heroics, to stay in command of the work and not let himself be carried away. His first version of the beginning of the battle at the collective farm is dramatic and colourful:

"By the time the sentry fired a burst from his sub-machine gun, the soldier was only fifteen metres from the hay. One of the bullets got him in the left hand, but he still managed to throw a Molotov cocktail into the largest of the ricks.

"The soldier dashed away. The sentry chased after him,

shouting and firing bursts from his sub-machine gun. Other sentries, who had been standing beside the tanks, also ran towards the soldier. The soldier suddenly stopped, loudly and merrily yelled out some powerful Russian obscenities, tossed a grenade at the Germans and slipped into a roadside ditch overgrown with tall, dust-covered weeds and grass. From there, he made his way back into the orchard. At this point the Germans lost sight of him. All they could do was fire at random, trying to guess at his whereabouts from the noise he made running between the low apple trees and brushing against their dense foliage. This soldier's bold act did a great deal to ensure the success of the night battle."

All this sounds too good to be true. Evidently realizing this, Grossman deleted both paragraphs and replaced them with a bleak statement of fact, "By the time the sentry turned his sub-machine gun on him, the soldier was only a few metres from the ricks. After throwing a Molotov cocktail into the hay, he fell to the ground – dead." And in the typescript, Grossman added a few more words to a sentence at the beginning of this episode. Casually, as if it didn't really matter, he mentions that no-one remembered the name of this soldier. The death of a single soldier is indeed quickly forgotten in a war between two huge states. In Grossman's view, however, it is these simple acts of individual bravery that lead the Red Army to victory.

Grossman's straightforward treatment of death was at odds with the prim, almost neoclassical conventions of Soviet war literature and it is not surprising that most of his descriptions of the dead and the dying were bowdlerized – weakened either by self-censorship or by editorial intervention. The clearest example of this is the passage about the two corpses – those of the old lawyer and Vera the young refugee – in the chapter about the fire-bombing of Gomel. First, Grossman deleted the clause, "The old lawyer's corpse was so mutilated." At a later stage, working with the typescript, his editors deleted two more clauses, "the whole upper half of his body was deformed – his skull smashed and his ribcage shattered." The following paragraph originally read, "The carter had just appeared. Evidently already accustomed to dealing with the dead, he took a rough hold of the young woman's legs and shouted crossly, 'Hey, you lot, someone give me a hand!'" Here too Grossman censored himself, aware no doubt that such forthrightness was unacceptable. His blander final version reads simply, "The carter had just appeared. He took hold of the young woman's legs and shouted, 'Hey, someone give me a hand!'"

3. Red Star, Pravda, the published book and the first translations

The People Immortal was first commissioned for publication in separate issues of Red Star (19 July–12 August 1942). This evidently determined the novel's structure. Grossman knew that many of his readers would not be able to count on receiving every issue of the newspaper, and so he divided the novel into eighteen short chapters, each of which can stand on its own. This structure also made it easy for him, later that year, to prepare a shorter, thirteen-chapter version to be published by Pravda as a small book.

Among the readers of the Pravda version was Vladimir Minorsky, a professor of Persian Studies at London University. Deeply impressed, Minorsky wrote both to Grossman and to Thomas Hudson-Williams, a fellow Orientalist and gifted linguist who had already published translations of Pushkin, Lermontov, Gogol and other Russian classics into Welsh. Hudson-Williams promptly translated *The People Immortal* and his version was published in 1945, in Caernarfon. The first English translation, by Elizabeth Donnelly and Rose Prokofiev, had been published in Moscow in 1943; and a slapdash adaptation of this, titled *No Beautiful Nights*, had been published in New York in 1944. The Donnelly/Prokofiev translation was republished in London in 1945.

Grossman's last revisions to the Russian text were in summer or autumn 1945, after the end of the war. He made several changes to the order of the chapters and divided some chapters into two. The new, twenty-two-chapter version included some previously unpublished passages. Grossman also chose to omit several of the fiercer expressions of hatred towards the Germans and the desire for revenge; no doubt, he felt the time to encourage such feelings had passed.

It is this revised and expanded version that *Pravda* republished as a separate book in 1945, with a print run of two hundred thousand copies, and that was republished in *The Years of War* (*Gody voiny*) in 1945, 1946 and 1947 and in all subsequent Russian editions. And it is this version – with the addition of numerous previously unpublished passages from the manuscript and type-script – that provides the basis for this new English translation.

Robert Chandler and Julia Volohova (September 2021)

Commissar Shliapin (1902–1941)

Grossman first met Nikolay Shliapin, the regimental commissar of the 50th Army, in late September 1941. Much of *The People Immortal* is based on Shliapin's account – recorded by Grossman in his wartime notebooks – of his escape from encirclement. Grossman's Commissar Bogariov is in many respects modelled on Shliapin; in *Stalingrad*, however, Shliapin makes a brief appearance under his own name. In October 1941, Shliapin fell into encirclement a second time, along with the entire 50th Army. He died later that month, possibly killing himself to avoid being taken prisoner.

The experience of encirclement is well described in a diary kept by Ivan Shabalin, the courageous and clear-minded head of the 50th Army's political section.[147] On 9 October, Shabalin wrote, "Our army is in a tragic situation: we no longer have any idea where the rear is, or where the front line is to be found – it is impossible to tell anymore. And we have suffered such terrible losses."[148] Shabalin was killed later that month. The historian Michael Jones sums up one passage from his diary as follows, "Shabalin, an ambitious NKVD officer responsible for army education, realized that he no longer needed to give political lectures or issue instructions to the men around him. The comradeship binding his group of fighters together was enough in itself. And as Shabalin realized that, he felt a remarkable sense of peace."[149] In *Stalingrad*, Grossman ascribes similar thoughts to Commissar Krymov – though Shabalin's diaries were first published only in 1974, ten years after Grossman's death. Here, as so often, Grossman's intuition was unerring.

The following two accounts – Shliapin's and his adjutant's – have been translated, without cuts, from the original manuscript of Grossman's notebooks.[150] Antony Beevor, surprisingly, omits these pages from his edition of *A Writer's Notebook*. He writes, "Shliapin's account was inevitably coloured by the Soviet formulae of the time and by exaggerated figures of enemy strengths and losses, yet the basic facts and the heroism of Shliapin's leadership were almost certainly accurate."[151] There is no doubt that Shliapin exaggerated many of his figures, but Beevor is wrong to see his account as formulaic. On the contrary, Shliapin is often astonishingly forthright.

★

Nikolay Alexeyevich Shliapin, Regimental Commissar, Member of the Military Council of the 50th Army. His account of how he broke out of encirclement

(He is intelligent, strong, calm, large and slow. People sense his inner power over them.)

September 1941. Briansk Front
On 24 July, the 94th division was in battle near the shtetl of Balashovo. One regiment was crushed by German tanks. The men fled, deciding to cross the River Vep at night. The enemy anticipated

this, occupied the crossings and opened fire; our men ran. I intercepted them in the forest and assembled five groups. With 150 men and four howitzers I decided to attempt a breakthrough near Mamonovo. On reaching the village, we were surrounded by 25 tanks and our guns were put out of action. Once again, everyone ran into the forest. There I assembled another group – 100 frightened, demoralized men, with four heavy machine guns. The division and the general had crossed to the other bank. A German tank group had concentrated close by; we could hear German speech. I ordered the men to rest and I sent out scouts; there turned out to be about 700 tanks. The forest round about was quite young, not at all dense. At ten in the evening, I gathered the men together and said, "We're not afraid of the Germans – it's the Germans who're afraid of us. We'll attempt another breakthrough. Agreed?" "Agreed!" Near Priglov the Germans sent up flares and everyone scattered. There were only 20 men left. I spent the night collecting our men together again. In the end there were 120 of us. I decided to move still further behind the enemy front line, to regroup. We came across some HQ staff and 40 more soldiers. We went deep into the forest, following a compass bearing due west. We encountered more men, along with the divisional HQ, under the command of Lieutenant Colonel Svetlichny. We decided to postpone the breakthrough. We found another 500 men and formed a regiment, in addition to the 2,000 men from divisional HQ. On 29 July we made another unsuccessful attempt to break through the enemy front line. Svetlichny escaped. We found a leaflet about how to act in encirclement; I interpreted it as an order. I took command, along with Lieutenant Colonel Beliavsky. Our goal now: not to break through the front line, but to go further west and strike at the German rear echelons. During the night of 30 July, the Germans sent three armoured cars into our forest. Our cannon put one out of action; the others withdrew. The Germans threw in an infantry battalion; we put it to flight. We continued west, still deeper into the German rear.

I still remember that first night, the first of our attempts at a breakout. I soon realized that we needed more time, that I could not achieve anything quickly with men like these. The Germans sent up flares. I shouted, "Do as I do!" – and lay down on the ground. The men lay down. We moved on. More flares. "Lie down!" I looked around. The men had all taken to their heels. They were running back into the forest. I held up a grenade. "Stop!" I yelled. "Or else!" I threw the grenade. No-one even looked back. At that, I lost my rag. "Well, you bastards," I said to myself, "I'll make heroes out of you yet." And so I did.

On 31 July I decided to divide the division into five detachments and divide each detachment into companies. We organized an HQ and titled ourselves a combined division. We set up a political section, a prosecutor's office and a Party department. I assigned each company and detachment a commander and a commissar, and I told these commanders and commissars that there was to be no more talk of a breakout. Our mission was to strike – and keep striking – at the enemy rear. I ordered everyone to wear collar tabs and to draw or sew on badges of rank. Any failure to give proper salutes was punished. For any slightest infringement of discipline, soldiers were subject to either two or three days of strict arrest. According to the rule book, they'd have been put on bread and water – but since we had no bread, they had to make do with water. All this had its effect. I ordered a few men to be shot. One was a sergeant who had grabbed a peasant woman by the throat.

My second task was to instil a taste for combat. We began with small things: an attack on a lone motorcyclist, taking a German prisoner. Taking two motorcyclists prisoner and seizing their motorcycles was a real morale-booster. On 4 August we captured another motorcycle. In reality, this meant little, since neither a man on a motorcycle, nor a man in a sidecar, can be combat-ready and no-one can shoot accurately from a sidecar. But getting my men onto motorcycles certainly did a lot for their spirits. We captured 20 motorcycles and an armoured vehicle. Then we carried out a major operation; we attacked a large column of 70 vehicles. Our artillery fired on them; we silenced their artillery and their infantry fled. Lieutenant Griniuk put a detachment of eleven motorcyclists to flight. This still further boosted the soldiers' morale. Then we captured twelve motorcycles, eight prisoners and two staff cars. We knocked out one tank and two armoured vehicles and attacked a column transporting a German regimental HQ – 800 men. We attacked a mortar battery and artillery positions.

We sent out scouts to check the river crossings and contact our main forces. One of our commissars was taken prisoner. The Germans did not feed prisoners, they ordered the kolkhoz workers to feed them. The kolkhoz workers gave their scythes to the prisoners, and about 60 of these prisoners made off into the forest, now armed with scythes.

On 7 July we were joined by General Boldin, along with a hundred men. On 8 July he took over the command. We sent out four groups of scouts, ordering one of these scouts, political officer Osipov, to contact Konev.[152] He did this. Konev set a date for a joint action. Meanwhile, we did not waste time. We learned that the Germans were about to slaughter 20 cows. We sent a party to kill the Germans, then brought back the cows. The Germans prepared another 28 cows. Kolkhoz workers informed us of this, and we took these cows too.

Political work: combining democracy and severity.

"Why aren't you defending your motherland?"

"Our commanders abandoned us!"

"I'm assigning you a task. If you fail, I'll shoot you!"

"Did you hear the shots?"

"Yes."

"Do you know the sergeant?"

"Yes."

"I shot him because of a woman kolkhoz worker. He seized her by the throat."

"You did right."

"Are you all ready for a breakout?"

"Yes, we are!"

Back at the beginning, I remember, we had to destroy two German machine guns. I said, "I'm going myself. Who'll go with me?" Not a word from a soul. "Who'll go with me? Raise your hand." No-one moved. "So – if there are no daredevils to hand, it seems I'll have to create some."

We captured a few signallers. Our men cut the cable and hid in the bushes. Then a signaller would show up. There's no need for mindless bureaucracy and no need to yell – you can make a brave man out of anyone. Discipline: stand tall, correct salutes, uniforms in good order. As a test, I ordered four commanders and two politinstructors to capture a truck on the highway. They came back empty-handed. "For this, I shall shoot you . . . Hey, get me a sub-machine gun." There they stand, drenched in sweat. At the last minute I say, "Or maybe you'd rather serve our motherland?" After that, they distinguished themselves. They destroyed a truck and an armoured car. I had no better men.

We ate meat without salt and without bread.

We had 70 seriously wounded. We treated all of them and took all of them with us. Some thought we should leave them for the kolkhoz workers to take care of, but I did not allow this. We took every one of them with us, we took all of them out of encirclement. One medical orderly came up with the idea of squeezing the juice from raspberries and blueberries. This really helped the men to recover.

Pashkov was captured during a reconnaissance mission. The Germans lumbered him with all their gear, with their equipment and ammo. They took him to their HQ. Immediate interrogation.

"Who is your commander there in the forest?"

"We have no commander."

"How many of you are there?"

"Thirty-eight."

"You making fun of us, you bastard?"

"No."

"Eating dead horse meat, I suppose?"

"What do you mean? We've got meat, cereals, butter, honey and bread."

After he'd replied like that, three Germans took him to the edge of the forest and gave him a spade. "Dig!" He dug about thirty centimetres deep. "All right. That's all you need. Off with your boots." They put bullets through both his shoulders. He fell to the ground and they threw earth over him. He got up out of the pit and crawled back to join us. Pale, half-dead, he was taken around the different units. He told everyone his story. It had quite an effect on the soldiers.

We began to publish a newspaper, *For the Motherland*. Five issues. We included SovInform Bureau bulletins we'd been listening to on a captured radio. We reported our men's exploits. The newspaper was a success. The editor was my adjutant, Lieutenant Klenovkin.

Thirteen of our men made contact with the women in a village. During the day, they mowed the hay, and at night they attacked the Germans. With time we got bolder and cheekier, and the Germans got more and more frightened. First they'd send in their tanks and unleash a hail of random fire into the trees – and then their trucks would tear through the forest at full throttle.

Our Communists took up their leading role again. At first, they'd kept rather quiet.

Our doctor unexpectedly encountered relatives in the forest – six Jews who'd escaped from Minsk, along with some old men and children. It was like in a fairy tale. We set three of the girls to look after the wounded. Then we came across another twelve people. One was a very old man indeed – a Jew with a cow harnessed to a cart. We got him out too, safe and sound. When we finally broke through, they all followed behind.

At first there were cowards saying we'd never get out in such numbers. Better to split up, they made out, so we'd be less conspicuous. There was a lot of fear at that time. I remember a conversation with the regimental chief of staff, Captain Lysov. "Comrade Commissar," he said, "you should tear off your collar tabs."[153] "Do you really think I'll let them take me alive?" I replied.

And Lysov had been decorated! There were a lot of men speaking in whispers then: "Comrade Commissar, allow me to report – the enemy!" But it was only the sound of birds.

At first, men didn't bother to wash or shave. I insisted on absolute correctness. And I myself washed and shaved like nobody's business.

My own biography's simple enough: Red Army soldier, then company librarian, then assistant politinstructor, then politinstructor, politlecturer, Party bureau secretary, instructor, regimental commissar, head of the political department, divisional commissar and Member of the Army Military Soviet. My background – working class, from Mariupol. In the army since 1919. A Bolshevik since a factory strike in 1916.

During those days in the forest, I got on well with the soldiers. One of the men gave me an embroidered tobacco pouch as a keepsake, along with some precious home-grown tobacco. Another said, "I've saved you a tin of meat." I told him to share it with his comrades.

And so, the day came for our real test, the decisive battle. We concentrated our forces. Everyone had rifles and cartridges. We had eight 76 mm guns, three 45 mm anti-tank guns, about 20 heavy machine guns, 60 light machine guns and some company mortars. And the men I had struggled so hard to bring together. We attacked the Germans from behind. Our well-coordinated blow caused panic. We killed 1,500 men, destroyed 100 vehicles, 130 motorcycles, two anti-aircraft batteries and one artillery unit. Our yells of "U-u-r-a-a!" were loud enough to reach Konev six kilometres away. One soldier yelled so loud and gave such a fright to three officers drinking coffee beside a bush that he managed to

THE PEOPLE IMMORTAL

shoot them with their own sub-machine gun. Another soldier killed three Germans, then sat down in their trench to eat a tin of their meat. I shouted at him. He replied, "Comrade Commissar, I've got to have something to eat – I'll deal with them bastards in a moment!"

I saw with my own eyes how a "coward" I knew put 40 Germans to flight, stabbing eight of them with his bayonet. Those who had run like hares on that first day fought like lions. As we approached the German HQ, shrapnel shells were bursting above us, but no-one bowed their heads. Everyone stood tall. Once again, I remembered the night everyone had fled in panic from the German flares. And so, we got everyone out – the wounded, the women and children, the old people who'd joined us in the forest. We even took our prisoners with us. And 70 sheep, 40 cows, 100 carts, etc.

Our meeting with the main Russian forces was wonderful. We hugged and kissed, they gave us makhorka and bread. We broke through on the 11th and were fighting again on the 13th. We'd held a meeting after 24 hours and someone had asked, "How much longer are we going to be sitting about doing nothing?" I found it sad to part with the men. They were all workers from Donetsk, my fellow countrymen.

(I heard all this from Shliapin himself. We were in a barn, lying on some hay, with bombs thudding round about. Later, in the same barn, young Valya turned on the phonograph and we listened to "Little Blue Kerchief".[154] Slim aspens trembled from all the explosions and tracer bullets were climbing up into the sky.)

★

Junior politinstructor Klenovkin, adjutant to Nikolay Alexeyevich Shliapin. His account

Klenovkin is as huge and broad-shouldered as Shliapin, but very young and thin. Here is his account:

Reconnaissance – movement, firepower. On hot days the horses snort. They tinkle and jangle their bits. We had to abandon them. To begin with, we ate them. There was a German HQ in the Sekachi district, in the village of Gunino. We saw the Germans shaving, drinking tea and listening to gramophones.

We watched from beside the road.

I was put in charge of provisions. I went to a village. I took one soldier with me. I could see through my binoculars that the village was full of Germans. We went to a second village – more Germans. Then two of our soldiers saw a broken-down German truck. It was carrying loaves of bread. The soldiers began to unload the bread into tarpaulins. A sudden noise, an armoured vehicle approaching. We dragged the bread into the bushes and watched. The Germans jumped out, babbled away and shrugged their shoulders. One of them fired a round into the forest – and off they drove.

On the 25th the commissar deployed us for battle – infantry in front and artillery behind. We came to a clearing, just outside a village. We entered the village, the commissar on a grey horse. We were quickly surrounded by tanks and armoured vehicles. The commissar gave the command, "Into battle!" We knocked out two tanks, but then the divisional commander got cold feet. The commissar ran to the gun crews and began to command them himself. The commissar ordered, "Retreat to the forest!" We retreated, firing back at the sub-machine-gunners. The commissar was calm and courageous, never flustered. If the men heard that he had appeared, they would all want to be with him. He spent all his time with the men, talking, listening, wanting to get a sense of the general mood. For something to smoke, we used dried clover leaves. We published seven issues of our newspaper, there were two women typists.

The commissar rode between the different units on a motorcycle.

We used a sapper's boat[155] to fetch water, from a forester's house by a stream. First, our observers watched from the trees while the Germans fetched water. Then they shouted, "All clear now!"

In battle the commissar walked about calmly and slowly. And his orders were calm and straightforward – you wouldn't have thought we were fighting. The men would all look at him, thinking, "The Commissar's with us."

Marshal Babadjanian (1906–1977)

In November 1945, Grossman wrote an article titled "A Soviet Officer" about Colonel Babadjanian, the model for the Captain Babadjanian of *The People Immortal*. Published in instalments, in five issues of *Red Star*, the article is interesting in many ways but is marred by excessive rhetoric. We have translated only the passages most relevant to *The People Immortal* and Grossman's two Stalingrad novels. And at some points we have substituted Grossman's notes from when he interviewed Babadjanian in Berlin; these are more concise, and sometimes very expressive.

One of the article's most striking features is the persistence with which Grossman repeats a simple thought – that the cost of victory must not be forgotten. In Berlin, in May 1945, one must remember the war's first months. Standing in a ceremonial uniform with medals on one's chest, one must remember the soldiers in wadded trousers and winter caps who battled tanks with only hand grenades or Molotov cocktails.

In July 1941, Babadjanian was a lieutenant colonel in command of an infantry regiment; by 1945, he was a full colonel in command of a tank corps. He eventually achieved very high rank indeed: Chief Marshal of the Soviet Tank Forces. During the war, he took part in both the Battle of Kursk (July–August 1943), the largest tank battle in history, and the Battle of Berlin. He was never in good health, he suffered from tuberculosis and he was wounded seven times – in the legs, chest, head, face and shoulder. In August 1944, in a battle with superior German forces, he survived only by a miracle. Incapacitated, coughing blood, with a damaged trachea, he was trapped in a burning tank. He was dragged to the cabin of another tank, but within a few minutes this tank too was ablaze. For a second time, he and another wounded commander were dragged out by a seemingly puny tankman. They then lay by a hayrick till nightfall, when they could be taken to a field hospital. The doctors could not understand how Babadjanian had survived ten hours with such severe wounds. Babadjanian, for his part, could not understand how a puny tankman could have twice rescued him and his fellow commander from a burning tank and then dragged both men a hundred metres, under fire, to the shelter of the hayrick. Grossman prefaces his account of this day with a paean to the depth of friendship between tankmen; like fishermen – he writes – tankmen understand that only an unfailing sense of brotherhood can enable them to survive in a hostile element, a world alien to human life. And he concludes – trying, no doubt, to counter the growing antisemitism of the time – with words of praise for the brotherhood of Soviet nations and a mention of the tankman being Jewish.

There is a paragraph about Babadjanian in Semion Lipkin's memoir of Grossman. It appears that Grossman stayed in contact with him after the war – and that he was, unsurprisingly, deeply pained when Babadjanian led a tank army to Budapest in November 1956, playing an important role in crushing the Hungarian Revolution.[156]

A comparison with other sources brings home how difficult it has always been for anyone – memoirist, journalist, historian or novelist – to write truthfully about the Soviet experience of the war. First, Babadjanian gives his date of birth as 1908, though he was, in fact, born in 1906; this may have been a slip on Grossman's part, but it is more likely that Babadjanian had got used to falsifying his year of birth, to avoid having to answer possibly awkward questions about his life before the Revolution. Second – perhaps out of vanity, perhaps to make a point about tactics and the importance of independent initiative – Babadjanian exaggerates his role in the battle of Yelnya; there is no mention of him in Jonathan Dimbleby's exhaustive history of Operation Barbarossa. Third, in his account of the battle by the River Kleven, Babadjanian fails to mention that his divisional commander, Colonel Akimenko, had refused his request for permission to withdraw to the east bank. Most important of all, Babadjanian does not so much as hint at the most terrible of the consequences of this refusal; according to Akimenko's personal account (a manuscript written in 1953 and preserved in a Ministry of Defence archive), when a German tank breakthrough isolated Babadjanian's regiment from its two neighbouring regiments, "an extraordinary incident occurred . . . About nine hundred men committed treachery. As if by command, this group rose up, threw away their rifles and, with raised hands, they proceeded to the side of the enemy tanks." Akimenko then ordered his artillery to fire on these men.[157] Babadjanian vividly conveys the desperateness of the fighting by the River Kleven; nevertheless, there was much that it would have been inconceivable for him to speak about except to the very closest of his family and friends, and in the strictest confidence.

By way of an introduction to Grossman's article we have translated this brief extract from a memoir by David Ortenberg, the editor of *Red Star*.[158]

★

Vasily Grossman's *The People Immortal* was published over eighteen issues of the newspaper, and readers' interest in it grew with each instalment.

Grossman and I spent eighteen evenings, sometimes nights, at my office, standing side by side as we proofread the chapter to be published the following day. He and I had no serious disagreements. But we had heated discussions over the ending: the much-loved hero, Ivan Babadjanian, dies. Both when I first read the manuscript and when I reread the last chapter in proof, I asked if it was possible to bring Babadjanian back to life.

Vasily Semionovich replied, "That would go against the truth of war." [. . .]

In autumn 1941, Grossman was in Ukraine, near the town of Glukhov. I learned that on the west bank of the River Kleven, on the few square kilometres we still held, Babadjanian's 395th Rifle Regiment was engaged in an unequal battle with the Germans. The regiment was fighting courageously, holding back the German advance and covering the withdrawal of the main part of our troops. Babadjanian more than once launched counter-attacks, even recapturing one village. Grossman saw this success as "a tiny seed of the great tree of victory". He decided to write about the heroes of this regiment and wanted to cross the river to join them. The political department did not allow this – it would have been too dangerous. Grossman was indignant, saying he could not write anything unless he met and talked to the combatants. He was still not given permission.

Later, when Grossman asked about the 395th Regiment, he was told that it had valiantly carried out its mission but had suffered heavy losses, and that its commander had been killed.

The heroism of the regiment and its commander became one of the plot lines of *The People Immortal*. As we were checking the proofs, Grossman talked about the fighting near Glukhov and said he had kept the real name of one of the characters – Babadjanian.

In spring 1944, Grossman and Kolomeitsev[159] were near Vinnitsa. They showed up at 38th Army HQ, where I was then head of the political department. I sent them on to Lipovtsy, to a tank brigade commanded by Lieutenant Colonel Hamazasp Babadjanian. This short, calm, cheerful man received them warmly. Grossman's name was well known to everyone at the front.

Babadjanian . . . At first Grossman paid little attention to the name; you come across men with the same surname often enough. Babadjanian talked briefly to Grossman and Kolomeitsev and then decided to send them back; his command post was being fired on. But he was somehow unable to get rid of the two journalists. They spent the whole day with the brigade. And when they were eating supper and, as often happens, people began to reminisce, it emerged that Babadjanian was that same 395th Rifle Regiment commander who had defended the west bank of the Kleven near Glukhov.

"Yes, I was there," said Babadjanian. And then, with a smile, "But you killed me."

Grossman took this in his stride. After a short pause he said simply, "I killed you, but I can bring you back to life too."

Grossman recounted all this on his return to HQ. I at once reminded him of our earlier disagreement. "Thank God that at least one of the men you've killed is still alive!"

Grossman made friends with Babadjanian, more than once going far out of his way in order to see him. And he wrote a long, vivid article, "A Soviet Officer", about this man who later became Chief Marshal of the Soviet Tank Forces – a man whom Grossman loved and whom he both killed and resurrected.

from "A Soviet Officer"

I

(abridged from the typescript of the Red Star article)[160]

The first time we war correspondents heard the name Babadjanian was in Ukraine, near the town of Glukhov, during the grim days of September 1941. [. . .]

The wheat in the fields was heavy and overripe, spilling its grains onto the earth with vain generosity. Fruit was falling from the trees, overripe tomatoes rotting in gardens, cucumbers and juicy cabbage wilting and cobs of corn drying up on their tall thick stalks. Forest glades were carpeted with intricate patterns of berries and there were mushrooms of all kinds in the grass and under the trees: white mushrooms, merry orange-cap boletus and grey birch mushrooms.

People's lives during that kind, generous Ukrainian autumn were grim.

At night, the sky turned red from the dozens of distant fires, and during the day the entire horizon was veiled in grey smoke.

The back roads were crowded with people, carts and animals heading east. Old men, women with children in their arms, cows, flocks of sheep, collective-farm horses – all were drowning in clouds of dust. Tractors roared deafeningly; day and night, train after train was carrying away machine tools, engines, boilers and other equipment. Because of the German onslaught, Ukraine was being stripped of everything that had enriched it since the Revolution: factories built during the five-year plans, tractor stations, scientific institutes, libraries and hundreds of higher educational institutions. Scientists, agronomists, heads of laboratory-huts, combine-harvester operators, tractor drivers, plant breeders, esteemed brigade leaders of both sexes – all were heading east. Fascism was returning Ukraine to the darkest times it has known. [. . .]

A few benighted people, reactionaries and obscurantists, supporters of the Black Hundreds,[161] held their heads up high, smirking as they watched the Red Army retreat. Day and night there was the drone of thousands of black German aircraft; the sky seemed about to sag under their weight. The earth groaned beneath the tracks of German tanks – steel tracks that mercilessly devoured, ground down and destroyed grass, wheat, berries, flowers, young birches, maples and fragile young firs. These steel caterpillars crawled over swamps and rivers, tortured the earth, shredded human bodies and killed everything in their path. [. . .]

The whole world watched in horror as these brigades of armoured brigands advanced deeper and deeper, further and further east. Every day the German telegraph agency Transocean reported the capture of dozens of towns and cities, of countless prisoners and quantities of military equipment. The war against the Soviet Union seemed to be progressing according to schedule, in accord with the precise timetable drawn up by Hitler's HQ.

Now, after our victory, as we celebrate the fearless and immaculate knights who took the full burden of the war on their shoulders, we must remember that time. We must remember that merciless adversary who surpassed us in both material strength and experience; we must remember the weight on the heart that all but stopped the breath of the Soviet people; we must remember the retreat that so undermined our physical and spiritual strength. All this must stay in our minds. We must recall it as we tell of people who met the enemy head-on in the dust and smoke of the year 1941, who did not lose faith in victory, who shed their blood only too readily at a time when some saw all struggle and sacrifice as in vain. A writer must recall all this when he writes a book about a hero. A reader must recall it if he decides to read such a book. Otherwise, writer and reader will fail to understand each other. Still less will they understand the hero; involuntarily they will find themselves wondering why he is considered so admirable. [. . .]

Lieutenant Colonel Babadjanian's first encounter with German infantry was in summer 1941, after our forces surrendered Smolensk.

Babadjanian, the commander of an infantry regiment, was very thin and suffering from a painful cough; sunburn, unremitting tension and many nights without sleep had made his dark complexion seem still more sombre. Together with his scouts he was sitting in a shelter near the edge of a forest, watching the German infantry – battalion after battalion, regiment after regiment – pass through a small village in the province of Smolensk. Men in black helmets – tall young soldiers with black sub-machine guns hanging from their necks – were marching past grey, tumbledown wooden shacks with small windows. Black regimental guns and mortars rumbled by in clouds of dust. Then came the tall, awkward-to-manoeuvre divisional artillery and a long line of black carts pulled by strong, well-fed horses with stout legs, stout faces and stout rumps. This fresh infantry division was moving forward in the wake of tank columns that had recently breached the Soviet front line. One smart-looking, rosy-cheeked officer was riding along on a new bicycle. Evidently wanting to escape the dust raised by thousands of boots and wheels, he turned off onto a path that skirted some vegetable gardens beneath a cliff. The path wound its way along the edge of the forest, between dense bushes. There was a quiet shot, but this was drowned by the sound of hundreds of wheels, the neighing of horses and the rumble of engines. The officer fell into some bushes. The spokes of his bicycle wheels went on gleaming in the sunlight. A minute or two later, Babadjanian was examining the man's documents; among them was a brand-new leather notebook. On the first page, written in a clear, round hand, were German phrases and their Russian translation: "You are a prisoner"; "Hands up!"; "What is the name of this village?" "How many *versts* to Moscow?"; and so on.

Babadjanian looked at the grim, exhausted faces of his scouts; at the grey shacks, which looked so small and defenceless; and at the endless stream of German troops. Overwrought, seized with pain and rage, he took from his tunic pocket the stub of a red pencil and wrote in large bold letters, almost filling the page,

"You will not see Moscow! And the day will come when we shall be asking, 'How many *versts* to Berlin?'"

And he slipped the notebook into his map case.

In the course of the war, I met Babadjanian several times. He told me many stories, but only at our most recent meeting did he mention this leather notebook. The meeting was in Berlin. It is a joy to recount this story today.

But what a weight of labour, time, blood and suffering separates that day in 1941, when Babadjanian wrote those words in a German notebook, from these joyful days of victory.

To write such words in the summer of 1941 took a great deal of faith, loyalty, simplicity and emotional strength.

How did such faith and loyalty come to be?

In early autumn 1941, when Babadjanian was fighting near Glukhov, I heard people say, "There is one regimental commander who does not know how to retreat."

His faith was never shaken: faith in the righteousness of his cause, faith in the friends fate had decreed he should fight alongside. Faith that it is better to die free than to live as a slave. [. . .]

2

(abridged from Grossman's notebooks)[162]

Hamazasp Khachaturovich Babadjanian, Armenian.

Born 1908, in the mountain village of Chardakhlu, 30 kilometres from the railway station.

Mainly cattle raising, arable farming.

Father – a peasant, 87 years old. Grandmother, aged 128 [sic! – R.C.], still knitting bags and chasing children out of the orchard with a stick.

⋆

Twenty Babadjanians served in the Red Army. One uncle feigned madness to avoid military service.[163]

⋆

1100 men from our village served in the Red Army – 136 lieutenants, senior lieutenants and captains, 30 majors, 4 colonels and 1 army general.
I went to a village school, I herded cattle in the mountains.
I wanted to study but did not know where.
In 1925, I was sent to the military school in Yerevan. Accepted – provisionally – in the infantry section. Was issued one big boot and one small.
How I got fully accepted: the director and senior students were shooting, with small calibre rifles, at a match 50 metres distant. "All right, shrimp, you have a go!" I hit the match. That got me fully accepted. [In the published article, Babadjanian explains that he considers his seemingly brilliant shot to have been pure luck – R.C.]
In 1926, I was transferred to the Transcaucasian Infantry School in Tbilisi.
I graduated top, my name is on the gold board.
I first studied Russian at the military school. Before then I did not know the language.
I was the course elder, very strict. Initially, no particular interest in military service. [...]

⋆

At military school, I loved mathematics and geography.
My hunger for the Russian language – at school I read 700 books. I read frenziedly, day and night, but I understood little.

⋆

Of the Russians, I love Tolstoy, War and Peace. And Lermontov. I'm less fond of Pushkin.

⋆

I also completed ten years of ordinary schooling.

*

I loved ancient history.

*

1929, graduated from the Tbilisi school.

*

At military school, my favourite subjects were tactics and the art of war.

*

In 1936, entered the Frunze Military Academy. A year off in 1937, to work. Graduated in 1942, with "fives" in all subjects. "Excellent."[164]

★

1929–32 – platoon commander.

1932 – secretary of regimental Party bureau.

1933 – company commander.

1934 – battalion commander and regimental chief of staff. From there to the Frunze Academy.

1937 – head of operations section at corps HQ.

1938 – wanting to work as a front-line officer, I was appointed deputy regimental commander, then commander.

May 1941 – deputy head of operations department at corps HQ.

(In the Finnish War – commander of a motorcycle regiment. Wounded.)

The War!

5 July – took command of 395th Rifle Regiment. Lieutenant Colonel.

September 1942 to August 1944 – commander of a light armoured brigade.

August 1944 – took command of a corps.

★

I have never felt disadvantaged because of my nationality.

★

22 June 1941 — the station, the train, the journey. We reached the front together with the Army HQ. We lost our troops, unable to find an entire corps. (!) Our troops were rushing towards the front line. The Germans pounded them on the road — by then they were bombing 300–400 kilometres behind the frontier. We had no secondary defensive line, nothing at all. And so our men were marching into a void, being pounded and pounded. At first, I thought the Germans would stop when they reached the old frontier.[165] Then I understood I was wrong.

3
(abridged from the typescript of the Red Star article)

Two forces determine the course of a war: human beings and equipment. Babadjanian had long understood the importance of a good relationship between a commander and his men; he had known this in peacetime and it had become still clearer to him during the Finnish War. He knew that, in the absence of stern discipline, success was inconceivable. But he also understood that discipline should not be mindless and mechanical. He knew that discipline is not a matter of a commander's whim but an inescapable necessity — and that it must be observed by a commander no less than by his subordinates. He knew that what matters most is that the commander should himself be disciplined. His sense of unwavering justice must extend to his own self; he must be willing to go to his death when his military duty requires it. Babadjanian not only understood with his mind but also felt in his heart that stern discipline — what is called iron discipline — requires a commander to attend fully to all his soldiers' requirements. Before taking care of himself, the commander must ensure that his soldiers are provided with all they need in the harsh conditions of war. He must ensure that they are given food that is tasty and satisfying; that they are issued with the right clothing – light in summer, warm in winter; that he doesn't thoughtlessly expose them to the pain of being left with nothing to smoke; and that their post is delivered to them correctly and without delay. He must allow his men to rest when the opportunity arises. He must not risk their lives without good reason; he must make it clear that every one of their lives is precious to him. Babadjanian understood all this; and he knew that a commander must not keep at a distance from his soldiers, that he must not appear aloof and inaccessible. [. . .]

The Battle of Yelnya was Babadjanian's first serious battle. On receiving his orders, he and his regiment made a sixty-kilometre night march, to the forward positions of the Soviet defences.

The divisional commander contacted Babadjanian by telephone and ordered him not to delay; he was to execute his mission and attack Yelnya. Such a mission, to be honest, was unusual in the summer of 1941. We had little experience of taking the offensive; few of our commanders understood how to go into the attack. This was the time of a long and difficult retreat. And when our commanders tried to attack, they simply launched themselves at the Germans head-on. They did not manoeuvre; they did not carry out bold outflanking movements that would have enabled them to strike at the enemy rear. Our tactics were unsuccessful and incurred heavy casualties.

The divisional commander was anxious. He kept telephoning Babadjanian, asking if his regiment had engaged with the enemy and could report any successes. Babadjanian replied that his regiment was already in combat – which was far from the truth. In reality, after talking to Pivovarov, the regimental commissar, Babadjanian had ordered his battalion commanders to give their men a good meal and then allow them to lie down and sleep.

Much water has flowed under the bridge since then – and Babadjanian's sin will be forgiven him. "What do you think, Pivovarov?" he went on to say, with a glint in his stern, dark eyes. "What I said is the truth, isn't it? Wouldn't you agree that, after a march like that, and before a difficult battle, eating and sleeping is a crucial part of the operation?"

It was a cloudless, moonlit night. While his men slept, Babadjanian crept through the forest to the front line, to his advance outposts.

In the light of the full moon, the entire area lay spread out before him. He looked for a long time at the hills and groves. He studied a deep, dark ravine beneath a high forest cliff. Straight ahead of him, brilliantly lit, stood a height held by large German forces.

A representative from HQ, lying there beside Babadjanian, pointed towards the height and whispered, "Attack here, capture this height – and we've done it!"

Babadjanian did not reply. He knew that the outcome of the battle depended on the decision he was about to take.

He returned to his observation post, where his signallers had just set up a telephone, took out a map and spread it out on his lap.

During the first months of the war, representatives from HQ and members of one commission or another were constantly making their presence felt everywhere. These men bore no responsibility, but they loved to advise and instruct, to interfere in a commander's work.

Several such men soon gathered around Babadjanian. The most senior said crossly, "What's there to think about, Lieutenant Colonel? Everything's clear as day. The Germans are here on this height – and this height is where we need to attack."

And the others joined in, "Couldn't be clearer . . . Our number one task . . . To take the height means to take back Yelnya. That's why the regiment's been sent here."

Babadjanian replied calmly, "I request you, comrades, not to interfere. It is I – not you – who am responsible for the outcome of this operation. It is I who will take this decision and it is I, not you, who will break into Yelnya."

After getting the telephone operator to connect him to regimental HQ, Babadjanian ordered the artillery and heavy machine guns to be moved forward immediately. In this respect he was well equipped; his regiment had been assigned seven batteries. He ordered half of these guns to be advanced almost to the edge of the cliff, directly opposite "the height of death". This height overlooking Yelnya had not been given this name for nothing – it had already seen several days of fierce fighting. Much blood had been spilled, but to no avail. It had been easy enough for the Germans to repel our attacks with dense, annihilating fire from their mortars and heavy machine guns.

The moon was still high in the summer sky when Babadjanian ordered a hail of fire to be unleashed on the height. Shells tore towards it, both from Babadjanian's heavy divisional guns and from the light regimental guns. The Germans heard the thunder of gunfire, the howl of shells and the crash of explosions; soon they were also being showered with long bursts of machine-gun fire. They prepared themselves for what was surely going to be a massive attack.

Around the same time, the Russian infantry battalions, after enjoying a hot meal and two or three hours of sound sleep, descended unnoticed to the bottom of a long, deep ravine.

The battalion commanders understood their mission, which Babadjanian had outlined to them clearly and simply. Not one of them so much as glanced at the height, where the Germans were by then well prepared to repel them.

Keeping to the ravine, avoiding any open terrain, Babadjanian's battalions continued their long march around the German positions. Russian shells roared over their heads; flames escaping from the barrels of Russian guns dimmed the calm, dead light of the moon.

The Germans were alarmed. The height had never before been subjected to such an extended barrage. The Russians, it seemed, were about to attack more fiercely than ever. This time, perhaps, it would not just be a single infantry battalion or regiment. Maybe the Soviet command had resolved to throw a whole division at the height?

Nevertheless, they were not so very alarmed. They were, in fact, smugly confident. They were well ensconced; the height was so well fortified and their guns so craftily and annihilatingly positioned that an entire Soviet infantry corps could lay down their lives on the slopes without even a single man reaching the crest.

In the meantime, Babadjanian's infantry and his remaining guns advanced further and further to the north-west, leaving the height behind them. Marching along back roads, through small woods and groves, through fields of tall, unharvested rye, they severed one road after another in the German rear.

The sun had already risen when the regiment concentrated for the decisive attack, but what they attacked was not the German fortifications east of Yelnya, nor even the eastern outskirts of Yelnya.

Instead, they entered the town from the west.

The soldiers saw their commander wave a hand in greeting. They smiled as they marched past him. Soldiers and commanders alike – all had understood his simple plan and were overjoyed by its success. The Germans fled. They prided themselves on their calm invincibility and iron discipline, but they had not expected to find a regular unit of the Red Army to their rear; they had not expected to be pounded from the west by machine guns, mortars and artillery.

Today an account of attacking the Germans in the rear and putting them to flight seems ordinary enough; there is nothing surprising about forcing German troops to surrender. But back then, in the summer of 1941, this was an important event. It carried meaning; it inspired; it strengthened people's belief in victory. In the eyes of many soldiers and commanders you could see tears of joyful excitement.

The battle was short and fierce. Babadjanian's regiment broke into Yelnya from the west, fulfilling their mission.

Babadjanian learned many precious lessons from this battle – his first victory as a commander.[166]

4
(First part from the typescript for the Red Star article, second part from Grossman's notebooks)

In September 1941, Babadjanian's infantry regiment, along with the rest of the division, was transferred from the Western Front to Ukraine. [. . .]

This was a time when black clouds hung low over the villages and cities of our homeland, when every Soviet heart was gripped by an iron hoop of anguish. Everyone could see the enemy's strength and successes; everyone knew that our armies were retreating, suffering cruel losses of both people and ordinance.

At this time, there were two kinds of people who turned out to be equally dangerous.

The first were those who had lost all strength of spirit, who grossly exaggerated the enemy's strength and underestimated our own. These people believed that the struggle was already lost; they said, and went on saying, that the war could only end tragically.

They sowed despair in the rear and on the front line. Like it or not, everyone somehow found themselves starting to lose hope as they listened to these people.

The second kind were those incapable of any real thought, who seemed unable to grasp the seriousness of our situation. Again, there were people like this both in the rear and on the front line. They did not see or understand the danger and, instead of mobilizing themselves and everyone around them to fight to the death, they basked in blissful confidence that all danger had passed.

If two or three days went by with no sightings of German planes, these people would say, "See – they no longer have any planes left. Or maybe they still have a few, but they can't do anything with them. They've run out of fuel."

If the front went quiet for ten or twelve days, these people would solemnly declare that the German army was exhausted and had for ever lost its ability to advance further. This cheery talk had the same effect as the pessimists' counsels of despair; it was a reason not to prepare oneself for the mortal struggle.

These two classes of people, apparently entirely opposite to each other, were in reality only too similar. Those who were most confident that an easy victory was already "in the bag", who pronounced that the Germans no longer had any planes left, were quick to turn into pessimists if they were shelled or bombed. And a report of some ephemeral minor success would be enough to make the pessimists suddenly see the world through rose-tinted spectacles and shout out excitedly that the war had already been won.

Really, they were one and the same breed – stupid, superficial people, with no mental or emotional stability. [. . .]

Babadjanian was an optimist of a different kind. When trouble bent him, he would draw himself up to his full height. When others were looking back, he would try to look forward. And during periods of ominous calm, he would be more vigilant than ever, refusing to deceive himself with the false hope that "Somehow it'll all be all right in the end."

When Colonel Akimenko, the divisional commander, ordered him to advance, Babadjanian knew he had little chance of success. [. . .]

The regiment crossed a small, boggy river and marched west. It was a low-lying area, overgrown with tall, bright green grass. In places it was a real quagmire, the water climbing up your leg the moment your boot touched the ground. Sometimes our guns sank into the water and it was a struggle to pull them out. The men would be up to their waists, even up to their chest, in a rust-coloured, foul-smelling boggy liquid.

The enemy retreated. It is possible that Babadjanian's advance was so sudden, his passage across the river and through the bog so swift, that the Germans were simply too taken aback to organize their defences in time. Kilometre after kilometre, Babadjanian's battalions marched west, brushing aside any resistance they met. They were now leaving the bog behind them; the forward units were already on solid ground, on arable fields.

The soldiers grew more and more excited – and not without reason. They had advanced eleven kilometres, always keeping west, fighting as they went. At that time of the war, this seemed an enormous success.

They had marched west, rifles at the ready. Instead of retreating, instead of abandoning their native land, they were freeing it from the invaders. The land they had liberated might have been mere bog, without villages and farms, but the commanders and soldiers were none the less overjoyed [. . .]

★

We were expecting an attack from the north, but the Germans outmanoeuvred us and attacked from the south. We were on our own. To our rear, the Germans had captured Rylsk. Bog everywhere. Enemy ahead of us, bog and the river behind.

We were in trouble. We held out on this strip of land for 11 days. They had tanks and aircraft; we had infantry and artillery. Their Ju-88 dive-bombers. My men were Siberians, they fought over every metre of ground. I was with them, there in their trenches, firing a rifle, working a machine gun. Once the Germans tried to hunt me down. Ploughed fields. I fell, I kept on running. The chief of staff broke both his legs. He burst into tears. He was carried away. Someone saying to me, "You will stay alive." My commissar, Pivovarov – he was killed. [. . .]

In the end, after three days of fighting without a break, there were 150 of us left. The Germans were in their undershirts, smoking cigarettes. They came on in a line. Our machine guns. A second line of Germans, 150 metres back. I was working a machine gun myself. This went on for three days and nights, we felled a great many of them. Then we retreated at night through the bog and across the water . . . I can barely walk, I haven't eaten for several days. I fall to the ground. "Leave me, boys, I'm a goner." Suddenly I see the great-coat of the dead Pivovarov. I get to my feet, grab it and drag it along. "I'll carry it," I say – and so I did. (In the published article, Grossman expands this passage, "Then something very strange happened. On the ground, just a few metres from him, was a sodden great-coat, riddled with bullets. Babadjanian recognized it at once. It was Pivovarov's. He got to his feet, held the heavy, sodden great-coat against his chest and began to carry it in his arms as if it were a living person.") That was hell – a green bog with countless pits left by mortar bombs. Shells, water, earth, sky – all jumbled together.

We carried back with us 70 wounded.

Akimenko hugged and kissed me. "You did a great job, you saved our front line from being breached. You enabled me to withdraw equipment, to deploy our reserves on a new line of defence."[167]

*

Tuberculosis throughout the war, fever, coughing blood in the spring.

5

(from Grossman's notebooks)

In late 1941 I came to fully understand the power of tanks. I saw how success-fully mobile infantry can work together with tanks. I did all I could to get my infantry onto Khasin's tanks, I rode in a tank myself.[168]

The best tactic during an offensive, after breaching the enemy's line, is *a lightning advance, firing on the move. If the enemy sees 100 tanks, he will never be able to knock out more than 10 or 15 of them. If you are deep behind enemy lines, create the illusion of an encirclement, attack him as he brings up his reserves. Fast, decisive movement symbolizes faith and confidence. Delay – in tank warfare – equals death. Only the most terrible swiftness can disrupt the enemy's defences and prevent him from constructing new defences and deploying his artillery. In good weather, it's best to avoid roads. Sweeping detours, outflanking manoeuvres, surprise thrusts at the enemy's rear.*

6
(abridged from the typescript for the Red Star article)

Above all, every branch of our armed forces was faced with a new task. During the first period of the war, Red Army commanders had to devote all their powers to the task of fighting for every smallest defensive line, the task of defending every river and patch of forest, of doggedly battling on in encirclement, of doing everything they could to slow the enemy's advance. Now, however, they had to learn to attack.

This new task necessitated not only a radical change in military tactics but also a psychological breakthrough. Babadjanian's long-held dream of an offensive became a reality. Encircling the enemy, dislodging him from strategic positions, fragmenting his defences, cutting his communication lines, surrounding him, splitting and destroying his forces, pursuing him day and night – these were the new tasks of our commanders. There were more than a few instances of fine commanders – commanders who had acquitted themselves well in defensive operations – struggling with these new tasks and mastering them only with time.

This period did not always go smoothly and straightforwardly for Babadjanian. He made mistakes and miscalculations. Sometimes he found it painfully difficult to eradicate weaknesses and shortcomings. Sometimes the enemy deceived or outplayed him. Sometimes the enemy slipped away or delivered counter-strikes where he did not expect them, inflicting severe damage that could have been avoided.

The Red Army's understanding of the offensive was not born in one day. Their grasp of this great and complex art was broadened, deepened and tempered through the stern reality of battle, through the routine demands of the war.

Babadjanian found in himself the strength and ability to master this art – just as he had earlier learned to fight fierce defensive battles. These new battles had similarities with the battles he had fought at Yelnya and Glukhov – battles within which the seed of the future had been lying dormant.

The future had now become the present; dream had become reality. [. . .]

Babadjanian had long understood that victory comes at a price, that it is always accompanied by risk, danger and sacrifice. [. . .]

Daring and a readiness for sacrifice enabled Babadjanian to achieve a remarkable success at Kazatin. This is a major railway junction, with lines to Fastov, Kiev, Dnepropetrovsk, Vinnitsa, Odessa and Shepetovka. The Germans were determined to put up a fight for the city – it was an important supply base and they had several thousand vehicles there. They were expecting long, stubborn battles on the outskirts and were truly stunned when Babadjanian's tanks burst into the city itself. Babadjanian had known that his only chance of capturing somewhere so heavily fortified lay in overwhelming surprise.

His tanks approached in the twilight. He did not wait until morning. He attacked immediately, at night. But he was not using the darkness for silence and secrecy – he was using it as a background, to make the power of the Red Army appear all the more dazzling and overwhelming. As he drew near, Babadjanian ordered all his vehicles – jeeps, tanks and armoured cars, and all the trucks pulling mortars and artillery pieces – to turn their headlamps on full. Hundreds of brilliant headlamps lit up simultaneously, cutting through the darkness like searchlights. The roar of engines, piercing hoots, artillery fire and machine-gun bursts merged into a single terrifying sound. Hurtling towards the city out of the dark winter fields was an avalanche of light. Babadjanian achieved his goal; he panicked the German troops and paralysed their defences. After a short, brutal battle, his tanks entered the city. [. . .]

On 21 March 1944, after heavy fighting, the German defences at Proskurov were breached. [. . .] In the afternoon, Babadjanian's brigade entered the breach. But the spring mud was so deep and viscous that any further advance seemed inconceivable. The fields of Ukraine had turned into bottomless swamps. And any movement on back roads was no less impossible.

The Germans were certain that the Soviet brigades would be unable to exploit this breach. Any move into such mud was unthinkable. It was Babadjanian who shouldered this unthinkable task. His brigade advanced through the fields, avoiding the roads, heading undeviatingly south.

Every metre of ground had to be conquered. The earth was like some sticky jelly. It sucked at the wheels of powerful three-axle trucks; tank engines let out howls of frustration. During the first day, the brigade advanced only twenty kilometres. At dawn, they got going again. Later that day, they entered Chertkov. Tankmen and tanks seemed equally exhausted. The men found it painful even to look at their struggling, tormented tanks; it was as if they could see beads of sweat on the hot metal. Nevertheless, Babadjanian, always so thoughtful with regard to his men, did not allow them to rest. He knew that the success or failure of a deep breakthrough depends entirely on speed. In Chertkov, his tanks moved onto the highway. That day, they covered sixty kilometres, outstripping German columns that were retreating along a parallel road. Babadjanian ordered his brigade not to engage with them. The Germans watched in horror as Soviet guns, tanks and motorized infantry trucks, spattered with mud, tore on towards the south. There were times in this mad advance when the artillery batteries got ahead of the tanks. By then Babadjanian's daring brigade had driven a wedge 150 kilometres into the German rear.

In this sector, the Germans were well equipped with planes. These first appeared two days after the initial breakthrough. Babadjanian's tank was positioned in a small hollow. Suddenly there were twenty-seven Junkers in the sky above him. Babadjanian looked around – there was nowhere to take cover. He glanced at his watch, climbed into the tank and closed the hatch.

The whistle of the first bomb was followed by a deafening explosion. The driver, lying on the floor of the tank, shouted desperately, "Down, Comrade Colonel! Get down! If they smash the turret, it'll be the end of you!"

Babadjanian lay down beside the driver. One after another, heavy bombs exploded close by. The tank bounced about, as if built of light plywood. It trembled, as if both it and the men inside it were dying in agony. To Babadjanian it felt as if his eyes and eardrums would burst from the tension, as if blood was about to gush from his throat. He might have been inside a huge, vibrating drum – with a heavy, cast-iron fist beating on this drum in mad frenzy.

With each new whistle, the half-conscious driver dug his fingers into Babadjanian's leg, as if this might ward off death. Later, Babadjanian felt pain in that spot, so forcefully had the man been gripping him. Suddenly everything went quiet. Babadjanian looked up and glanced at his watch. The bombing had lasted for twenty-two minutes.

When they opened the hatch and looked around, they were appalled; all around them were vast craters, like mass graves, their edges right up against their tank. It seemed like a miracle – an intact tank, covered in mud, amid craters and slabs of earth torn apart by explosions. For the tank to be able to move, they had to fill in one of these craters. It was as if the German pilots had deliberately surrounded their tank with an enormous ditch.

Babadjanian at once ordered the brigade forward. An hour later, the bombers came back. The command tank was destroyed by a direct hit. Fortunately, Babadjanian and the crew were not inside – they had managed to find somewhere to shelter. The moment the bombers left, Babadjanian gave the same command, "Forward!" These fierce raids continued throughout the day. The brigade suffered heavy casualties, but after each raid, Babadjanian ordered, "Forward!"

That day, the tanks covered seventy kilometres and reached the cold, dark Dniester.

Once again, the attentive, caring Babadjanian did not allow anyone to rest. He ordered the brigade to cross the river immediately. Men crossed on logs, on homemade rafts, on bits of fencing and on gates they had wrenched off their hinges. A ford was found for the tanks and other vehicles – and the steel herd, snorting mistrustfully, made its way through the swift, malevolent water. The water washed away the tanks' dense coating of mud, revealing the countless dents from the impact of bomb splinters. The brigade completed the crossing before any Germans could attempt to hinder them. Once again, Babadjanian gave the command. "Forward!"

Soon, his advance tanks were approaching Stanislavov, 200 kilometres behind the German front line. Babadjanian had fulfilled his mission.

7
(abridged from the typescript for the Red Star article)

Winter 1944–45. On the west bank of the Vistula, south of Warsaw, the First Belorussian Front was about to launch an offensive. The Commander-in-Chief, Comrade Stalin, was preparing a mighty blow; the Red Army was to clear all western Poland and enter the territory of Nazi Germany.

Along with several other tank formations, Babadjanian's corps was to move forward through a breach in the German front line.

The vehicles and equipment on the bridgehead were so densely concentrated that the ground seemed as if it might give way.

The artillery commanders were like communal apartment tenants, constantly bickering. There were so many artillery pieces that it was difficult to find room for them all. [. . .]

In this offensive, Babadjanian's prime consideration was speed. Ninety kilometres a day was now seen as normal. There were days when the tanks covered one hundred and twenty kilometres. Sometimes they crossed rivers without first constructing a bridge. This saved them two or three hours.

Colonel Gusakovsky was a friend of Babadjanian and one of his brigade commanders. On seeing that the Germans had blown up the bridge across the River Pilica, he ordered his sappers to detonate the ice. He then sent his tanks forward, across the river bed. Their front plates ploughed through the ice, lifting it up and sending it crashing down onto their turrets. This ice ford won the brigade precious hours. And our men enjoyed laughing about comic incidents when they encountered German officers and officials who thought they were far from the front line and who were not expecting to be confronted by Soviet tankmen. [. . .]

And then – the beginning of the last offensive. The words Babadjanian wrote on a dusty summer afternoon in 1941, after the fall of Smolensk, had proved true: "The day will come when we shall be asking, 'How many *versts* to Berlin?'" [. . .]

The last battle among the blossoming gardens on the outskirts of the city were cruel and bloody. Death hovered over Babadjanian's head. In this last battle, as in the war's first battles, he did not flinch or try to flee danger. This time, fate was kind to him. [. . .]

Here, on the night of 2 May 1945, near the smoking walls of the Reichstag, our turret gunners fired their last shells at the enemy. Berlin surrendered. I met Colonel Babadjanian again. I had met him several times during the grimmest days of the war. How things had changed.

Back then, in our memories of 1941: bogs, dugouts, the dusty roads of retreat, the wind howling across deserted, snow-covered fields, men in caps with earflaps and wadded trousers and jackets. And now: the impeccable discipline of victors, smart uniforms all spick and span, HQs located in palaces, with carpets, armchairs and mahogany tables. Past and present: two opposite poles, like night and day, like a cruel winter and a generous summer.

I thought how everything had changed – and how little this man had changed. Calm, modest and restrained, hard-working and incapable of complacency, he was the same in every way. In every respect he remained a soldier, ready at any moment to meet his fate, no matter how harsh this might be.

He has, of course, gained in experience of war; his knowledge is now immeasurably wider and deeper. During these last four years he has learned much that cannot be found in any book. But the inner world of this man has not changed. This is how he was in the green bogs near Glukhov, in the life-and-death battles of the retreat – infantry regiment commander Babadjanian. And this is the man I met in the days of victory in Berlin – Babadjanian, the commander of a powerful tank corps. Ascetically modest, a simple soldier, an honourable knight, he lived through the whole war. And I said to myself that the strength of the Soviet people lies in their inner constancy. Their faith and loyalty are eternal and unchanging.

Tacitus

Publius Cornelius Tacitus (c.56–c.120 CE) was ancient Rome's greatest historian, and his most important work was the *Annals*, a history of Rome under the emperors following Augustus: Tiberius, Caligula, Claudius and Nero.

The classicist Anthony Barrett sums up his account of Tiberius's reign as follows, "Augustus had established a system that was inherently corrupt, and Tacitus's great achievement was to trace the degradation of Roman politics through the course of Tiberius's reign, to show that his character and personality were unable to withstand this debasing force of the imperial system." Barret goes on to say that few rulers so powerfully exemplify the truth of the saying that all power corrupts – and absolute power corrupts absolutely.[169]

In his summary of Tiberius's reign, Tacitus writes, "Ordinary human interaction had been destroyed by the power of fear, and with the growth of the savagery came the exclusion of pity."[170] And towards the end of his introduction to the *Annals*, Barrett writes, "Tacitus's experience of the destructiveness of tyranny has made the *Annals* a work of special relevance to the contemporary reader in the light of our experience of the last century. The dark pessimism engendered by two world wars [. . .] is totally in tune with the dark message of the *Annals* and its grim picture of imperial duplicity."[171]

★

There is little doubt that the old lawyer who dies with a copy of the *Annals* beside him would have been thinking about Stalin as he read the book. Three years earlier, in 1938, Grossman had read the *Annals* himself – and been prompted to write the following page in his notebook. Needless to say, Grossman avoids any explicit comparison of Stalin with Tiberius or Nero, which – if seen by the NKVD – would have led to his arrest or execution; even the more abstract reflections he did entrust to the page were heretical, contradicting the belief in humanity's moral and intellectual progress that was central to Soviet Marxism–Leninism.

The Soviet translation of the Annals was titled *Annaly*, but the old lawyer's copy is titled *Letopisi (Chronicles)* – the title given to earlier Russian translations. This makes the scene still more poignant – evidently, the lawyer had been hoping to save a rare old copy of the work, probably the 1858 edition, translated by A. Kroneberg.

★

Extract from "A Few Notes" on Tacitus's *Annals*

A beautiful soul – he admires courage, nobility, intelligence, just decisions, truthful speeches, faithfulness in marriage, a son's love, lasting friendship.

He condemns lies, denunciations, flattery, cowardice, cruel murders, debauchery, incest, greed and servility.

His moral vision is identical to our own. In every colour and half-tone of good and evil, of light and shadow, it corresponds to our own moral and ethical views.

It is true that he is rich in the prejudices of his time – prejudices and superstitions that even our most benighted old women have left behind them: divinations, signs in the heavens, two-headed calves, women giving birth to monsters, appearances of mythical birds, etc.

Each century has its own "personal" prejudices.

Tacitus calls Christians vile and dirty. They offend the fastidiousness of his ethics and rationality.

In historical reading, people find similarities between their time and distant eras; this brings them pleasure and joy. If their behaviour is like that of the ancients, then everything – they imagine – will become clear to them. But things can be similar yet no less incomprehensible.

Equal causes give rise to equal consequences, because people remain the same. The amount of good and evil, of fidelity and intelligence in them remains the same. People do not become worse or better over the centuries and millennia.

Mankind is fully completed yet imperfect.

Historical reading does not give rise to horror and joy.

I would not say that people were terrible but have become good. People remain the same.

Their prejudices are different, but their minds and souls are unchanged; they are as they are and they will probably stay like that until the end of mankind. Human beings are not going to develop any further. They must have already attained their peak – their "ceiling" – and, most likely, they attained it several millennia ago. After all, elephants do not grow to be the size of a mammoth with the passing of centuries. An elephant is the conclusion of a particular development, not one of its stages. Evolution will continue, but we have already come to a stop. The river will flow past us, as it will flow past a ship that clings to the bottom and finally ceases to move altogether.

"Nemnogie zapisi" (1938)

Vasily Grossman and the Stalin Prize

Western readers have long tended to divide Soviet writers into two classes: corrupt time-servers and heroic, dissident martyrs. It was hard for a Soviet writer to attract widespread attention in the English-speaking world except through some major international scandal. *Doctor Zhivago* became a bestseller because the Soviet authorities coerced Boris Pasternak into declining the Nobel Prize. Joseph Brodsky became known after being tried in court and then sent into exile in the far north. Alexander Solzhenitsyn became ever more famous as the authorities stepped up the pressure against him and eventually deported him in 1974. Great writers with less dramatic biographies often went unnoticed. Andrey Platonov, for example, has only slowly gained Western recognition. And Vasily Grossman was ignored for several decades – until we learned the story of the KGB "arresting" the manuscript of *Life and Fate*.

Between them, Soviet repression and Cold War propaganda created many myths about Soviet writers and artists. Soviet admirers of a particular writer, wanting to help him or her to be published, exaggerated their Soviet credentials; Western admirers, wanting a writer to achieve recognition in the West, exaggerated their anti-Soviet credentials.

The poet and translator Semion Lipkin was a close friend of Grossman. He played a key role in sending microfilms of *Life and Fate* to the West and he wrote an important memoir about him, first published in 1986. Wanting to make Grossman appealing to Western readers, he downplayed the degree to which he was a part of the Soviet establishment and emphasized or exaggerated everything about him that was in any way dissident. Since Lipkin is a gifted and engaging writer and there are no other memoirs of comparable length, the myths he created gained wide circulation; I have, I regret, repeated many of them myself.

One of the most persistent myths is that Stalin personally, three times, "vetoed" Grossman's being awarded a Stalin Prize – for his Donbas novel *Stepan Kolchugin* in 1941, for *The People Immortal* in 1943, and for *For a Just Cause* (the long novel titled *Stalingrad* in our recent English translation) in 1952–53. According to Lipkin, Stalin strongly disliked or mistrusted Grossman. It is surprising that this assertion went unchallenged for so long. Once one begins to question it, its absurdity soon becomes obvious. Apart from anything else, what could have made normally timid Soviet literary functionaries stubbornly go on nominating a writer known to have incurred Stalin's personal enmity? And why would Soviet publishers have continued publishing and republishing Grossman's work in large print runs? In any case, we now know, from documents about the Stalin Prize declassified in 2006, that *Kolchugin* was never even nominated. The title does not appear in the list sent to M.B. Khrapchenko, the head of the prize committee, nor did Khrapchenko himself attempt to bring the novel to Stalin's attention.[172] There is no doubt that Lipkin created, perhaps on the basis of rumours already circulating in the literary world, a myth that he knew would be helpful to the reputation of a writer he loved and admired.

In 1943 Grossman truly was a contender for a Stalin Prize, at least at one stage. *The People Immortal* was one of six novels listed in the Prize Committee's discussions on 3 and 4 March 1943. The lists compiled on these two days are not identical, but Grossman figures on both; his name, however, is absent from later lists. We do not know who chose to omit him or why.[173] But this does not indicate any serious fall from favour. Four separate editions of *The People Immortal* were published in 1943 and five in 1945.[174] In 1945 and 1946 three editions of *The Years of War*, a selection of Grossman's wartime journalism together with *The People Immortal*, were published in Moscow, while a fourth was published in Stavropol. And in 1950 a volume of Grossman's short stories, also including *The People Immortal*, was published in Moscow. Most of these publications were in large editions and the top Soviet writers received high royalties. If not at the very summit of the Soviet literary establishment, Grossman was not far below it.

The novel's failure to win a Stalin Prize is, in any case, unsurprising. *The People Immortal* is set during the first months of the war, a time of headlong retreat. The list of prizewinners was published on 19 March 1943, six weeks after the Soviet victory at Stalingrad. Though reviewers praised Grossman for his ability to discern in those early defeats the seeds of victories to come, the subject matter of *The People Immortal* now seemed dated. The theme of the day was now victory – not courageous retreat.

Nevertheless, we yet again find the writers of memoirs invoking Stalin's personal enmity. In 1966 Ilya Ehrenburg wrote, "The star under which Grossman was born was a star of misfortune. [. . .]

I was told that it was Stalin himself who deleted his story *The People Immortal* from the list of books nominated for the prize." Ehrenburg goes on to assert that Stalin must have hated Grossman for "his love of Lenin, for his genuine internationalism".[175] And in 1980, in a memoir published in Paris, Natalya Roskina, a younger friend of Grossman, came up with a slightly different version of what is essentially the same story: "It was certainly not love for Lenin that was the reason for Grossman being constantly in disgrace. It was exclusively the fact that Grossman never sought Stalin's love. It was Stalin who deleted the novel from the list of laureates."[176] The only element of truth here is that Grossman did not "go out of his way" to seek Stalin's love. He was certainly not "constantly in disgrace".

Like Ehrenburg, Roskina does not name her source; it is clear, though, that she has borrowed from Ehrenburg. Ehrenburg was the first memoirist to claim that Stalin hated Grossman – and he almost certainly did this with the best of motives. By asserting that Grossman loved Lenin and was hated by Stalin, he was probably hoping to pave the way for a Soviet publication of *Life and Fate*; the novel could, after all, have been published in a heavily censored version. Ehrenburg was politically shrewd and he seldom acted without some ulterior motive; Roskina's memoir is more spontaneous and freer from political calculation.

Writing in 1986, twenty years after Ehrenburg and six years after Roskina, Lipkin picked up their central idea. He too was doing what he could to further Grossman's reputation. Ehrenburg, however, was trying to salvage Grossman's standing in the Soviet Union, while Lipkin was trying to promote his reputation abroad. And where Ehrenburg and Lipkin led, Western scholars and journalists were glad to follow. Cold War politics, together with the seductions of the image of the courageous, truth-telling artist, made it almost impossible for them to do otherwise.

Grossman truly was a great and courageous artist. He truly did love the truth and he was entirely free of grandiosity. It goes without saying that he would have wanted his life story to be told truthfully.

Robert Chandler and Yury Bit-Yunan

(2020)

Material confiscated from German and
Italian prisoners-of-war

As deputy head of the Front Political Directorate for work among enemy troops, Bogariov regularly interrogated German prisoners, read their letters and diaries, and studied orders from the German High Command. His experiences and reflections during those first weeks of the war have much in common with Grossman's. Grossman was present at interrogations of German POWs and he collected and studied a variety of confiscated material – both official documents and personal letters and photographs; like Bogariov, Grossman wanted to understand what motivated the Germans. Among the material in Grossman's files in the state literary archive, there are photographs and postcards taken from German soldiers; a German–Russian phrasebook, remarkable for the brutality of the phrases it lists; documents about Russian POWs and *Ostarbeiter* (Russians and other East Europeans sent to Germany to work as slave labourers); a warning to the population of Warsaw about "retribution" for attacks on German military personnel; letters sent to Hitler during the last months of the war, blaming him for leading Germany into disaster; and even essays and dictations written by German schoolchildren, explaining why it is wrong to pass on bad news that might demoralize their fathers at the front.

Few people then had access to such documents and Grossman would probably have studied them in considerable detail. The two letters sent to Hitler, for example, could have given him insights not only into the mood of the German civilian population but also into the workings of the repressive mechanisms of a totalitarian state; it is clear from the various official stamps on these letters that they were forwarded first to Hitler's secretariat – and then to the Gestapo. The war was already nearly over, but the German security services were still functioning efficiently.

Pocket phrasebook for soldiers at the front – German–Russian.

1. Halt!	Stoj!	Стой!
2. Hände hoch!	Ruki wwerch!	Руки вверх!
3. Ergib dich!	Sdawajssja!	Сдавайся!
4. Wer da?	Kto idjott?	Кто идет?
5. Rauskommen!	Wyhadi!	Выходи!
6. Die Waffen nieder!	Brassaj orushije!	Бросай оружие!
7. Hinlegen!	Lashissj!	Ложись!
8. Aufstehen!	Fstawaj!	Вставай!
9. Halt den Mund!	Maltschi!	Молчи!
10. Ruhe	Tische!	Тише!
11. Ich schieße!	Budu streljatj!	Буду стрелять!
12. Ich erschieße dich!	Sastrelju!	Застрелю!
13. Antworte!	Atwetschaj!	Отвечай!
14. Antworte, ja oder nein!	Atwetschaj, da Ili njet!	Отвечай, да или нет!
15. Antworte, schnell und klar!	Atwetschaj, bystro i jassno!	Отвечай, быстро и ясно!
16. Vorwärts!	Fperjott!	Вперед!
17. Zurück!	Nasatt!	Назад!
18. Waffen her!	Dawaj arushije!	Давай оружие!
19. Papiere her!	Padaj dokumenty!	Подай документы!
20. Wo liegt dein Truppenteil?	Gdje twaja tschastj?	Где твоя часть?
21. Wo ist der Stab?	Gdje schtab?	Где штаб?

5

1. Halt!; 2. Hands up!; 3. Surrender!; 4. Who goes there?; 5. Show yourselves!; 6. Lay down your weapons!; 7. Lie down!; 8. Stand up!; 9. Be quiet!; 10. Silence!; 11. I'm going to shoot!; 12. I'm going to shoot you!; 13. Answer me!; 14. Answer yes or no!; 15. Answer quickly and clearly!; 16. Forward march!; 17. Go back!; 18. Hand over your weapons!; 19. Hand over your papers!; 20. Where is your unit?; 21. Where is your headquarters?

22. Wo ist der Regiments- (Bataillons-) Stab?	Gdje schtab palka? (bataljona?)	Где штаб полка? (батальона?)
23. Wo sind MG-Stellungen?	Gdje pulemjoty?	Где пулеметы!
24. Wo sind die Posten?	Gdje pasty?	Где посты?
25. Wo ist die Artillerie?	Gdje artillerija?	Где артиллерия?
26. Wo ist die B-Stelle?	Gdje nabljudatelny punkt?	Где наблюдательный пункт?
27. Wo sind Panzer?	Gdje tanki?	Где танки?
28. Gibt es russische Truppen im Dorf?	Jestli russkije wajsska fselje?	Есть ли русские войска в селе?
29. Gibt es Posten in der Nähe ja oder nein?	Jestli pasty wblisi — da Ili njet?	Есть ли посты вблизи — да или нет?
30. Gibt es hier Partisanen?	Jestli sdjessj partisany?	Есть ли здесь партизаны?
31. Bei Fluchtversuch wird geschossen!	Pabjeshisch — sasstrelju!	Побежишь — застрелю!
32. Sage die Wahrheit!	Gawari prawdu!	Говори правду!
33. Wo ist die Telefonzentrale?	Gdje telefonnaja stanzija?	Где телефонная станция?
34. Wo ist das Haus der Roten Armee?	Gdje dom krassnoj armii?	Где дом Красной Армии?
35. Wo ist das Haus der GPU.?	Gdje dom NKWD.?	Где дом НКВД?
36. Wo ist die Post?	Gdje potschta?	Где почта?
37. Wo ist der Dorfsowjet?	Gdje sseljssawjet?	Где сельсовет?

6

22. Where is your regiment (battalion) headquarters?; 23. Where are your machine-gun positions?; 24. Where are your sentry posts?; 25. Where is your artillery?; 26. Where is observation post?; 27. Where are your tanks?; 28. Are there Russian troops in the village?; 29. Are there sentry posts in the area, yes or no?; 30. Are there partisans here?; 31. Those who try to escape will be shot; 32. Tell me the truth!; 33. Where are your signals?; 34. Where is the Red Army HQ?; 35. Where is the NKVD HQ?; 36. Where is the post office?; 37. Where is the village soviet?

38. Wo ist hier das Stadthaus?	Gdje sdjessj gorkom?	Где здесь горком?
39. Wo ist der Bahnhof?	Gdje waksal?	Где вокзал?
Wo ist das Krankenhaus?	Gdje balniza?	Где больница?
Wo ist das Lazarett?	Gdje lasarjet?	Где лазарет?
40. Geh voraus!	Idi fperjott!	Иди вперед!
41. Wie heißt dieser Ort?	Kak nasywajetza eto ssjelo?	Как называется это село?
42. Wohin führt diese Straße?	Kuda wjedjot eta daroga?	Куда ведет эта дорога?
43. Ist sie gut befahrbar?	Wasmoshen panjej prajesd?	Возможен по ней проезд?
— ja — nein?	— da — njet?	— да — нет?
44. Ist die Brücke noch heil?	Most jeschtscho zel?	Мост еще цел?
45. Spricht hier jemand deutsch?	Kto gawarit pa nemetzki?	Кто говорит по немецки?
46. Wir brauchen Benzin!	Bensin jestj?	Бензин есть?
Wir brauchen Öl!	Masslo jestj?	Масло есть?
47. Ist hier eine Motor- und Traktoren-Station?	Jestj sdjessj MTS?	Есть здесь МТС?
48. Wir brauchen Autoschlosser!	Nam nushny aftomechaniki!	Нам нужны автомеханики!
— Mechaniker!	— mechaniki!	механики!
— Schlosser!	— ssljessari!	слесари!
— Elektriker!	— elektromechaniki!	электромеханики!
— Fahrer!	— schoffjory!	шоферы!
— Zimmerleute!	— plotniki!	плотники!

7

38. Where is the town party committee?; 39. Where is the train station? Hospital? Field hospital?; 40. Go ahead!; 41. What's this place called?; 42. Where does this road lead to?; 43. Is it passable – yes – no?; 44. Is the bridge still intact?; 45. Does anyone here speak German?; 46. We need petrol! We need oil!; 47. Is there a motor-/tractor-repair workshop near here?; 48. We need car mechanics! –mechanics! –metal workers! –electricians! –drivers!–carpenters!

German	Transliteration	Cyrillic
— Tischler!	— stoljary!	столяры!
— Maurer!	— kamenschtschiki!	каменщики!
— Klempner!	— wadaprawodtschiki!	водопроводчики!
— Schuster!	— ssaposhniki!	сапожники!
— Schneider!	— partnyje!	портные!
49. Kann das hier repariert werden? wo?	Moshno eto sdjessj patschinitj? gdje?	Можно это здесь починить? Где?
50. Wann wird das fertig?	Kagda gatowo?	Когда готово?
Wir brauchen Leute!	Nam nushny ljudi!	Нам нужны люди!
10 — 20 — 30 Mann!	djessjatj — dwattzatj — trittzatj tschelawjek!	десять — двадцать — тридцать человек!
Wir brauchen Pferdegespanne!	Nam nushny loschadi!	
51. Das ist eilig!	Eto spjeschno!	Это спешно!
52. Mach schnell!	Shywa!	Живо!
53. Schneller!	Skareje!	Скорее!
54. Schnell — langsam	Skora — medlenna	Скоро — медленно.
55. Schlecht — gut	Ploha — harascho	Плохо — хорошо.
Schlecht gemacht!	Ploha ssdjelana!	Плохо сделано!
Gut gemacht!	Harascho ssdjelana!	Хорошо сделано!
56. Idiot — Dummkopf!	Idiott — durack!	Идиот — дурак!

8

–joiners! –masons! –plumbers! –cobblers! –tailors!; 49. Can this be repaired here? Where?; 50. When will it be ready? We need people! 10 – 20 – 30 men! We need horses and carts!; 51. It's urgent!; 52. Hurry!; 53. Faster!; 54. Fast! – Slow!; 55. Bad – Good/That's a bad job!/Well done!; 56. Idiot – Blockhead!

Note on Russian Names

A Russian has three names: a Christian name, a patronymic (derived from the Christian name of the father) and a family name. Thus, Maria Timofeyevna is the daughter of a man whose first name is Timofey, and Sergey Alexandrovich Bogariov is the son of a man called Alexander. The first name and patronymic, used together, are the usual polite way of addressing someone or referring to them; the family name is used less often. Close friends or relatives usually address each other by one of the many diminutive, or affectionate, forms of their first names. Seriozha, for example, is a diminutive of Sergey, and Vasya is a diminutive of Vasily; Sima is one of many possible diminutives of Semion; Lionya and Lionochka are both diminutives of Leonid; Tima and Timka are both diminutives of Timofey; and Masha, Mashenka and Marusya are all diminutives of Maria.

Note on the Peasant Hut

In northern and central Russia, where wood was plentiful, a hut (*izba*) was built of logs (in the south it was of brick). Usually it was one storey high, with its floor raised two or three feet above ground level; this formed a cellar space beneath the house. On the outside, this part of the building was often surrounded by an earth ledge (*zavalinka*) – heaped earth held in by boards – which stopped cold air getting under the house and served as a bench in the summer.

Between the outer door or porch and the habitable room or rooms was an unheated entrance room (*seni*). This provided further insulation from the cold and could be used for storing tools and firewood or for housing animals.

In the long, cold Russian winter, the question of heating has always been all-important. A Russian stove was a large brick or clay structure taking up between one fifth and one quarter of the main room. It was used for heating the house, for heating water, for baking bread and for all the cooking, for drying linen and foodstuffs, for conserving grain and plants, for protecting small farm animals (holes were made in its walls for them), and sometimes for taking a steam bath: when the fire had burned out a person could climb right inside the stove's mouth.

Loaves or pies to be baked were placed deep inside the stove after the fuel had burned out or had been raked to one side; they were handled by means of an oven fork – a long iron stick with two prongs, heavy enough to need two hands to lift it. Soup was cooked in a large cast-iron pot.

Beds as such were rare, but several sleeping places were arranged in relation to the stove. A sleeping-bench might be attached to one side of it to share its warmth; a wide shelf extended under the ceiling above it and could be slept on; and people often slept directly on the warm brick surface of the stove itself; this might be a few feet above the ground or as high as a person.

Notes

1   Vasily Grossman, *Gody voiny*, 1989, p. 247.
2   Ibid.
3   Frank Ellis, *Vasiliy Grossman* (Oxford: Berg, 1994), p. 48. There are similar accounts by people who first read Grossman's articles in Leningrad, during the Blockade; some are quoted in A. Bocharov, *Vasily Grossman: Zhizn', tvorchestvo, sud'ba* (Moscow: Sovetsky pisatel', 1990), p. 132.
4   The Polikarpov I-16, nicknamed "the Donkey" (*Ishak*), was the main Soviet fighter during the first year of the war. It was obsolescent and on the verge of replacement by later, superior models.
5   In service from 1936 until the end of the war, the multi-role Junkers Ju-88 was one of the Luftwaffe's most important aircraft. The Heinkel He-111 bomber was also in service throughout the war.
6   Every unit of the Red Army had both a military and a political leader. The military leaders were called "commanders" until 1943, when the word "officer" was officially reintroduced. The political leaders were known as "commissars", except for the most junior rank, "political instructor" (*politruk*). Catherine Merridale writes, "An individual *politruk* was likely to combine the functions of a propagandist with those of an army chaplain, military psychiatrist, school prefect and spy." *Ivan's War* (Faber, 2006), p. 56.
7   The Marx–Engels Institute was established in 1919 as a library and archive attached to the Communist Academy. In 1931, it was merged with the Lenin Institute to form the Marx–Engels–Lenin Institute. In the typescript, Grossman changes the institute's title from "Marx-Engels" to "Marx–Engels–Lenin". This seemingly minor change illustrates the extreme sensitivities around this institute. The longer title would have been a little safer, since its use would have indicated that Bogariov only began working there after the arrest of David Riazanov, its dangerously free-thinking director. See Afterword, pp. 259–61.

8   Paul Lafargue (1842–1911) was a French Marxist, journalist, literary critic
     and activist. He was Karl Marx's son-in-law.

9   In spite of the instance of self-censorship described in note 7, very little
     of these last two paragraphs (from "The directors of the Marx–Engels
     Institute . . .") was included in any of the published versions. This last
     paragraph (from "She also found something touching") was deleted by
     Grossman himself; he may have thought that his editors would consider
     it inappropriate for the novel's hero to exhibit such helplessness. Here
     and elsewhere, however, there is some variation as regards which details
     were included in which editions. See Afterword, pp. 260–63.

10   A "Front" was equivalent to a German Army Group. According to Rodric
     Braithwaite, "A Front contained up to nine mixed armies, up to three tank
     armies, one or two air armies and various supporting formations. A mixed
     army contained five or six rifle divisions and supporting arms." *Moscow
     1941* (Profile, 2006), p. 268, note 6. The word "Front" was used only after
     the German invasion; the earlier term was "Military District". Throughout
     this translation we distinguish between "Front", as above, and "front"
     or "front line" in a more general sense.

11   All five of these places in Belarus and Ukraine were shtetls. All had a high
     proportion of Jewish inhabitants, most of whom were massacred by the
     Nazis in September 1941. Antisemitism – both official and unofficial –
     was a persistent force in Soviet society, and it was growing more powerful
     throughout the 1940s. This made it difficult, though not impossible, for
     Soviet writers and artists to address the theme of the Shoah directly. Here,
     as elsewhere in his wartime stories and articles, Grossman takes every
     opportunity to hint at it.

12   Like most of the passages about Bogariov's pre-war, "philosophical" life,
     this paragraph was deleted from the manuscript by Grossman himself.

13   Grossman deleted from his manuscript the two sentences from "All these
     officers . . ." The long Soviet retreats of 1941–42 were a sensitive issue.
     See Afterword, pp. 251–53.

14   We have reinstated from the manuscript the passage from "just as they
     had in the past" up to "oldest cultures".

15   This paragraph was included in *Red Star*, but not in subsequent published
     editions. Grossman had in his possession a copy of an information
     bulletin about the morale and general thinking of German soldiers.
     This bulletin (published 27 February 1942, in a small print run, for Soviet
     commissars, commanders and war correspondents) consists mainly of

extracts from diaries and letters found on German prisoners-of-war. As well as complaints about Hitler's mistakes and the lack of winter clothing, there are indeed many mentions of geese, pork, honey and *smetana* (sour cream). It is unclear whether it was Grossman or his editors who deleted this paragraph from the published editions.

16 Otto von Bismarck (1815–1898), the "Iron Chancellor", masterminded the unification of Germany in 1871. Helmuth von Moltke (1800–1891), chief of staff of the Prussian army for thirty years, was considered the embodiment of Prussian military organization and tactical genius. Count Schlieffen (1833–1913) was chief of the Imperial German General Staff from 1891 to 1906; his name lived on in the "Schlieffen Plan" for a war against France. Frederick the Great (1712–1786), King of Prussia from 1740 to 1786, is now generally thought to have been a gifted general and an enlightened monarch.

17 The original meaning of *soviet* is simply "council".

18 Heinz Guderian (1888–1954), a pioneer of the blitzkrieg approach, was Hitler's most celebrated Panzer general.

19 Prince Ivan Paskevich (1782–1856) was an important general, diplomat and political figure. In 1834 he bought an estate in the city of Gomel, in what is now Belarus.

20 Grossman's Yeromin is clearly the historical General Andrey Yeromenko, at this time the commander of the Central Front. In summer 1942 Yeromenko was appointed commander of the Stalingrad Front.

21 The official newspaper of the National Socialist Party, published weekly from December 1920 and daily from February 1923.

22 Nearly all of the previous fifteen lines (from "They did not understand the harsh, complex laws") were omitted from the published editions. Only the sentence beginning "The *Völkischer Beobachter*" was published. See note 13.

23 Maurice Gustave Gamelin (1872–1958) is remembered, above all, for his disastrous command of the French Army at the beginning of the Second World War. The three sentences from "He had a broad understanding" were omitted from the published editions; they may have been considered too complex.

24 General Mikhail Kutuzov (1745–1813) was the commander-in-chief of the Russian army that defeated Napoleon in 1812. He was brave, intelligent and popular among his troops.

25 The George Cross was the supreme award for bravery. There were four

grades; the two lower were silver, the two higher were gold. Semion's father had been awarded a very high honour indeed.

26 See Note on Russian Names.

27 A bond issued in 1917 by the Provisional Government, rendered valueless after the October Revolution.

28 Evidently, a lieutenant – not such an important boss as he leads Marusya to think.

29 The four lines from "all girls" were omitted from all the published versions, perhaps because light-hearted humour was considered inappropriate in a novel about the war.

30 Factories of all kinds were "evacuated" to the Urals and Siberia on a scale that is hard for a contemporary reader to imagine. The historians Wendy Goldman and Donald Filtzer write, "In contrast to the state's initial failures on the military front, it managed to act decisively and, by and large, effectively on the home front. [. . .] The Soviet for Evacuation [. . .] by fall 1942 had organized the transport of more than 2,400 industrial enterprises, almost 8 million animals, and up to 25 million people." Goldman and Filtzer, *Fortress Dark and Stern: the Soviet Home Front during World War II* (OUP, 2021), pp. 5–6. Sheila Fitzpatrick, in a review of this book, writes, "Perhaps a little more than a third of the occupied regions' industrial plant was salvaged and re-established in the Urals and Siberia." "Miracles on the Home Front" in *Australian Book Review*, September 2021, no. 435.

31 Much of this chapter corresponds to passages in Grossman's notebooks about his time in Gomel; he witnessed the city being firebombed on the night of 7/8 August. There are probably two reasons why he chose not to name the city. First, *The People Immortal* is set much later in August. Second, he may have preferred to create a more universal image of the destruction of a peaceful city.

32 Important factories were dismantled and shipped further east, often to the Urals or Siberia. Most employees were evacuated along with their factories. Children and the old, for the main part, were not evacuated. Many of the stronger and healthier set off on foot, but this old Jewish woman – like Grossman's lame mother – does not have that option.

33 Grossman deleted from his manuscript the twelve lines from "He had particularly disliked" to "struggling to hold him back!" He may well have thought that his portrayal of Mertsalov was too negative to be acceptable. We have reinstated the passage because it presents a

paradox that troubled Grossman: that all too many commanders thought nothing of risking their lives on the battlefield yet were terrified of showing any true initiative, of doing anything that might be seen as an infringement of orders. See Afterword, pp. 253–55.

34 Georgy Plekhanov (1856–1918) came to be revered by the Soviet Communist Party as one of the first revolutionaries and an important theoretician. From the 1905 Revolution until his death, however, he was fiercely critical of Lenin and the Bolshevik Party.

35 The ten paragraphs from "They got talking again" up to "said Bogariov" were not included in any of the published editions. This is not surprising. The old lawyer clearly belongs to the first generation of revolutionaries – men whom Stalin found threatening and most of whom he eliminated during the Great Terror of 1936–38. There are similar figures in many of Grossman's other works – from Verkhotursky in the story "Four Days" to the various Mensheviks and Old Bolsheviks in German and Soviet labour camps in Life and Fate.

36 A senior field officer rank, equivalent to group captain (air force) or colonel (ground forces).

37 In one of his memoirs Ortenberg writes, "Grossman and I spent eighteen consecutive evenings or nights checking the three-column pages of the proofs of his story for Red Star. During that time, he told me new details of what he had been through. He praised Troyanovsky [the more experienced journalist whom Ortenberg had detailed to accompany Grossman – R.C.]. A German bomb had set fire to the three-storey building where they were billeted and everyone had rushed out into the yard. Grossman had then realized that he had left his notes behind, in a room on the top floor. Troyanovsky had run back in to rescue them. What Grossman did not mention was that he himself had then rescued Troyanovsky from a burning staircase. That I learned only later, from Troyanovsky." D. Ortenberg, Vremia ne vlastno (Moscow: Sovetsky pisatel', 1979), p. 314. In another version of his memoir Ortenberg explains that Troyanovsky had lost consciousness. "Vasily Grossman – Frontline Correspondent" in Letopistsy Pobedy (Moscow, 1990), p. 42.

38 Much of these three paragraphs corresponds to a striking passage in Grossman's wartime notebooks, "The Bombing of Gomel. A cow, the howl of bombs, fire, women. The smell of perfumes – a chemist had been bombed – momentarily overpowered the smell of burning. The colours of smoke. Printworkers composed the day's newspaper by

the light from burning buildings. A picture of blazing Gomel in the eyes of a wounded cow." *Gody voiny*, 1989, p. 254. As always, Grossman has an eye for a vivid detail. The addition of Bogariov's thought about how he himself was taking in the city's destruction, exemplifies something perhaps still more important: Grossman's ability to make unexpected use of such details.

The *Red Star* version includes an additional paragraph immediately after "peaceful and ancient city": "As long as I live, as long as I breathe, as long as my fingers have the strength to move and I have the strength to utter even just one word," he said to himself, as a slow, stern thought, like a solemn oath, passed through his overheated brain, "let nothing exist for me but the work of a fighter. May I put all my heart and soul into arousing hatred and the thirst for revenge. Oh, let it be so!" This is one of several passages about hatred and the thirst for revenge that Grossman omitted from all the post-war editions. See Afterword, p. 266.

39 Many of the harsher physical details of this passage were omitted from the published versions. See Afterword, pp. 264–65.

40 Tacitus's most important work, usually known as *The Annals*. In 1938, towards the end of the Great Terror, Grossman was reading this himself. See Appendix p. 309.

41 Here too, the harsher details were omitted from the published versions. See Afterword, pp. 264–65.

42 Instituted in 1934, this was the highest Soviet award, for heroic deeds on behalf of the Soviet state. Recipients received a certificate and a Gold Star medal.

43 We have reinstated from the manuscript the first six sentences of this chapter, from "Divisional command" to "extremely self-confident".

44 Here we have reinstated two passages from the manuscript: from "He was someone who" to "some preconceived view"; and from "You're not saying much" to "everything becomes clear".

45 We have reinstated from the manuscript much of the preceding four paragraphs. The sentence beginning "Bogariov noted" is present in the manuscript but was omitted in all the published versions. Grossman himself deleted from his manuscript the four lines from "And then, when Kozlov suggested" up to "anything of the kind". We have also reinstated from the manuscript the word "gravely" and the sentence "Everyone laughed." Grossman's implied criticism of the commanders for their excessive concern with bureaucratic regulations was clearly controversial.

46 We have reinstated from the manuscript the two short paragraphs from "Excuse me" to "loudly and angrily". Grossman's emphasis on Myshansky's defeatism may have been considered excessive.

47 We have reinstated from the manuscript the three sentences from "And please forgive me again" to "helpless despair".

48 The philosopher and literary critic Nikolay Chernyshevsky (1828–1889) is best known for his utopian socialist novel *What Is to Be Done?* This greatly influenced Lenin, one of whose political tracts bears the same title.

49 For von Schlieffen see note 16.

50 Grossman deleted this sentence from his manuscript. He may have thought it inadequate; he certainly understood that the genesis of antisemitism is more complex than Bogariov makes out. Or he may have realized that it was unacceptable to suggest that there might be similarities between Russia and Germany. Since this may well be the first place in Grossman's work where he draws any such parallel with regard to antisemitism, we have reinstated the sentence.

51 A metal stove on wheels, with a square opening through which it was fuelled, and which might sometimes be left open.

52 Mess tins were sometimes in short supply, especially during the first months of the war. It was not uncommon for soldiers to have to share.

53 Here we follow the manuscript and typescript version of this sentence, which is identical to a sentence in Grossman's notebooks (*Gody voiny*, 1989, p. 254); Grossman evidently heard a soldier speak these words. In *Red Star*, this sentence was omitted. It was included in subsequent published editions, but only with a change to make it ideologically acceptable; the words "but people fight for supremacy" are replaced by "but Germans fight for supremacy". The soldier's words evidently made a deep impression on Grossman and he returns to them in *Life and Fate*, in Ikonnikov's essay on "senseless kindness".

54 Ortenberg recalls, "(Grossman) told me about a conversation with a middle-aged infantry sergeant, formerly a carpenter, who had been through a great deal during the war. The two men talked about bravery and cowardice. Grossman asked if he found fighting difficult: 'Wasn't it frightening?' The man replied, 'Why frightening? It's work. We worked back at home. And we're working here.' These words stayed in Grossman's mind. This carpenter, who had worked without a break all his life, saw his front-line duties simply as necessary hard work for the defence of his homeland. This theme – the difficult feat of labour on the

front line – runs through all Grossman's wartime writings. Grossman considered it his duty as a writer to work without interruption towards victory over the Fascist invaders. And he went on working without giving so much as a thought to whether or not what he was doing was dangerous." *Vremia ne vlastno*, p. 315.

55 The Junkers Ju-87 dive bomber and ground-attack aircraft played an important role during the years 1939–42. It provided crucial support to German ground troops and was seen as a symbol of German military might.

56 Very little of the seven paragraphs from "True enough" to "fight well" was included in any of the published versions. Grossman himself deleted the two paragraphs from "True enough" to "taken back the farm". The paragraph beginning "As for Bogariov" was published in full. Grossman deleted the two paragraphs from "Kudakov turned to Mertsalov" to "thought Bogariov". And from "Then he turned to Kudakov" to "we'll fight well" is present in the manuscript but omitted from all the published versions. Grossman's editors were clearly uncomfortable with his mentions of Soviet defeatism.

57 A *kolkhoz* is the standard Soviet term for a collective farm. It is a portmanteau word, derived from **kollektivnoye khoziaistvo**, meaning "collective holding".

58 The original meaning of *kulak* is "fist". During the late nineteenth century the word acquired the meaning of "prosperous (i.e. tight-fisted) peasant". In Soviet times, peasants were classified as either poor peasants (*bedniaki*), who had no property of their own, middle peasants (*seredniaki*), who owned property but did not employ hired labour, and rich peasants or *kulaki*, who both owned property and employed hired labour. During collectivization, the *kulaki* were deported en masse.

59 See note on the Russian peasant hut, p.323.

60 This sentence exemplifies the minor editorial interventions to which Grossman's text was subjected. Two phrases are present in the manuscript but were omitted from the published versions: "magnificent, compact" and "powered by multi-cylinder engines". Grossman's emphasis on German technological superiority was not controversial, but it may, at this point, have been considered excessive.

61 This is reminiscent of the practice of mutual forgiveness at the beginning of Lent, when one person bows down to the ground before another, saying "Forgive me" – to which the standard response is "God will

forgive". Here, the mother's imaginary bow is an expression of humility, reverence and a grateful acceptance of fate; she wants her son to understand that she is not blaming him for her imminent death. Grossman may, perhaps, have been hoping, that if the Germans had killed his mother, she might have felt something similar.

62   Maria Timofeyevna's primary allegiance appears to be to Lenin rather than Stalin. In this, she is similar to Bogariov, whose rapport with her son is very close.

63   The two sentences from "This impending murder" to "annihilations" are present in the manuscript but were omitted from all the published versions. Grossman's editors may have felt uncomfortable with some of his more thoughtful passages, perhaps uncertain whether or not they were in accord with the Party line.

64   The last part of this sentence, from "the desperate cries" to "the previous week", was omitted from all the published versions. Grossman's emphasis on the sufferings of the civilians in occupied territory may have been thought excessive.

65   There is a brief mention in Grossman's notebooks of a real prototype for Kotenko: "An old man was looking forward to the Germans' arrival. He put out a smart tablecloth and a spread of delicacies. The Germans wrecked and plundered. The old man hanged himself." *Gody voiny*, 1989, p. 311.

66   Founded in 1924 as a fortnightly journal for "Working Youth", *Smena* had a large circulation. During the 1930s it had sometimes published work by major writers, but its general standard, especially during the war years, was very low. Bogariov treats Nevtulov and Rumiantsev with great tact, but he is clearly well aware of the absurdity of Nevtulov's account of their elimination of several German artillery batteries and an entire infantry regiment. It is easy to imagine this episode being based on reality; eager young commanders may well have shown writings of this kind to Grossman himself.

67   We have reinstated from the manuscript this whole simile, from "like musicians" to "important concert". Editors often preferred to omit Grossman's more original or fanciful images.

68   In a notebook entry, Grossman writes, "Heinkels and Junkers flying at night. They crawl about among the stars like lice. The darkness is filled with their hum. The thud of bombs. Burning villages round about. The dark August sky grows brighter . . . If people see a shooting star or

hear a clap of daytime thunder, they take fright and then laugh, saying, 'That was from the sky, from the real sky.'" *Gody voiny*, 1989, p. 254.

69   During the first months of the war there was often too little time to construct proper trenches. These small foxholes all too often served as the soldiers' graves.

70   During the Spanish Civil War and the Second World War, tape was often applied to shop windows in order to reduce the risk of shards of glass flying across a street during an air raid. See https://madridnofrills.com/wartime-art/.

71   A kind of coarse tobacco, widely used in Russia throughout much of the last century.

72   The two mentions of Sedov swearing have been reinstated from the manuscript. In many respects, the Soviet Union was an extremely puritanical society. Even in an army newspaper like *Red Star* the taboo with regard to swear words and obscenity was surprisingly strong. Grossman, naturally, was interested in how soldiers actually speak, and his notebooks contain several mentions of swear words. One of the most amusing is this: "Ponomarenko: someone says to the general, 'Don't you dare curse and swear about members of the Central Committee.' The general, embarrassed, 'It was just cursing – it wasn't *him* I was cursing.'" Panteleimon Ponomarenko (1902–1984) was First Secretary of the Belorussian Communist Party Central Committee from 1938 to 1947. *Gody voiny*, 1989, p. 257.

73   In the typescript: "Babadjanian said to Rodimtsev." This is almost certainly a mistake. Here we follow the published version, which makes better sense.

74   Another vivid detail omitted from the published versions – either because it was thought unseemly or because it might have evoked the readers' pity.

75   Throughout his life and work, Grossman consistently emphasized the value of labour. In a notebook entry he observes, "A Russian may labour very hard and live a difficult life, but deep down he lacks any sense of the inevitability of this hard labour and difficult life. During this war I have observed only two attitudes towards what is happening: either extraordinary optimism or absolute, unrelieved gloom. The transitions from optimism to gloom are quick and sharp, and they happen easily. There is no middle ground. Nobody lives by the idea that this is a long war, and that only hard, unremitting work, month after month, will lead to victory. Even those who say things like this do not really believe what

they say. There are only two feelings: first, that the enemy has been totally defeated; second, that the enemy *cannot* be defeated." *Gody voiny*, 1989, p. 314.

76 Babadjanian is treating these fleeing soldiers leniently; his duty, according to Stavka Order no. 270, is to shoot them. Compare Colonel Babadjanian's words when Grossman interviewed him in Berlin in 1945, "In 1941, I was not one for having men shot. If someone took flight, I'd say, 'Where are you going? You're a defender of the Motherland.'" (*Skazhesh begushchemu: "Kuda zhe vy, vy ved' zashchitnik Rodiny."*) (RGALI, 1710-3-31. listy. 1–12)

77 This whole paragraph – a fine example of Grossman's determination to avoid grandiosity – was omitted from the published editions. It is all the more moving because Grossman has just done all he can to ensure that at least five of the dead *will* be remembered. Politinstructor Yeretik's death is also mentioned in his notebooks. *Gody voiny*, 1989, p. 306.

78 A related notebook entry reads, "Driver Kuptsov was on horseback a hundred metres away from the main position. The unit began to retreat, leaving an artillery piece behind. Mortar bombs were raining down. Instead of galloping off to the rear, Kuptsov rode up to the gun and dragged it out of the bog. When the politinstructor asked him where he had found the courage to confront an all but certain death, he replied, 'I've got a simple soul. Cheap as a balalaika. It's not afraid of death. It's people with precious souls who get scared.'" *Gody voiny*, 1989, p. 254.

79 Most of this sentence has been reinstated from the manuscript. The published versions read simply, "Yes, he often wanted Lisa to look at him now." Grossman himself deleted from the manuscript the words, "a scholar and philosopher, studying day and night in the Marx–Engels Institute". And his editors deleted "one of the cooks tending to the fiery cauldron of the war".

80 A network of special high-frequency telephones, set up during the 1930s and used by the government, the military and the security services. The Supreme Command in Moscow, established on 23 June 1941, was known as the Stavka; its members were Stalin, Semion Timoshenko (the defence commissar), Georgy Zhukov, Viacheslav Molotov, Kliment Voroshilov, Semion Budionny and Nikolay Kuznetsov. This paragraph was omitted from the published versions. Grossman's editors may have felt that his treatment of something so important as a conversation with Stalin was too cursory. Or it may have been Grossman's own wish to

omit the paragraph; he was well aware of the atrocious state of Soviet communications at the time and would have known that he was painting too rosy a picture.

81   We have reinstated from the manuscript the ten lines from "To be honest" to "from metal". Yeromin's open, straightforward love of war must have been considered politically incorrect – as, of course, it would be today.

82   Here, Grossman is delicately inserting himself into the story. It is clear from his notebooks that he attended the Central Committee meeting just described. And he was, at this point, still being accompanied by the war correspondent Pavel Troyanovsky, and by the photographer Oleg Knorring. *Gody voiny*, 1989, p. 257.

83   A prose work by Alexander Pushkin, based on notes taken during his unauthorized journey to eastern Turkey during the Russian–Turkish war of 1828–29.

84   Vsevolod Garshin (1855–1888) was a Russian writer and critic. He volunteered to serve as a private soldier in the Russian–Turkish war of 1877–78, during which he was wounded. His best stories evoke the reality of war as experienced by ordinary soldiers.

85   A love song, popular during the war years.

86   Kliukhin evidently thinks of the name "David" as exclusively Jewish.

87   Grossman deleted these three adjectives from his manuscript.

88   The corresponding notebook entry reads, "He is very cruel and very brave. He told us how, not wanting to put on civilian clothes, he escaped the encirclement on foot, wearing his medals and his Gold Star. He was alone, in full uniform, and carrying a stick to fight off the village dogs. 'I'd always dreamed of getting to Africa,' he said, 'of chopping my way through tropical forest, alone, with just an axe and a rifle.' He has a great love of cats, especially kittens, and he spends a lot of time playing with them." *Gody voiny*, 1989, p. 271.

89   The corresponding notebook entry reads, "Everything has been taken away from the empty huts; only the icons remain. All very different from Nekrasov's peasants, who rescued their icons but yielded the rest of their belongings to the flames." *Gody voiny*, 1989, p. 273. Nikolay Nekrasov (1821–1877) – an editor, publisher and the most popular poet of his time – was fiercely critical of serfdom and the autocracy. Much of his work is devoted to the plight of the Russian peasantry. It is unclear whether Grossman's peasants left their icons behind in order to protect their huts, or because they no longer cared about the icons, or because they were

afraid that the icons might attract unwelcome attention from the
authorities as they fled east.

90   Here Grossman quotes almost verbatim from his notebooks: "Elderly
     mistress of the hut, 'Who knows whether God exists or not. I pray to
     Him. It's not hard work. Bow to him twice – maybe he'll hear.'"
     Gody voiny, 1989, p. 273.

91   Grossman's Samarin is modelled on General Mikhail Petrov (1898–1941),
     who died in October 1941 during the Briansk Encirclement, along with
     Commissar Nikolay Shliapin. Most of what Grossman tells us about
     Samarin – his love of cats, his lecturing his cook about baking techniques,
     his conversation with the old woman – comes straight from the wartime
     notebooks. Altogether, Grossman portrays Petrov three times – in his
     notebooks, as Samarin in *The People Immortal*, and under his real name in
     Stalingrad. It is clear from all three of these portrayals that Grossman
     admired Petrov – and not only for his remarkable courage. Antony Beevor
     is wrong to suggest that Grossman's descriptions of Petrov "read like a
     terrible satire of the Red Army". *A Writer at War*, p. xiii. Grossman portrays
     him as severe but fair – and occasionally selflessly generous – in his
     treatment of his subordinates. See *Gody voiny*, 1989, pp. 271–73.

92   Kissel is made of pureed fruit or peas, thickened with potato starch.
     Depending on the proportion of starch, it can be the consistency of a
     smoothie, a soup or a blancmange.

93   Ignatiev himself can hardly, at this stage of the war, have "tramped
     thousands of kilometres". Grossman seems to be thinking of him as a
     collective being, as an embodiment of the Red Army's collective soul.

94   That is to say, a German soldier from whom they hope to be able to
     extract information.

95   A common refreshing drink, lightly alcoholic, usually made from old
     bread.

96   A standard formula, pronounced in acknowledgement of official praise
     or the receipt of an official award.

97   Grossman deleted from his manuscript the three sentences from
     "There was nothing" to "forgotten all discipline". This was probably
     self-censorship – he would have understood that he was presenting too
     negative a picture.

98   Desertion from the Red Army took place on a large scale and discussion
     of it remains a sensitive issue even today. Grossman's wartime notebooks
     were first published, in an almost uncensored edition, at the height of

Gorbachov's liberal reforms. The following is one of the very few entries that were entirely omitted, "Thousands of men from Chernigov are running away. At night, German radio loudspeakers call out, 'Men from Chernigov, go home!' And so they do." See A. Bocharov, *Vasily Grossman*, p. 130.

99 Grossman deleted from his manuscript the words, "and some were not carrying weapons".

100 No matter what the military situation, it was considered important to maintain standards of dress and general appearance. In a notebook entry, Grossman writes, "A commander asked a soldier why he was unshaven. 'Because I don't have a razor,' the soldier replied. 'All right,' said the commander. 'You can pass as a peasant. I'll send you on reconnaissance behind enemy lines.' 'Comrade commander, I'll shave today, without fail.'" *Gody voiny*, 1989, p. 248.

101 In the manuscript, this is followed by one more sentence, which Grossman himself deleted: "Yes, in this war, everyone must become a hero." Grossman may perhaps have been struggling to find a way to reproduce the more vivid – but unpublishable – words of the real Commissar Shliapin, "I held up a grenade. 'Stop!' I yelled. 'Or else!' I threw it. No-one even looked back. At that, I lost my rag. 'Well, you bastards,' I said to myself, 'I'll make heroes out of you yet.' And so I did." See Appendix p. 272.

102 We have reinstated this paragraph from the manuscript. Grossman himself deleted the first three sentences; the last three sentences were probably omitted by his editors. It is significant that Bogariov concludes by invoking "the heart of Lenin". Most commissars would, at this moment, have paid the obligatory homage to Stalin, but Bogariov appears not to accept Stalin as Lenin's true heir. See our discussion of the Marx–Engels Institute in the Afterword, pp. 259–61.

103 This paragraph was omitted from the published editions – as were many of Bogariov's philosophical reflections.

104 The heroine of Pushkin's *Eugene Onegin*. Like Tolstoy's Natasha Rostova, she is often seen as the embodiment of true Russian womanhood.

105 During the first decades after the Revolution, scientists working at the Pasteur Institute made important and original contributions in the fields of microbiology and immunology. Many of these scientists were executed or sent to the Gulag during the 1930s. Grossman deleted this

sentence from his manuscript – aware, no doubt, that mention of this institute might be too controversial.

106   Trofim Lysenko (1898–1976) was a Soviet agronomist, a charlatan and a favourite of Stalin's. At his instigation, a network of "laboratory-huts" – supposedly a Soviet equivalent of research stations – was established on collective farms. Data from these laboratory-huts was collected only through questionnaires, which made it easy to falsify the results.

107   A standard pre-revolutionary measure of distance, slightly longer than a kilometre.

108   A related notebook entry reads, "A lieutenant colonel was making his way east from Volkovysk. In the forest he came across a three-year-old boy. He carried him hundreds of *versts*, through bogs and forests. I saw them in our HQ. The boy had fair hair and he was asleep, his arm round the man's neck. The man had red hair and his clothes were in rags." *A Writer at War* (Harvill Press, 2005), p. 21.

109   Bogariov – and Grossman himself – see both time and space as working in the Russians' favour. As time passed and the *Wehrmacht* penetrated deeper into the Soviet Union, it became ever harder for the Germans to keep their troops supplied, let alone to cope with the dense autumn mud and an exceptionally cold winter.

110   We have reinstated from the manuscript the four sentences from "He laughed" to "closer to defeat". Nearly all Bogariov's reflections on the duration of the war were omitted from the published versions of the novel. See Afterword, pp. 251–53.

111   This thought was important to Grossman. Commissar Krymov expands on them in *Stalingrad*. Grossman put it most succinctly in a notebook entry: "The dialectics of war: the ability to shelter and so preserve one's life – and the ability to fight and sacrifice one's life." *Gody voiny*, 1989, p. 254.

112   Red Army soldiers and commanders were expected to sew a narrow strip of white cloth to the inside of their tunic or jacket collar, leaving two to three millimetres showing above it. This served both to preserve the collar and to create the illusion of a shirt.

113   In an October 1941 notebook entry, Grossman writes, "War is an art. In it elements of calculation, cold knowledge and intellectual experience meet with inspiration, chance and something entirely irrational. [. . .] These elements all meet together. Sometimes, though, they conflict with one

another. All this is like musical improvisation – and without brilliant equipment it cannot happen at all." *Gody voiny*, 1989, pp. 313–14.

114   This whole sentence was omitted from the published editions. Grossman's emphasis on the need for commanders to take responsibility was controversial.

115   Kudakov is, of course, referring to Stavka Order, no. 270. See the last pages of the Introduction. For this sentence, we have followed Grossman's manuscript. The *Red Star* version of this sentence ends, "aware of Samarin's severity with regard to every order about retreat". The book versions omit the last phrase, ending with the words, "aware of Samarin's severity".

116   We have reinstated this sentence from the manuscript. Like other humorous details, it was omitted from the published versions. Humour and comedy were, for the main part, considered inappropriate in works about the war.

117   The Fronde was a series of civil wars in France, between 1648 and 1653. King Louis XIV eventually defeated the Frondeurs – an alliance of the princes, the nobility and the law courts, along with much of the French people. The king's victory marked an important step in the establishment of an absolute monarchy.

118   Literally, "Black Death". This was the Ilyushin-2 ground-attack aircraft, produced in large numbers from 1941. The Russians often called it either the "Hunchback" or the "Flying Tank".

119   *Zrazy* is a meat roulade dish popular in Poland, western Belorussia and Lithuania. *Flaki* or *flaczki* is a traditional Polish meat stew. It is named after its main ingredient: thin, cleaned strips of beef tripe.

120   *Kluski* is a generic Polish name for all kinds of soft dumplings, usually unfilled. A *mazurek* is a sweet flat cake baked in Poland for Easter. A *knish* is a traditional East European Jewish snack food – a filling (usually cheese, *kasha* or mashed potato) covered with a baked or fried dough.

121   A distilled spirit made from rye, drunk mainly in Poland and Lithuania.

122   An *arshin* is a basic unit in the Russian system of measurements used until 1925. Usually it was a measure of length, 28 inches, the equivalent of an English cubit. Here, though, it is being used as a measure of area.

123   A sleeveless dress worn by peasant women.

124   The Renaissance humanist philosopher Thomas More (1478–1535) published *Utopia*, a work of fiction and political satire, in 1516.

125   Robert Owen (1771–1858) was a Welsh socialist and social reformer.

Marx, Engels and Lenin all engaged with his ideas and reinterpreted them.

126 Vissarion Belinsky (1811–1848) was an important Russian literary critic, strongly opposed to the tsarist regime and a single-minded advocate of Realism in art and literature.

127 Alexander Herzen (1812–1870), a philosopher, journalist, publisher and revolutionary, spent much of his life as an exile in western Europe, including twelve years in London. He is best known for his autobiography, *My Past and Thoughts.*

128 Andrey Zheliabov (1851–1881) was a Populist revolutionary. As a member of the executive committee of the terrorist organization *Narodnaya volia* (The People's Will), he helped plan the assassination of Tsar Alexander II in March 1881. He was executed along with his fellow-conspirators.

129 Alexander Mikhailov (1855–1884) was another Populist revolutionary. Sentenced to life imprisonment, he died in solitary confinement, from pulmonary oedema.

130 Piotr Alexeyev (1849–1891), a textile worker, was one of the first Russian revolutionaries to come from the working class. A speech he gave in March 1877, while on trial along with other Populists, made a great impression on Russian progressive society as a whole. The following sentence became almost proverbial, "Millions strong, the Russian people will raise their muscular hand – and the yoke of despotism, defended by the bayonets of soldiers, will crumble to dust."

131 We have reinstated from the manuscript the words "for a land that does not know slavery, for a life built on the laws of reason and justice".

132 Grossman deleted from his manuscript the phrase beginning, "yet it was the motherland". The final sentence is present in his manuscript but was omitted from all the published versions. It seems from this and from the omission mentioned in the previous note that Grossman's editors were alarmed by the intensity of Bogariov's internationalism and love of freedom.

133 Alexandra Popoff, *Vasily Grossman and the Soviet Century* (Yale University Press, 2019), p. 128.

134 See Grossman, *Stalingrad* (NYRB Classics, 2020), pp. xviii–xx.

135 *A Writer at War*, pp. 31–35.

136 Gosudarstvennyi literaturnyi muzei, otdel rukopisei, f. 76, op. 1, ed. khr. 6.

137 Ibid.

138   Jochen Hellbeck, *Stalingrad: The City that Defeated the Third Reich* (Public
       Affairs, 2015), pp. 433–34.

139   I. V. Stalin, *O Velikoi Otechestvennoi voine Sovetskogo Soiuza* (Moscow, 1947),
       p. 24.

140   *Gody voiny*, 1989, p. 249.

141   See "How Victory is Forged" in *The Years of War* (1946), p. 424. The title of
       this article could be translated more literally as "The Creation of Victory"
       or "The Creative Work of Victory".

142   For a sensitive discussion of the similarities between Ignatiev and Tiorkin,
       see A. Bocharov, *Vasily Grossman*, pp. 123–26.

143   RGALI, 1710-1-88 and 1710-1-89.

144   See Beevor, *A Writer at War*, p. 113. We have slightly revised the translation.

145   The Soviet security service was renamed many times; the most important
       of its names and acronyms, in chronological order, are the Cheka, the
       OGPU, the NKVD and the KGB.

146   Victor Serge, *Memoirs of a Revolutionary* (NYRB, 2012), p. 291. In 1903, the
       Russian Social-Democratic Labour Party split into two factions, which
       became known as the Bolsheviks (led by Lenin) and the Mensheviks.
       After Lenin's death in 1924, there were two main groups opposing Stalin's
       rise to power: first, the "Left Opposition" (led by Leon Trotsky), and then
       the "Right Opposition" (led by Nikolay Bukharin).

147   Shliapin and Shabalin are similar names and both men served in the
       50th Army, one as a commissar, the other as a NKVD officer. This – along
       with inconsistent transliterations – has led some writers and readers to
       imagine them to be one and the same man. There is no doubt, however,
       that they are separate figures – at one point in his diary, Shabalin
       describes a meeting with Shliapin.

148   Quoted in Dimbleby, *Barbarossa* (Penguin Viking, 2021), p. 317.

149   Michael Jones, *The Retreat* (John Murray, 2009), p. 67.

150   RGALI, 1710–49, with thanks to Oleg Budnitsky.

151   *A Writer at War*, p. 34.

152   During the first months of the war, General Ivan Konev was in command
       of the 19th Army. He fought a number of defensive battles during the
       Red Army's retreat to Smolensk and then to the outskirts of Moscow.
       In 1944, he was appointed a Marshal of the Soviet Union.

153   Captain Lysov was, no doubt, aware of Hitler's notorious "Commissar
       Order" of 6 June 1941. Any prisoner of war identified as a commissar was
       to be summarily executed as a proponent of "Judeo-Bolshevism".

154 One of the most popular Soviet songs of the time. A young woman wearing a modest blue kerchief waves goodbye to her boyfriend as he departs for the front. She promises never to forget him. Valya may well be the "campaign wife" of one of the senior commanders.

155 A simple wooden boat, about 7 metres long, used to ferry infantry or light field guns across a river.

156 Semion Lipkin, *Kvadriga* (Moscow: Knizhnyi Sad/Agraf, 1997), p. 531.

157 Dimbleby, *Barbarossa*, pp. 271–76. For Akimenko's manuscript see *Tsentral'nyi Arkhiv Ministerstva Oborony*, f. 1047, op. 1, d. 12, l. 11–12.

158 David Ortenberg, *God 1942* (Moscow, 1982), p. 293.

159 Piotr Kolomeitsev was another *Red Star* war correspondent.

160 RGALI 1710-3-31; l. 12–70.

161 A nationalist – and violently antisemitic – movement in early twentieth-century Russia and Ukraine.

162 RGALI 1710-3-31; l. 12–70.

163 The published version is very different: "His uncle feigned madness for a year – anything not to have to serve the tsar, not to have to live in a military barracks."

164 Established in 1918, the Frunze Academy was one of the most prestigious Soviet military educational institutions. Most Russian exams and tests, at school and university alike, are graded from one to five – with five being the top mark.

165 That is, the Soviet–Polish frontier before the Molotov–Ribbentrop Pact of 23 August 1939 allowed Nazi Germany and the Soviet Union to divide up Poland between them.

166 The Battle of Yelnya (30 August–6 September 1941) was one of the first Soviet offensive operations of the war. Alexander Werth, a British journalist based in Moscow, wrote, "Here was not only, as it were, the Red Army's first victory over the Germans; here was also the first piece of territory – perhaps only 100 or 150 square miles – in the whole of Europe reconquered from Hitler's *Wehrmacht*." *Russia at War*, p. 188. Yelnya was indeed liberated, but the larger Soviet offensive following this victory was a failure. Dimbleby, *Barbarossa*, pp. 271–76.

167 Even if this is true, there is more to be said. According to the official divisional records, in the course of the battle "Babadjanian lost 605 men killed, wounded, or missing in action; a further 850 were described as having 'surrendered as prisoners of war'." Dimbleby, *Barbarossa*, p. 294. See note 155.

168 In early 1942, Grossman himself visited a tank brigade commanded by Colonel Khasin. See *A Writer at War*, p. 96.

169 Tacitus, *The Annals*, tr. J. C. Yardley (Oxford World's Classics, 2008), p. xix.

170 *The Annals*, p. 194.

171 *The Annals*, p. xxviii.

172 RGANI (Russian State Archive of Contemporary History). f. 3; op. 53; delo 3; l. 17–19; 30–40.

173 Committee for Stalin Prizes in the realm of Literature and Art (Moscow: 1939–1956), RGALI, f. 2073, op. 1, ed. khr. 7–8. Also ed. khr. 7, l. 85–87.

174 In Moscow, Leningrad, Magadan and Khabarovsk; and in Moscow, Leningrad, Voronezh, Sochi and Rostov-on-Don.

175 Ilya Ehrenburg, *Liudi, gody, zhizn'*, vol. 3 (Moscow: Sovetskii pisatel', 1966), pp. 211–12.

176 Natalya Roskina, *Chetyre glavy. Iz literaturnykh vospominanii* (Paris: YMCA-Press, 1980), pp. 107–109.

Further Reading

During the last twenty years a great deal has been published about the German–Soviet War and the Battle of Stalingrad. Richard Overy's *Russia's War* (Penguin, 1998) and Antony Beevor's *Stalingrad* (Viking, 1998) were among the first such books to reach a large readership. Listed below are a few other books I have found particularly helpful:

Antony Beevor, *The Second World War* (Weidenfeld & Nicolson, 2014).

Chris Bellamy, *Absolute War* (Pan, 2009).

Maria Bloshteyn, *Russia Is Burning: Poems of the Great Patriotic War* (Smokestack Books, 2020) – an excellent, comprehensive and well-translated anthology.

Anna Bonola and Giovanni Maddalena, *Vasily Grossman: A Writer's Freedom* (McGill-Queen's University Press, 2018).

Rodric Braithwaite, *Moscow 1941* (Profile, 2006).

Jonathan Dimbleby, *Barbarossa* (Penguin Viking, 2021).

Frank Ellis, *And Their Mothers Wept* (Heritage House Press, 2007) – a comprehensive account of Soviet and post-Soviet fiction about the Second World War.

Frank Ellis, *The Damned and the Dead: The Eastern Front Through the Eyes of Soviet and Russian Novelists* (University Press of Kansas, 2015).

Frank Ellis, *Barbarossa 1941* (University Press of Kansas, 2015) – includes an interesting chapter about the treatment of the German invasion in works by Grossman and two other Soviet writers.

Ian Garner, *Stalingrad Lives* (Montreal: McGill-Queen's University Press, 2022) – a selection of articles published by Grossman and many other journalists in *Red Star*

Vasily Grossman, *A Writer at War*, ed. Antony Beevor and Luba Vinogradova (Harvill Press, 2005) – extracts from Grossman's wartime notebooks, with a useful commentary.

Vasily Grossman, *Life and Fate* (NYRB Classics and Vintage Classics, 2006), tr. Robert Chandler.

Vasily Grossman, *The Road* (NYRB Classics and MacLehose Press, 2010), tr. Robert and Elizabeth Chandler.

Vasily Grossman, *Stalingrad* (NYRB Classics and Vintage Classics, 2020), tr. Robert and Elizabeth Chandler.

Michael Jones, *The Retreat* (John Murray, 2009). A powerful account of the first year of the German–Soviet war, focusing on the successful defence of Moscow and the subsequent German retreat.

Michael Jones, *Total War: from Stalingrad to Berlin* (John Murray, 2012).

Catherine Merridale, *Ivan's War* (Faber & Faber, 2006) – a sensitively written, psychologically informed evocation of the experience of the rank-and-file Red Army soldier.

Richard Overy, *Blood and Ruins: The Great Imperial War, 1931–1945* (Allen Lane, 2021).

Alexandra Popoff, *Vasily Grossman and the Soviet Century* (Yale University Press, 2019).

Brandon Schechter, *The Stuff of Soldiers: A History of the Red Army in World War II Through Objects* (Cornell University Press, 2019) – an almost encyclopedic account of the material side of the lives of Red Army soldiers: their rations, uniforms, weapons, etc.

Alexander Tvardovsky, *Vasily Tiorkin* (Smokestack Books, 2020).

Alexander Werth, *Russia at War* (Pan, 1964).

Articles

Yury Bit-Yunan and Robert Chandler, "Vasily Grossman: Myths and Counter-Myths", *Los Angeles Review of Books*, 13 November, 2019.

Robert Chandler, "Vasily Grossman, Writer who Caught the Reality of War", *The Critic*, July/August 2020.

In Russian

Yury Bit-Yunan and David Fel'dman – their many articles and books are the most important recent publications in Russian.

A. Bocharov, *Vasily Grossman: Zhizn', tvorchestvo, sud'ba* (Moscow: Sovetsky pisatel', 1990) – still the best introduction to Grossman's work.

Vasily Grossman, *Gody voiny* (Moscow, 1989) – an almost-complete Russian text of the wartime notebooks; it is censored only lightly.

Semion Lipkin, *Kvadriga* (Moscow: Knizhnyi Sad/Agraf, 1997) – his engaging and well-written memoir has influenced almost all subsequent writing on Grossman but is sadly unreliable.

P. Polian, *Esli tol'ko budu zhiv: 12 dnevnikov voennykh let* (Nestor-Istoriya, 2021) – twelve wartime diaries kept by very different figures: Gulag inmates, NKVD officers, men who collaborated with the Germans, penal battalion soldiers, etc. A remarkable volume.

Acknowledgements

Our thanks, above all, to the staff of the Russian State Archive of Literature and Art (RGALI); to Yevgenia Mikhailovna Varentsova and Yelena Iosifovna Pogorelskaya of the V. I. Dal' State Museum of the History of Russian Literature; and to Alexey Gusev for his help with regard to the history of the Marx–Engels Institute. We are also deeply grateful to Tatiana Dettmer for translating passages of German, and to her and Ian Garner for allowing us to draw on unpublished work of their own; to Yury Bit-Yunan and Oleg Budnitsky for help in obtaining archival material; to Meic Pattison for information about the Welsh translation of The People Immortal; and to him, Rodric Braithwaite, Elizabeth Cook, Jonathan Dimbleby and Garrett Riggs for reading through complete drafts of our translation and their many helpful suggestions.

Julia Volohova wishes to express her especial gratitude to Anna Shmaina-Velikanova, who has shown her for many years, through personal example, that nothing can be more important in any scholarly endeavour than the search for truth.

Many, many others have also answered countless questions about language, military terminology, Soviet clothing and diet, etc. Among them are Michele Berdy, Alexander Nakhimovsky, Natasha Perova and Anna Pilkington, David Powelstock, Oliver Ready and Paul Richardson, Lisa R. Taylor. Thanks, as always, to all members of SEELANGS, a remarkably helpful and generous email group without which this work would have been a great deal more difficult. And apologies to anyone whose name we have inadvertently failed to mention.

Biographical Notes

VASILY SEMIONOVICH GROSSMAN (1905–1964) was born into a Jewish family in Berdichev, in what is now Ukraine. In 1934 he published both "In the Town of Berdichev" – a short story that won him immediate acclaim – and the novel *Glückauf*, about Donbas miners. During the Second World War, he worked as a reporter for the army newspaper *Red Star*; his vivid yet sober "The Hell of Treblinka" (1944) was one of the first accounts of a Nazi death camp to be published in any language. His long novel *Stalingrad* was published to great acclaim in 1952, then fiercely attacked. A new wave of purges was about to begin; but for Stalin's death in 1953, Grossman would probably have been arrested. During the next few years Grossman worked on his second Stalingrad novel: *Life and Fate*. In February 1961, the KGB confiscated his typescript and working notes for this, but he was able to continue working on *Everything Flows*, which is yet more critical of the Soviet regime, until his last days. The short stories he wrote during his last three years are among his supreme achievements; English translations are included in *The Road*. Grossman died on 14 September 1964, on the eve of the twenty-third anniversary of the massacre of the Jews of Berdichev in which his mother had died.

ROBERT CHANDLER's translations from Russian include works by Alexander Pushkin, Teffi and Andrey Platonov, as well as novels, short stories, essays and a memoir by Vasily Grossman. He has also written a short biography of Pushkin and has edited three anthologies of Russian literature for Penguin Classics. He runs regular translation seminars and has worked as a mentor for younger translators.

ELIZABETH CHANDLER is a co-translator, with her husband, of Pushkin's *The Captain's Daughter* and of works by Vasily Grossman and Andrey Platonov.

JULIA VOLOHOVA is an independent scholar. She has been research-ing the life and work of Vasily Grossman since 2014 and she works as an editor for "The Laboratory of Unnecessary Things", an innovative, non-commercial educational project under the auspices of the Indepen-dent Moscow University.